JACK JONES

OFF TO PHILADELPHIA
IN THE MORNING

SONGS OF PRAISES,
I WILL EVER GIVE
TO THEE

PENGUIN BOOKS
IN ASSOCIATION WITH
HAMISH HAMILTON

FIRST PUBLISHED 1947
PUBLISHED IN PENGUIN BOOKS 1951

MADE AND PRINTED IN GREAT BRITAIN
FOR PENGUIN BOOKS LTD
HARMONDSWORTH, MIDDLESEX
BY C. NICHOLLS AND COMPANY LTD

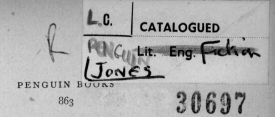
PENGUIN BOOKS
863

OFF TO PHILADELPHIA
IN THE MORNING

JACK JONES

CONTENTS

Dedicated
to the memory of
JOSEPH PARRY
Mus.D.(Cambridge)

CHAPTER I

Never Heard of Him, said the Traveller

ON towards evening of a day in May, 1941, a commercial traveller was driving himself home along a by-pass road in South-west Wales. He was hoping to get back to where he lived in a Cardiff suburb before black-out time. He had had to take over what was new territory to him when several of his younger colleagues had joined the Army and Air Force. He, a Bristolian himself, had served throughout the First World War, from which he returned, with one leg shorter than the other, to cover the West of England for his firm. Now he had the coastal belt of South and South-west Wales to do as well. Still, it could not be helped. There was a war on, and as he saw things in May of 1941 it was going to take us all our time to get out of it as well as we had got out of the last. This war had to be fought from the doorsteps of Britain to the ends of the earth, and if it was not won on the doorsteps and along the home front then it would not be won at all.

He was clear of the by-pass road and entering the steel and tinplate town at its eastern end. A boy on a bike rode recklessly out of a side-street and across the road just in front of his car, so he had to apply his brakes until they screeched to avoid knocking the boy and the bike for six. The young fool ... These Welsh people have no road sense, he told himself. He was getting to know and to like the Welsh people a little better by now, but as for understanding them and their language – hullo, what's all this?

He slowed down on seeing the huge crowd that was completely blocking the street on which a large chapel dwarfed shops, pubs and houses. Capel y Bryn, which the English might call the Chapel on the Hill, was the largest Non-conformist chapel in Wales, and being the largest it was sometimes referred to as the Nonconformist Cathedral. But a chapel it was when all's said and done, a chapel and not a church, remember. A church is a church and a chapel is a chapel is what most people in Wales insist. The one is tied to the Established Church and the other is free. That is something which people from other countries should bear in mind when in Wales.

The commercial traveller drove at a snail's pace to stop a few yards away from the edge of the crowd. He beckoned to a man who was standing in the doorway of a grocer's shop which, like all the other shops in the street, was closed. Yes? said the man. What's all this, what's wrong? said the traveller. Nothing wrong as I know of, said the man. Where are you going? I'm on my way back to Cardiff, said the traveller. Oh, said the man. Then go back the way you came as far as the cross, down the left by the Puddlers' Arms and along the old road till you come back on to this one by the bridge this side of the steelworks. Wasn't there a policeman on the Square to tell you? To tell me what? said the traveller. That you can't go with your car this way, said the man. Why not? said the traveller. What's all the excitement about?

The man looked hard at the traveller. Don't sit there in the car and tell me that you don't know, he said. If I knew what it was all about would I have asked the question? said the traveller. The man nodded and said: I see. You're a foreigner. I'm nothing of the kind, said the traveller. I'm as British as you are any day. But not as Welsh as I am into the bargain, said the man. For if you were you would have known why this crowd is out by here and why nearly as many again are packed till they can't move inside that chapel. You would have known that this is the first great gathering of the Parry Centenary Celebrations. What Parry is it you're talking about? said the traveller. What Parry do you think I'm talking about? said the man. I'm talking about Doctor Joseph Parry, of course. Never heard of him, said the traveller.

The Welshman looked at him pityingly and said: Pity for you. You English don't know much about Wales and her great men, do you? He bent himself forward to bring his head level with the head of the traveller seated in the car. Nor I don't suppose you've heard of 'Aberystwyth' either, he said. That's where you're wrong, said the traveller. I've been to Aberystwyth several times. The Welshman sighed and said: Listen now. I have talked more in the thin English tongue to-day for your sake than I have talked all the time since this war started. I was not talking about Aberystwyth as a place but about the hymn-tune which Doctor Joseph Parry made and called 'Aberystwyth'. Oh, I see, said the traveller. Yes, said the man, but what you can't see from where you are sitting in your car is that you are now an island surrounded by people. Look, look, more and more people have closed in behind you. I'll soon shift 'em, said the traveller, sounding his horn. Stop that noise and listen, said the man as the crowd outside took up the singing which the people inside the chapel had given them the lead for. There you are, said the man to the traveller, there's 'Aberystwyth' for you now.

The man threw back his head and joined in the singing of the famous hymn and the traveller sat listening in his car. He recognized the tune, having sung 'Jesu, lover of my soul' to it many a time, but now all these people were singing words that were double-dutch to him.

> 'Beth sydd i mi yn y byd
> Ond gorthrymder mawr o hyd ...'

The traveller rightly assumed that they were Welsh words but as for their meaning ... Anyway, it was the most thrilling disturbance he had ever heard. A wailing most mighty and in perfect harmony by nearly five thousand people within and without the Nonconformist Cathedral. He was content to sit in his car to listen to the end, and when it was ended he nodded and smiled at the Welshman he had conversed with before sounding his horn and putting his car into reverse.

The traveller managed to get the car out of the crowd before they, the crowd within and the crowd without, joined in singing another of the late Dr Joseph Parry's hymn-tunes. The sound of the singing followed his car for a mile or so before leaving him to his thoughts. Rather good but a bit on the doleful side, was how he summed up the singing after he had heard the last of it. Dr Joseph Parry ... ? No, he had never heard of him until that day.

*

Joseph Parry was born in the town of Tydfil the Martyr in 1841 and he was the youngest but one of the eight children of Daniel and Elizabeth Parry. Three of the children died in infancy and little Joseph nearly died more than once before he learnt to walk and talk. But after his third birthday in May, 1844, his parents felt certain of rearing him to be a man. For he was strong on his legs and he had plenty to say for himself. Already he could sing like a bird, as most Welsh children of his age could in those days, when it was said that the Welsh did all the singing and the Irish did all the drinking in the town of Tydfil the Martyr. That saying was not altogether true. Some of the Welsh did their share of the drinking too.

Joseph loved the town in which he was born and throughout his life his proudest claim was that he was a 'Bachgen bach o Ferthyr, erioed, erioed', which in English simply means 'a little boy from Merthyr, always, always'. He fell in love with the town as soon as he was able to take it in and he never fell out of love with it. Its name took his fancy when he first grasped its meaning. The town of Tydfil the Martyr, abbreviated by the English to 'Merthyr Tydfil', and by the Welsh to 'Ferthyr Tydfil', the Welsh for Martyr being

10

'Ferthyr', was anything but lovely during Joseph's child-hood and boyhood days. But it was a vital and thrilling town in which to grow up. It was not hungry in the hungry 'forties, when the Irish by the thousands flocked there from their own distressful country. For there were four large iron-works and many coal-pits in and around the town, then the world's largest industrial town, and the population of the town and district was upwards of forty thousand.

This population had been drawn from Welsh agricultural counties and from Ireland and England. A very small per-centage had come there from Scotland. In the dirt and smoke of the place there was good money to be earned and, in the case of employers, nearly all of whom came there from England, lots of money to be made. Joseph's parents had come into the dirt of the place from clean, but far from prosperous Welsh agricultural counties, so had most of the good people of the town. But many bad people, people wanted by the police, had fled from elsewhere into the smoky upland industrial metropolis of Wales, where the police who followed in search of them were at a loss to find them.

That was the kind of town in which Joseph was born and where he lived as a child and a boy, loving every minute of his life there. He lived inside one of the ironworks, the famous Cyfarthfa Works, yes, literally and truly lived right inside the works. For Chapel Row was right inside Cyfarthfa Works and it was named Chapel Row because it was near to a chapel of ease which the Crawshay who was the founder of the family fortunes had had built – goodness only knows why – in his works. The works was within the walls, 'the Cyfarthfa Works walls', as the people said, and so was Chapel Row within the walls too.

So Joseph was one of the few children 'on the inside', so to speak, and wonders were performed before his childish eyes by day and by night. Heavy-booted men, puddlers and rollers and other ironworkers, combined to throw flames into the sky for him to wonder at every night including Sunday night. Then by day there were the canal barges in and out of the canal terminus only a matter of yards from the door of the house in Chapel Row in which Joseph lived with his parents and brothers and sisters.

It was a fairly substantial house, one of five such houses which made a row. The position of Chapel Row was unique, for in addition to being inside one of the greatest ironworks in the world, the Glamorganshire Canal was practically washing their front doorsteps and the Taff River did as much for the doorsteps at the back. So Chapel Row was situated on a strip of 'made' ground between the Glamorganshire Canal and the River Taff, both parallel with the row of houses. The Glamorganshire Canal had been more or less eclipsed by the Taff Vale Railway, which was opened for traffic from the town of Tydfil the Martyr right down to Cardiff the very year Joseph was born. This was annoying, to say the least, for Mr Crawshay, who practically owned the canal which started at the sea at Cardiff and at great expense had been made to climb about twelve hundred feet in the twenty-five miles of its length to where it finished in Mr Crawshay's great works and near the doorstep of Joseph's home. Until the Taff Vale Railway was opened for traffic the year Joseph was born Mr Crawshay had had the other ironmasters of the town and district where he wanted them as far as the transport of coal and iron down to the port of Cardiff was concerned anyway. But once the Taff Vale Railway was opened, right from this town named after Tydfil the Martyr, down to Cardiff, the other ironmasters were able to send their coal and iron down to the port of Cardiff by rail. It was Sir John Guest, Mr Crawshay's most powerful rival and competitor, that was mainly responsible for the building and opening of the Taff Vale Railway. His works at Dowlais were bigger than Mr Crawshay's at Cyfarthfa, and it had been most galling for Sir John to be so dependent for transportation on the canal which was practically owned and controlled by Mr Crawshay, who had built a castle to overlook Cyfarthfa Works and had called it Cyfarthfa Castle. There were sixty-two acres of park-land and a lake and everything, and the Park was walled-in and there were lodges and lodge-gates at three points of the outer walls. This castle, built at a cost of £30,000, had for sixteen years before the birth of Joseph been the envy of all the other ironmasters and their wives, who were only human after all. So they felt they had to do something to bring Mr Crawshay down a peg and Mr Guest before he was made a baronet went to meet some people with whom he discussed the possibilities of making a railway from the port of Cardiff right up to the town of Tydfil the Martyr. Mr Crawshay was not invited to take part in those discussions. The Glamorganshire Canal, which had served him well for over forty years, was good enough for Mr Crawshay. His father had been most proud of the canal which was twenty-five miles long and had forty stepping-up locks from the sea at the port of Cardiff to where it finished in Mr Crawshay's ironworks in the town of Tydfil the Martyr. He was still as proud of it as ever, even prouder of it than his father before him had been. Well, said the other ironmasters now that they had the Taff Vale Railway, well, they said in effect, you can have your canal all to yourself now, Mr Crawshay. By now the main inspiring industrial force behind the making of the railway was Sir Josiah John Guest, Bart., better known as Sir John Guest, and that didn't make plain Mr Crawshay feel any the sweeter towards him either.

These are matters which concerned only the big people, the English coalowners and ironmasters who were the real rulers of industrial Wales during Joseph's childhood and boyhood. They spoke little or no Welsh and Joseph spoke little or no English. But he saw their works and lived by their grace. His father, Daniel Parry, worked for Mr Crawshay, as a refiner in his ironworks, where he earned 24s. per week or 4s. per shift. Joseph's mother, Elizabeth Parry, better known as Betty Parry, had to do the best she could for seven all told on that amount of money per week. With five hungry children it was hard to make a go of it with flour at 43s. a sack and potatoes 5s. 6d. a hundredweight. Then tea was 4s. a pound – and how the women whose husbands spent money on drink that was stronger than the strongest tea managed to live was more than Betty Parry could make out. Her husband, her Daniel, had never in his life spent one penny on the drink, but he had to have a couple of ounces of tobacco each week. Then there was a shilling a week for their chapel, Bethesda Chapel. So between everything it was a tight go each and every week. Daniel was chafed in spirit by the never-ending struggle Betty was engaged in to make ends meet, and many a night after the children had gone to bed he talked about going to America some day –

But before he and Betty go into that again perhaps it would be just as well to go upstairs and see their five children, being as they are the main reason why Daniel wants to go where he thinks he can better himself. But before looking at the children in the two beds in the one room upstairs it may as well be said that there was more than a little of the Chartist spirit in Daniel Parry. Anyway, the children, three girls in the one bed and the two boys in the other. The three girls in the biggest of the two beds which fill the little room to the exclusion of everything else with the sole exception of what the children called 'the po' are Ann, Elizabeth, and Jane. Ann is the eldest of all five children sharing the two beds, the little mother who is such a help to the real mother who is with the father downstairs. Until recently she was home helping her mother all the time, but now she goes out working three days a week at the house of the minister of their chapel, the Rev. Daniel Jones, who succeeded the more famous Rev. Methusalem Jones at Bethesda Chapel. Ann's mother had been in service in the home of the Rev. Methusalem Jones and it was he that had taught her to read. He was a giant in the pulpit and he had led the congregation from their first meeting-place in a room behind a blacksmith's shop into a sacred edifice worthy of being called God's house. Then, full of years, he died and was succeeded by the Rev. Daniel Jones, in whose time Bethesda Chapel was rebuilt and enlarged to accommodate the growing congregation.

Now Ann went three days a week for sixpence a day and her food to work in the house of the Rev. Daniel Jones, but she came home to sleep. She was nearly twelve years old and very pretty and, like all the Parry children down to little Jane who was only two years old, she was a good singer. No wonder, for their mother was one of the finest singers in the town of Tydfil the Martyr. Yes, Betty Parry led the singing of the hymns at Bethesda Chapel from the time she first went there fresh from the west country of Wales. As a servant in the house of the then minister, the Rev. Methusalem Jones, she was expected to go to his chapel twice on Sundays for the preaching, praying and singing, and also to the Sunday School on Sunday afternoons for two hours' learning from the Bible, the Welsh Bible. I think it should be explained that she did not conduct the singing but only led it, struck the first note of the hymn first for all present to follow her. There was no one like her for leading the singing of hymns. Now twelve-year-old Ann was almost as good as her mother in that and other respects.

Elizabeth was nearly nine years old and a good little girl about the house. She was, if anything, a prettier girl than Ann, though Ann had nicer eyes. Between Ann and Elizabeth in the bed was the baby of the family, two-year-old Jane. She had not been sleeping upstairs very long, about three months perhaps. Before that she had been sleeping with her parents in the bed which filled the downstairs bedroom, which is on the right as you step into the living-room from outside. Now her two sisters were doing their best to spoil her, but that was not Jane's fault. Anyway, they did not succeed in spoiling her.

The two in what was called 'the boys' bed' were Henry and Joseph. At this time Henry was seven and Joseph was four years old. I won't say anything about the three children who had died in infancy beyond mentioning the fact that one of them was taken by what was called the 'old cholera' in 1832. There had been some talk this night before Ann made them all shut up and go to sleep. Joseph had listened to the talk for a while before he said: I don't like the old canal in front of the house but I like the river at the back.

Why don't you like the canal? said Ann. It doesn't walk or talk or sing, said Joseph. It came all the way up from Cardiff and it hasn't moved since. Only waits all time for boats to go over it. The river don't wait. It goes all time and talks and sings as it goes. I am older than you, our Joseph, said Henry, but I have never heard the river at the back of the house talking. Have you, our Ann? I have heard it making a noise when in flood, said Ann. It shouts then, said Joseph. Shouts? said Elizabeth. No, I am wrong, it does not shout, said Joseph. When full of the rain of the streams of the mountains it sings loud, sings like the people in the singing festival sing halleluia, as it rushes down to the sea that takes people over the big world. Go to sleep now, good boy, said Ann. Not like the old canal saying nothing all the time, said Joseph. If it don't say anything it does plenty, said Henry. Bringing boats with men and things in them all the way up from Cardiff by the sea. It don't bring them up, it's the horses pull the boats up from Cardiff, said Joseph. Whether or no, go to sleep when I tell you, good boys, said Ann. I asked the boy who walks the canal-bank with the horse and he told me, said Joseph. The boy knows that the old canal could not move a boat without him and the horse. Same with the railway that started from here down to Cardiff the year you were born, said Ann. No trucks can go on the railway without the engine and the man to drive it. But go to sleep now, good boys. I would not be afraid to go on a train down to Cardiff, said Henry. Then I would, said Elizabeth. I would not dare go on the old train from here to Pentrebach. I shall be bound to smack you all if you don't go to sleep quick, said Ann. No, I don't like the canal in front of the house, said Joseph, turning on his right side to go to sleep. He had the last word. The talk was in Welsh, for they spoke only Welsh, and it was only Joseph had picked up a few words of English from the boys who came up from Cardiff along the canal-bank and in the canal barges. When they got tired walking the canal-bank with the horse which drew the barge along by a rope attached to both horse and boat, the boy got on the boat, as it was generally spoken of, to take a rest when it came up out of one of the forty locks. So by talking to these boys at the terminus of the canal, which was close by Joseph's home, Joseph had picked up a little English by the time he was four.

Joseph's parents spoke only Welsh and felt a sense of guilt when they unconsciously spoke an English word, one of the few which had come to them through contact with English and Irish people or pedlars who came to the door. Both parents and children, with the exception of little Jane, could read Welsh from the Welsh Bible and Welsh hymn-books. This they had learnt to do in the Sunday School of Bethesda Chapel, which was wholly conducted in Welsh. But neither parents nor children could write in any language. The mother, Betty, and Ann, her eldest child, could also read music if it was tonic solfa. None of the children had been to a day-school and Betty saw no reason why she should pay 2d. per week for her children to learn things in English in a dame- or day-school. In any case she was not able to afford the cost of such education for her children, and had she been able to afford it she would have considered it a waste of money to pay it. Her children could get their schooling where she got hers, in the Sunday School, in Welsh, where the ancient Welsh language was not polluted by words in English or any other tongue. There was only one way in which the Welsh language could be kept alive under the pressure of alien influences, that way was by continually speaking and reading Welsh – and also writing in Welsh if one could. There was a line in the Welsh national anthem which Betty often quoted for the benefit of her children, and the line was: 'O bydded i'r hen iaith barhau,' which might be translated as: 'O see that the old language shall last.' Betty was doing all she could to make it last. There had about this time been issued a report on Education in mining districts of South Wales, a report which implied that the Welsh language was the main reason why the Welsh people were as ignorant as the Report tried to make them out to be. That Report roused the righteous anger of the Welsh people of the mining districts of Wales, but it satisfied the British Parliament, the Lower House of which was composed almost entirely of Englishmen. Henry W. Lucy said this about the House of Commons who considered that Report: 'A more respectable body of the gentlemen of England it would be difficult to gather together. With the possible exception of one or two political adventurers there is probably not a man in the House who is not well born or at least rich ...'

Those gentlemen of England notwithstanding, Betty Parry was determined that she and her husband and children should remain as Welsh as possible for as long as she lived. But Daniel was growing more concerned about a more spacious way of living than was possible in Wales – for me, anyway, he said. America is where I would like to go to. So you have said many times, said Betty. But men have to work there same as they have here, remember. Yes, but ... He sighed and she said: But what, Daniel? No odds anyway, he said. I'm never likely to have the money to pay my own passage let alone yours and the children's. He had to start working on the night-shift the week that was coming and he hated night-work. It made him wish he had never left the farm in Pembrokeshire, made him wish he had the money to pay for his passage to America, and it made him say to Betty this night that he had a mind to go to his father and brothers on the farm and ask them to lend him the money to pay his passage.

Betty would not hear of it. If you must go then you'll pay for your passage with your own money. Being as you're set on going sooner or later we'll start saving as – Save, indeed! said Daniel. Out of what I'd like to know? I was going to say that we would start saving as soon as Henry starts to work, said Betty. We can put him to work next year and all he will earn we will put by towards your passage-money. Not that I hold with your going the other side of the world to live and work, but I can see that you will never be content any more here. No doubt Ann will be able to get a couple more days' work each week too, and that will be another shilling a week towards what will take you over the sea.

What Henry will start earning next year and the shilling a week extra Ann will earn soon will not amount to much in five years' time, said Daniel. I shall put Elizabeth to service with some tidy family as soon as I can, said Betty. That will be another few pounds a year – and go you shall now. We must all help so as you won't have to live with your head in one place and your heart in another. But you must be patient, Daniel, through the years it will take us to save the money to pay your passage. I would like to go before I am past my prime, said Daniel. And you shall, said Betty. Content your mind now and sleep well tonight. I wouldn't be in America long before I would be able to send money for you and the children to come over the water to me, said Daniel. I am not so much for America as you are, but wherever you go me and the children will follow, said Betty. Come now to bed. The night is very near gone.

*

A night must have an end, an end of joy and sorrow, of love

19

and hate, all men and all things must have an end in the world without end. But before this night ends for the town of Tydfil the Martyr, the darkness over which is lightened only by the intermittent rising and spreading and contracting light from enormous furnaces, we must climb to the high place from which many a distinguished visitor has looked down on the town and district on a dark night when the town and district seemed to be hell-bound within a crazy square made by its four great ironworks. A most wondrous sight, said Borrow when he came later to look down on it. Lord Nelson and his lady-love were taken up to the high place by the first of the Crawshays on a dark night long before and they were immensely impressed by the smoky and fiery lay-out from the table-land above Dowlais to the broad valley in which the town of Tydfil the Martyr was situated. The Grand Duke Constantine of Russia and many other less distinguished visitors were all taken by their respective hosts to one or other of the high places overlooking the town and district which was the coal and iron capital of the world. Their hosts and guides pointed first with pride to their own huge corner of the four-square smoky and fiery lay-out below, then just before returning to the waiting horses or carriages to ride or be driven back to where they were honoured guests their hosts and guides would wave a hand contemptuously in the direction of the works of their rivals and competitors. If the host was a Crawshay of Cyfarthfa Castle he referred to Sir John Guest, who was the Member of Parliament for the town and district, in a way that left his guest or guests in no doubt as to what the Crawshays of Cyfarthfa Castle thought of the Guests of Dowlais House. As for the other ironmasters of the 'big four' who were the real rulers of the town and district – well, they and theirs could make the most of their time in Plymouth House and Penydarren House. For William Crawshay of Cyfarthfa Castle and Sir John Guest, M.P., of Dowlais House, were both convinced of their ability to produce all the coal and make all the iron the world required from the town and district. So the Penydarren and Plymouth ironworks would soon be surplus to requirements.

But to return to the night and its life and work, this night of decision so far as the Parry family is concerned. From this night forth the word 'America' is the name of a distant star to which the head of the Parry family is preparing to hitch his wagon. This family so small and yet so great in its home in the coal and iron capital of the world may make its mark in the world in the days to come, make its mark in the new world and the old. As they sleep furnaces are roaring and sending their angry light skywards. Wheels are turning over pit-mouths which belch forth coal and power. Men and boys and a fair percentage of women and girls are straining and sweating through the night which must have an end. A percentage of these night-workers on and under the surface of the town and district associated with the name of Tydfil the Martyr are burning or bleeding. But the sleep of the day-workers is none the less sweet.

All are not asleep in the town of Tydfil the Martyr. Many of the windows of Cyfarthfa Castle are ablaze with light from within, gaslight from gas made by a small plant behind the Castle. William Crawshay is entertaining a large number of people whom he has invited from far and near to meet the young lady his son and heir, Robert Thompson Crawshay, is to marry before so long. All the notabilities of the town and district with the exception of Sir John and Lady Charlotte Guest were present to meet Robert's fiancée. Sir John and his lady had not been invited. They were in London, where they had dined that night with the Disraelis. Mrs Disraeli's first husband, Mr Wyndham Lewis, had made a lot of his money through his connexions with Mr Guest and the Dowlais Works, and now Mr Disraeli had about £4,000 a year of that money, with which he hoped to convince the 'gentlemen of England' that he was no mere political adventurer. It may have been possible to find a worse use for the late Mr Wyndham Lewis's money. Still, most of the money made in such towns as that of Tydfil the Martyr sooner or later finds itself in London.

But to return to where the money was made in the first place. The two hundred public- and beer-houses of the town and district have just closed, for it is eleven p.m., and they have been open since five-thirty a.m. The dozen policemen who maintain law and order to the best of their ability and limited strength are at pivotal points of the town. The usual number of drunken men and a few drunken women have been turned out of the pubs and beer-houses into the streets and the policemen stand and wait. Drunkenness they did not in the least object to, but when drunken men or women were also disorderly then the policemen, with sighs of regret, had to do something. We are only a dozen all told, said a policeman, and what's a dozen of us in a place this size?

What, indeed? Upwards of forty thousand people to keep an eye on and some of those people would not think twice before they bashed a policeman. So many of the people had bashed one or other of the dozen policemen. It was only natural for the policemen who had been bashed not once or twice but many times, it was only natural that they should try and get their own back. The trouble was that the magistrates were too lenient in the cases of those found guilty of disorderly conduct and of assaulting the police. But now that Mr Henry Austin Bruce had been appointed Stipendiary Magistrate for the town and district it was confidently expected that transgressors against the law would be firmly dealt with. It was also expected that the force of a dozen policemen would be considerably strengthened, possibly doubled. Two dozen policemen would be none too many to cope with the wild Irish, the many other bad eggs of different nationalities who had come into the town and district from elsewhere, and, of course, those natives of the place who took a delight in trying to get the best of a policeman. But the crimes committed by the natives of the place were less than half the number committed by the population as a whole. More than half the number of crimes were committed by natives of Ireland and England who had come to live and work in the place.

This very night there was likely to be trouble with the Irish, for there was a Wake in progress in Quarry Row, in which nine out of every ten houses were occupied by Irish families. There was also a free fight going on in the district of Caedraw and another in the neighbourhood known as the Ball Court. Then in the district called 'China', where policemen went in couples but never alone, there was a bit of a disturbance. But on the whole the town of Tydfil the Martyr was not bad. The vast majority of the people of the town and district were hard-working, sober and respectable, and more than half of them were deeply religious as well. Those who stated that the place had more public- and beer-houses than any other place of like size in Britain forgot to add that it also had more chapels than any other place of like size in Britain.

Now that the district called 'China' has been mentioned, we can stop a minute to observe a masked man and a little girl who evidently live in that district. Hand in hand they walked over the cobblestones which formed the roadway over the Iron Bridge and hand in hand they went under the dark archway and out of sight. The masked man was obviously drunk but not reeling drunk. He held himself upright and walked as though he were defying the drink with which he had filled himself from head to toe to slacken his frame or stagger his walk. The face of the little girl when seen at the height of the light of the largest of the Cyfarthfa Works' furnaces was as serious-looking as that of a grown woman, yet she could not have been more than eight years old.

A tall, fat, dark-whiskered man had followed the little girl and the masked man over the Iron Bridge, but he did not follow them under the dark archway into the district

23

called 'China'. He stopped outside the archway and called after them. Goodnight, Myfanwy. Goodnight, Dick. Goodnight, Ieuan, they both said in reply and went to wherever they were going. The tall, fat, dark-whiskered man went up the little hill to Castle Street and turned left this side of the Lamb Inn to go to where he lived in Lamb Lane. A strange trio to meet in the streets of the coal and iron capital of the world, on the streets without gaslight and no moon to be seen in the sky. Why was that man masked? If that little girl was his own little girl then why had he kept her up and about until this time of night? It was getting on for midnight. Then that tall, fat, dark-whiskered and distinguished-looking man, who and what is he and why was he so closely following the masked man and the little girl across the Iron Bridge? Where have they all been until this time of night?

At the Puddlers' Arms, that's where they have been from seven until eleven p.m. The man wearing the black mask is none other than Richard Llewelyn, better known as Blind Dick, the singer. The little girl is his daughter, Myfanwy, and she lives with her father in a cellar-dwelling in the district called 'China'. The people who live in this district are no angels and no motherless little girl should be left to grow up among them. Yet they are kind to her, and when the river rises during winter floods and she and her father have to leave their cellar-dwelling to escape drowning, they have been welcome to stay in the pick of the homes on the higher level until the River Taff goes down again.

It was not always this way with them. Time was when Richard Llewelyn was a sober and industrious ironworker and a singer of good repute. He went to chapel and was in every way well thought of until he married an Irish girl named Cathleen Daley, Big Jim Daley's only child. Soon after that he started to drink and he went on drinking defiantly, now that his own people, the Welsh, had more or less ostracized him because he had dared to marry an Irish girl and a Catholic. His wife also drank and that made the

Welsh chapel people feel more bitter than ever against the man who in their opinion had disgraced Wales and the Welsh by marrying an Irish girl and a Catholic in the first place.

Soon after Myfanwy was born Dick was carried home from the ironworks in a terrible state. Accidentally he had been splashed with molten metal. It made a horrible mess of the upper part of his face and blinded him permanently. The works physician and surgeon did all that could be done for him and no doubt saved his life, which Dick gave him no thanks for. His wife, Cathleen, could not bear the sight of him and it was she that insisted on him wearing the black mask which she made to hide the upper part of his face and his hairless head. For the first year after the accident he was confined to bed in the little house in Company Row, where he and his wife and child lived on the charity of his wife's relatives and the neighbours, most of whom were Irish.

Little Myfanwy was two years old when Dick went out of the house for the first time since his accident. He was wearing his black mask and holding his little girl's hand that first morning he returned to the world outside the little house in Company Row. Cathleen, his wife, had said it was all she could do to put up with the sight of him in the home let alone walk the streets with him. It was the sight of him without sight and no hair on his head, and the new skin of the upper part of his face shiny and tight, that had driven Cathleen to drink more and more and to go with men easier to look at and lie with than Dick now was.

The rent of the little house in Company Row was in arrears but the Company agent, now that Dick was up and about, did not worry him about the arrears. But from now on, he said, you must try and find the rent each week. So Dick took to singing along the streets of the town of Tydfil the Martyr, accompanied by little Myfanwy, who said thank you in Welsh and in English for what people were good enough to give. Sometimes her father was invited into public-houses to sing and she went with him and collected

25

what she could from those who listened to her father singing. Some wanted to give him beer to drink instead of money which would pay the rent and buy food, but for three years Dick refused to touch the drink. I am blind enough already, he said, laughing, making a joke of it so as not to offend those who would press him to drink. Then when he and little Myfanwy would go home they more often than not found Cathleen drunk and more than once found some man in the house with her as well. This went on for about three years until Cathleen ran away from her blind husband and little daughter to live with some man over in the Tredegar Valley.

Then it was that Dick took to the drink again and got himself drunk twice a day whenever he could. Little Myfanwy had all she could do to keep from her father enough to pay the rent out of the money she collected. They had food given them in the public-houses at which her father sang day after day and night after night, Sundays included. They did not go short of food. Landlords and landladies of public-houses were only too willing to feed them, for Dick was a singer without an equal in the town and district and wherever he happened to be singing was always crowded. His tenor voice, like a silver trumpet, drew people off the streets into the public-houses. He knew hundreds of songs and he could also stand in the long-room of a public-house and make up a song in his head there and then and sing it straight off.

He could also take a pint full of strong beer and drink it straight off, in one long intake of breath. His breath-control when singing and drinking was perfect. In the morning early he would be holding his head and demanding money from Myfanwy to raise the latch of the nearest public-house. Some nights little Myfanwy was alone in the little house in Company Row without a penny in her purse, nights when her father would ask her for her purse as they were walking home. It's only the money for the rent when the man comes, she would say. Never mind the rent, give me the purse, 'Fan, he would say, using only the second of the three syllables of her christian name and softening the f to v to make it sound like Van.

It was no good telling him when whatever it was had hold of him. Once he had the money out of the purse in his hand he was off to some place and to someone. It could not be to any public-house, for they were all closed. He came home with the dawn of the morning by himself and as dirty as though he had been working in the works or down a coal-mine and he would fall on the bed like a log and sleep until middle-day. Where can he have been? Myfanwy used to ask herself when only five years old. And how did he find his way to wherever he has been and find his way home again? She would know soon enough, God help her. Poor Dick had been sleeping up the coke-ovens with one of the women from the district called 'China', the women who took men up to the coke-ovens after all the public-houses were closed for the night. Sometimes they took drink with them to make a night of it.

It took Myfanwy the best part of three years to find out about this. It was one such woman that had caused Dick to move out of the little house in Company Row to this one-roomed cellar-dwelling in the district known as 'China'. But she had long since grown tired of Dick and his black mask. Other women had taken him on only to cast him off and by the time she was eight years old Myfanwy had seen and heard enough to make her appreciate the fact that life and love as between men and women can be very dirty and low. She loved her blind father for all that, loved him when the mask was off as well as she did when the mask was on, and she had many times vowed to herself that she would look after him for as long as God spared him. At his best he was a grand man, she thought. All the songs of the world were in his head, she believed, and her belief was strength-ened by the fact that John Thomas, better known as Ieuan

27

Ddu, had followed her father about for as long as she could remember. It was from her father's singing that Ieuan Ddu had written down in the writing of music many of the Welsh airs he put in a book and called it *The Cambrian Minstrel*.

That book Myfanwy had and thanks to Ieuan Ddu she was able to read in that book the very words she had heard as they came out of her father's mouth. But she could not yet read the music writing which Ieuan Ddu had put to her father's words – and the tunes were her father's too, but it was Ieuan Ddu had put the tunes into the writing of music so that other people could now sing them if they wanted to and bought the book. She did not have to buy the book. Ieuan Ddu gave her a copy for herself and her father and taught her to read words but not the music signs so as she could read it to her father. Her blind father was excited and delighted when she managed to read the title page right first time for him to hear when she was only seven years old. The long words in English she read as easy as the short words and when she had finished reading the title page her father cried: Well, done Ieuan Ddu. He is making a scholar of you, Van. Read it for me again, good gel. And she read it for him again:

'THE CAMBRIAN MINSTREL,
being
A Collection of the Melodies of Cambria
with
Original Words in English and Welsh,
together with
Several Original Airs
by
John Thomas (Ieuan Ddu),
Merthyr Tydfil

––––––––––

Merthyr Tydfil
Printed for the Author by David Jones, High Street.
1845.'

Well done, him, cried Blind Dick. Out of the heads and mouths of me and others he has put it all on paper and made a book. He must have had good schooling in the first place, Van. Now we know why he used to follow us about, don't we? Into the public-houses and wait for the song to come out of my head through my mouth. That's Ieuan Ddu all over, Van. He would go down to hell itself if he thought somebody there would remember and sing an old long-forgotten Welsh air for him to put down on paper. For paper lasts longer than men, Van. If only my eyes had been left in my head and I had kept myself as sober as Ieuan Ddu does then perhaps I should have – no, no, never. When I gave my heart to your Irish mother she sold me body and soul to the devil, Van. Leave her alone, God help her, wherever she is and whatever she is, said Myfanwy. If you want to talk nasty about anyone then talk about yourself and the bad women you have gone up the tip to the coke-ovens with. Shut up now and let me take off your mask to put some more goose-grease where it's sore just under where your eyes used to be. But what good me put goose-grease if you will drink and drink and drink and drink? I asked the doctor when he was getting up into his trap outside the surgery and he told me it's the drink is killing you and stopping your face under your eyes from getting better. To hell with my face and to hell with the doctor, cried Blind Dick. Shut up and lie quiet on the bed and don't knock the candle over, said Myfanwy.

As she gently applied goose-grease to the affected part she went on talking soothingly. You must have clean rag to wear under your mask to go out tomorrow, she said, helping him to undress. I'll have to patch a bit of this trousers before going to sleep, she said. He was lying awkward on the bed with only his shirt on and crying like a baby, as he did most nights in his drink. You won't leave me, will you, Van? he said this night again. Get in the clothes, she told him, going with the candle and his trousers to patch it sitting on her own bed in her own small corner of the room. He got himself under the bedclothes and again he said: But you won't leave me, will you, Van? Who is talking about leaving you? she said. I am, because I'm afraid that you will, he said. Go to sleep, she told him. I will if only you'll tell me, he said. Softer you are getting, she said. How could I ever leave you with no eyes in your head? Your mother did, didn't she? he said. Go to sleep and leave my mother alone I tell you, she said. Then you won't leave me? he said. Haven't I told you I won't, she said. Right, Van, now I'll sleep, he said. You and the doctor are quite right about the drink. No more, Van. Finished, he said. Humph, was all she said, having heard him say that hundreds of times. Yes, finished, he said. You'll see ... tomorrow. Never inside a public-house again. No, Van. Live tidy ... find a tidy house. Sing for money not for beer. Then perhaps they'll take us back into the chapel ... sing in oratorio again ... eisteddfods ... prizes ... He was asleep and she went on patching his one and only pair of trousers.

In a house at the corner of Lamb Lane the distinguished-looking man who had followed Blind Dick and Myfanwy as far as the archway leading into the district called 'China', where he had said goodnight to them both, this man was now writing by the light of an oil-lamp. One would think that he was writing in the waiting-room of the Taff Vale Railway Station instead of in a room in his own home. For he was writing fully-dressed and with a three-quarter height top-hat on his head. There was an air of greatness about the man even now when sitting down and wearing his hat where there was no need to wear it. He was writing an introduction to a book he had written but not yet published, a book he had entitled *Cambria Upon Two Sticks*. He sat back after he had finished another paragraph and thought for a few seconds before starting the next, which gives some idea of the type of man he was. He was writing in English but the sentences and the paragraph as a whole have a Welsh lilt –

for the man was a poet as well as many other things. Listen to him, this man who in a room in his own house is writing with his hat on after midnight.

And may I who have in this Wales sung thousand times to the wall of my school-room strains from Handel, Haydn, Kent and other masters, without a hope that I should be able to get even half-a-dozen young persons to persevere sufficiently to make their performance even of one piece approach in intonation that of English professionals. I ask may I not wonder at the present number of our choirs? I know how difficult it has proved to bring into, and preserve in, existence the first choir or glee party I had formed, and how impatiently every pupil would listen to my admonition as to tune and time. As to intonation and that articulation which should be as remarkable for its distinction as for its freedom from harshness, Welshmen had never thought of it, and no one doubted that he could give the diatonic intervals as truly as the best tuned organ. Mr David Francis, who had his lessons of me, has not forgotten, and never will forget, how much I laboured in this way; and he has, with many others, seen how much Welshmen can do, when once any number of their fellow-countrymen have seen their efforts once crowned with success ...

Easy to tell from that that he was a schoolmaster and musician. Anyone could be a schoolmaster in his time. There were forty-seven common day-schools scattered over a half-dozen mining districts and there was not a real schoolmaster in charge of any one of them. Females had the care and supervision of five and of the males who had charge of the remaining forty-two only ten had received some little instruction for the profession of teaching. The other thirty-two were made up of men who had failed in some retail business or other, miners and labouring men who had lost their health or met with accidents in mines or ironworks, ministers of the Gospel who had been found wanting and an ex-parish-clerk or two.

But Ieuan Ddu was a scholar and his school was a private school which was founded by the famous Taliesin Williams, whose bardic title was Ab Iolo Morgannwg. Ieuan Ddu was in every way a worthy successor to the famous bard – with this exception. Ieuan Ddu was not as good a teacher as his predecessor. Ieuan was too many things himself to be a very good teacher. He would sit at a high desk near the window, with his hat on more often than not, writing a book or a poem or music, in school, if you please. Now and again he would look to see what the boys in the schoolroom were up to and if they were not making too much row he would resume work on his epic poem, 'The Vale of Taff', or whatever he happened to be working on at the time. Only when the boys were too bad did he thunder at them with a bass voice which sounded like the lower register of an organ in a temper. Be quiet, he would then shout, and let me have quiet to go on with my work.

First thing each morning he would briefly give his boys a line along which to work throughout the day. One day painting – for he was a talented painter as well – and the next English. His music pupils got the best for their money for he talked well and at great length to them about music, particularly about choral singing. But geography, arithmetic, mathematics and English history he only referred to in passing, as it were. The only glimpse of history afforded the boys was the one caught on the rare occasions when Ieuan would read to them from North's translation of *Plutarch's Lives*. This might be called an annual event and a great event and experience for the boys, for Ieuan's voice, when he read aloud from a book he liked, made what he read sound like grand opera to his boys.

Yet he was not, definitely not a good schoolmaster in the opinion of the majority of the people of the town and district. His religious belief was an offence to most people; being a Unitarian he was regarded unfavourably by people of all creeds and denominations. Still, he had as many boys to educate as his little schoolroom behind his house at the corner of Lamb Lane could hold at all times, and those boys managed to pick up a good deal that was of educational value at Ieuan's school. He dropped crumbs which the boys picked up and somehow thrived on, but there was little or no method in his teaching. He left the boys to educate themselves during the greater part of their time with him. Many a morning he would place them under the senior scholar and on their honour before leaving them to catch the train – or the coach that left the Castle Hotel for Abergavenny to spend the day at some eisteddfod or other. For he competed both as a singer and as the conductor of his choir and glee party. Other days he would leave the boys to go and do what he regarded as important research work, which simply meant that he went to visit men who knew old Welsh airs and made them sing and sing until he had written down in the writing of music the tune of the air.

Then there were mornings when he would go and discuss the publication of a book or a poem with David Jones, the printer. And what about the thousand and one mornings and afternoons when, as he himself wrote against himself as schoolmaster, he sang to the wall of his school-room? 'And may I who have in this Wales sung thousand times to the wall of my school-room strains from Handel, Haydn, Kent and other masters ...' He looked and sounded magnificent when he stood with his back to the boys singing Handel's and Haydn's arias to the wall. The choruses he would also sing, changing his own glorious bass voice to false tenor, soprano or alto as required. No wonder it was his rendering of the choruses in four different voices that the boys liked best. At the end of a chorus or aria Ieuan would feel for the handkerchief and bring it out of the pocket inside the tail of his coat to wipe the sweat off his brow and face. He would turn around and see the boys all looking at him and he would remember them again and say: Why don't you go on with your work, good boys? You come here to learn, re-member, so stick to your work and never mind me. Then he would turn to face the wall and start singing again.

When he had finished singing to the wall he would send the boys home and after a cup of tea he would go on writing out the choruses of the 'Messiah'. He had only the one printed copy and the choir with which he hoped to perform the work for the first time in Wales was forty strong, all carefully selected and tested voices. So he had to write out at least forty sets of the choruses for the members of his choir. Such copying work would have been a weariness to Ieuan's flesh were it not connected with a masterpiece of musical composition. The copying helped Ieuan to plan his treatment of the choruses and sometimes whilst at work copying he would put down his pen and rise to sing no matter whether it was the middle of the day or the middle of the night. Many a time in the middle of the night he nearly frightened the life out of his wife, his first wife, for he married twice, by singing in the school-room in the middle of the night as though it were the middle of the day. Then, being as she was awake, she would go downstairs in her night-dress and with his old slippers on her feet and go out to the school-room behind the house with only a small shawl over her shoulders over her nightdress.

When are you coming to bed, Ieuan? she would ask. Do you want to catch more cold again? he said. What about you catching more cold? she said. If you go to bed and leave me finish I won't be long, he said. Will you ever finish? she said. No man can ever finish anything in this world but he can do a bit of something if only he's left alone, he said. Then you should have done something by now for I have left you alone most of our married life, she said. If you must work middle night try not to sing out loud, good boy. Wonder is you have not woke your niece and all the people of Lamb Lane and along the Glebeland. It will take more than my singing to wake my niece after the sleep has got her fast, said Ieuan.

His wife would nod and sigh and go back to bed and leave him to come when he liked. She had no children to turn to in the night. Her husband's niece lived with them and she was as tidy a young woman as a woman could wish to have about the house, and she was a great help, in the house and in the school behind the house, when Ieuan was away somewhere or other. The senior scholar left in charge on those days was glad of her help in restoring order when the boys, who had been placed on their honour by Ieuan, got beyond the senior scholar's control. Then he went and opened the door between the school-house and the house and called out loud for Gwenny. That was enough to make the boys scurry back to their places and when she came from the house into the school-house they were all like mice.

Yes, I know you, she said, looking them over sternly. Not enough of the stick do you get from my uncle, but you'll get it from me if you don't behave. Sometimes she was as good as her word and gave a couple of the worst offenders what for. Gwenny was a strong young woman and she was courting David Price at the time, she and David being members of her uncle's choir that had won many prizes and was now getting ready to perform the 'Messiah' for the first time in Wales. Yes, she was a great help but she was not the same as a daughter would have been to Mrs Thomas. However, the niece slept through whatever noise her uncle made at his work middle night. It was Mrs Thomas that he woke and it was she that went downstairs to ask him to try to be quiet and to come to bed before morning.

He had not made any row this night when writing the introduction to his book to be entitled *Cambria Upon Two Sticks*, but his wife woke up to find herself still alone in bed and she wondered what he was doing this night again. She could not hear him moving about or singing or anything. Had he come home? She had gone to bed early because she was not feeling very well. What time was it? The clock was downstairs and it could not be taken upstairs because it was a grandfather clock standing as tall as she did. But before going downstairs to see if Ieuan was in and to

35

see what he was doing if he was in, she would lie quiet until the clock struck the hour to tell her what the time was. She did not have to lie quiet for long before the clock struck two.

She got out of bed and put her feet in Ieuan's old slippers and put the little shawl she called a 'turnover' over her shoulders and went downstairs and found him busy writing with all his clothes and his hat on. Don't you know that it is two o'clock in the morning, Ieuan? she said. Never, he said, without looking up. Didn't you hear the clock strike? she said. No, he said. I won't be a minute now – don't say anything more for one minute. She sat down on a chair and looked at him and smiled and noticed how fat he was getting. He grew fat on work but she grew thin until she could not be much thinner and stand on her legs. She had not been feeling well for a long time but she had not said anything about the way she felt to him. What a fine head he had. She tried not to cough and disturb him so busy writing. What was he writing now again? He did not like to be asked what he was writing. Whatever it was it was coming fast from his pen – she had to cough now but it did not disturb him. He wrote:

But once the teacher of teachers is removed by death or by his calling, too often does his removal prove the decay, if not the deathbed, of what he had created ...

He sat back with a sigh of satisfaction and said: There. We'll leave it at that for now. You haven't touched the supper I left ready on the table for you, she said. I'll have it now – you go back to bed before you catch more cold, he said. And leave you to bother your head for another couple of hours? she said, getting up to take his hat off his head. Go to the table and I'll put a stick in the fire to boil the kettle. What time did you come home?

He collected his papers and put them away in the drawer of the old oak dresser. It was after eleven, he said, going to the table. Where were you till then? she said. In the Puddlers' Arms most of the time – but not drinking. All I took was two pints of shandy-gaff. We must do something about that little girl, he said. What little girl? she said. Blind Dick's little girl, he said. Public-houses every night and a cellar in China to sleep in is not right for a little girl. What can you do when she won't leave her drunken scamp of a father? she said, using the bellows to liven-up the fire under the kettle. Yes, what? he said. I told her that she could come and live here and sleep with Gwenny but she won't. I can't say that I blame her either. Dick may be a drunken scamp but he has more real music in his soul than any other dozen men you could name. He hears a drover from the other side of the Black Mountain humming a tune once and before you know it Dick has got it all in his head. Quick he is in his blindness to pick up the old songs from little more than a hint. Then the way he sings them in the gutters or the public-houses of Merthyr makes little gems of each and every one of them. At his best he is a better singer and musician than I am.

Mrs Thomas came to the table with the tea-pot and poured tea for Ieuan. I may as well drink a cup of tea now that I've made it, she said. Whatever he is as a singer and a musician he is no good as a father. Put in jail he should be for taking that little girl to live with him in that cellar down China. Whatever will she grow up to be in such a place? I am not so much afraid for her as for him, said Ieuan. It is he is the child of the two. Out of the scraps of learning she has had by coming here to me for an hour when she can she has made a mind of her own. None of the bad women who live down China can hurt the soul of that child. But living in that cellar where the smell of the river in the dry summer is so poisonous to the body – that's what I am afraid of. Mind to give her plenty to eat every time she comes here for her lesson. I always do and give her food to take home as well, said Mrs Thomas. If only I could get Dick off the drink and out of that cellar to live amongst tidy people I would make him the talk of Wales, said Ieuan. His voice is phenomenal and it's being wasted in public-houses and along the gutters of this town – and what a memory he has! Once – no, twice I sang falsetto the big aria from the 'Messiah' to test him. Then he gave it back to me better a hundred times than I had given it to him. I could hardly believe my ears. If I get half as good a tenor from London to sing the tenor part when I perform the 'Messiah' I shall be lucky. Have you finished your supper? said Mrs Thomas. Yes – and little Myfanwy is like her father in that respect, though she hasn't much voice yet, said Ieuan. But she is full of music and her memory may prove to be too good now that she is coming to me to learn to read and to read music as well. If she develops as I think she will and I had her and her father to train, then I should have to adopt two entirely different methods with them. Are you ready for bed now? said Mrs Thomas. Yes, said Ieuan. Light a candle for me to blow the lamp out.

CHAPTER 2

Haymaking

DURING the haymaking season Daniel Parry and Betty and their five children spent every Saturday afternoon and evening – weather permitting, of course – at one or other of the few farms still left on the outskirts of the town of Tydfil the Martyr. In addition to the few farms which had stubbornly held out against the industrialization of the area which for long had been known as the coal and iron capital of the world, there were about a dozen green fields here and there inside the industrial belt. There was haymaking on those fields during the haymaking season but it was not such fun as it was on the hayfields of the farms on the outskirts. Those fields within the black belt and at the foot of ash, clinker and slag-tips were dirty and it was rats and not rabbits that ran

38

out of the last patch when it was surrounded by the mowers with their scythes.

It was to the farm known as Danygraig, which in English means Under the Rock, that the Parry family liked best to go haymaking. For old Watkins the 'Graig was the last of the old farmers, those whose families had farmed the land for centuries before the coal-owners and ironmasters were thought of. Watkins hated them and their works. Old Ben Watkins would have it that he was ninety-two years old – and it's I that should know never mind how I look – was what he said when people looked at him incredulously and shook their heads. But I am, he insisted. I was born in seventeen-fifty-four and if I wasn't then my mother was a liar – and don't you call my mother a liar.

No one had called his mother a liar, yet few in the town and district could bring themselves to believe that he was as old as he claimed to be. Eighty at most they thought he might be and yet, when they remembered his eldest son who was farming in Breconshire, and his son's sons, who were farming in the same county, they had to admit that it was possible he was ninety-two years old after all. Whether or no he did not look anything near as old as that. He walked about on his own two legs or rode about on a mettlesome horse as well as any man of sixty could. His hearing was a bit bad and that was all that was wrong with him. Born and bred and lived all my life on this farm, he said proudly. Never slept a night away from it, never will. I'm going to keep it green and clean and sweet no matter what happens. The works and pits have closed in on Danygraig with their dirt and smoke but they shan't smother or dirty Danygraig. My farm it is, but no thanks to the coalowners and ironmasters and the lawyers who cheat for them.

He could have been had up for libel any day of the week for what he was always saying about the coalowners and ironmasters and their lawyers, but there was too much truth in what he said to warrant those he attacked taking action

39

against him. So they let the old man say what he liked and then kept a damper on it by sympathetic references to the decay of his faculties and so on. So Ben was left to say what he liked and he said quite a lot in Welsh, never a word in English. Another of his boasts was that he had never dirtied his tongue with an English word. He still rode considerable distances to fairs, starting off early in the morning and returning to Danygraig before night. He was said to be worth his weight in gold and he was considered to be one of the best to work for. His bark is worse than his bite, was what the three men who worked on the farm for him said. He was one of the elders of Bethesda Chapel but not a teetotaller. He drank beer but not much, and when the harvest was in he had a Noson Lawen, which means Night of Gladness in English, on his farm, in the house and outbuildings. Noson Lawen at Danygraig was something much more memorable than any of the forms of entertainment at Cyfarthfa Castle or Dowlais House, the residences of the two leading iron-masters.

Are they the only people who can entertain? said Watkins the 'Graig. Must we leave all the money and the pleasure to the English and we Welsh have all the dirt and pain? What? No, no, a fair share of pleasure is no sin. The drop of drink, did you say? Well, if the deacons at Bethesda Chapel object to me sitting in the big seat with them then they know what they can do. Tut-tut-tut. I have lived to be nearly a hundred and have never been seen worse for drink, have I? My father before me the same and he was farming here before the valley of Merthyr was dirtied at all. Well, then? What are you talking about?

It was he did most of the talking and it was others that had to do the listening. They did not mind, for old Ben Watkins was worth listening to. In the stream of talk that flowed from his lips there was much of it that was rich talk, rich in local history, humour and humanity.

Daniel Parry liked going to mow and make hay at

Danygraig. Before coming to the town of Tydfil the Martyr
he had worked on his father's farm in Carmarthenshire and
now that he was an iron-worker he enjoyed the afternoons
of Saturdays in the harvest season when he could lead the
mowers with their scythes and afterwards make the haystack. His sons, Henry and Joseph, went with him on the
Saturday afternoon when he and five others were going to
mow two fields of Danygraig that same afternoon and evening. Our dad knows how to cut hay, doesn't he, our Henry?
said Joseph as they stood back out of the way whilst their
dad led the mowers. The scythes swished and the grass fell
leaving a little lane almost as clean and smooth as the face
of a man who has just been shaved by a good barber. Six
men and six scythes and Joseph's father leading the van. Up
the field and then back down, for the fields of Danygraig
Farm were all on the slope above the town of Tydfil the
Martyr. From Danygraig one had a panoramic view of the
town and district from Dowlais Top down to Aberfan.

Now dad's sharpening his big knife, said Joseph. Scythe,
corrected Henry. I know, but a knife it is all the same, said
Joseph. Now they are going to start again. Daniel Parry
tossed the sharpening stone into the hedge a dozen yards
forward from the last cut and noted where it fell. Then he
led the way again and the other five mowers followed after.
If I could write the music I would make a song of dad and
those others cutting hay, said Joseph. They heard the sound
of a horse walking and when Joseph and his brother looked
over the hedge they saw it was Mr Ben Watkins riding up
the lane between the two fields. He stopped his horse near the
gate of the field to watch the six men mowing and when they
came to the end of the downward cut he raised his hand and
shouted: Well done, boys. A good day, good hay and good
cutting. There's beer and small-beer and plenty of everything in the corner of the field, remember. Right-o, Mr
Watkins, shouted Daniel. That's a fine horse, said Henry, as
Ben Watkins rode on up to the farm. I would like some

41

small-beer, said Joseph. So would I, but we shall have to wait till dad and the others stop cutting to have a drink and perhaps a bit to eat as well.

The 'small-beer' the boys were thirsting for was non-alcoholic herb beer which, when the cork was taken out of the bottle or jar, made as much fuss as though it were champagne. It gushed out all over the place until the gas or whatever it was grew tame. There were several kinds of non-alcoholic small-beer and they were all good drinking. Some kinds were white and others a pale brown. There were scores of recipes for making small-beer and nine out of every ten were good. Many men took it to work in preference to cold tea. It was cheaper to make than tea at 4s. a pound. Some people said that in some places in England the small-beer was as alcoholic as big beer and would make you every bit as drunk, but that was not the case with the small-beer brewed in the homes of the town of Tydfil the Martyr.

After a fine week the two fields of hay which Daniel and his fellow-workers had cut was fit to be got in. So all the Parry family, Daniel and Betty and the five children, went up to Danygraig Farm the following Saturday afternoon. There were about a dozen such families all told and the three farm-servants and the daughter of the woman who had kept house for Ben ever since his wife died ever so long before. The weather was lovely for the job and everybody worked with a will. Daniel was already cart-high on the stack he was making and it seemed almost certain that the hay of the two fields would all be got in before dark. Betty led the singing as surely as she led it on Sundays in Bethesda Chapel, the singing of the women and girls who were doing the raking and loading on to the wagons. Joseph went to sit under the hedge to listen as he would listen to singing at a concert or eisteddfod, critically, that's how he listened, and him only six years old. He was satisfied with his mother's lead but some of the women and girls dragged on her lead, he felt. They broke the rhythm ...

It was nearly five o'clock in the afternoon when Blind Dick and Myfanwy came out from the district called China through the archway over which there was the living-room of the shop to the right of the archway. Dick stopped and sniffed the air. Is it to the Three Salmons or to the Eagle you're going to sing tonight? said Myfanwy. I can smell the hay, said Dick. Before I go to the smoke and sawdust take me through the town and up to where I can fill my inside with the smell of the hay. What prank is this again? said Myfanwy. No prank, Van, I want to go close to the clean hay for a minute, that's all, said Dick. Then come, she said. With his hand resting lightly on her left shoulder they walked together up the little hill leading to Castle Street. Ieuan Ddu was on the lookout for them on the corner near the Lamb Inn, and not until after they had passed him did he loudly say: Hullo, where are you going that way? He's taken it into his head to go anear the hay, so I'm taking him up the lane between the fields of the 'Graig Farm, said Myfanwy. Coming, Ieuan? cried Dick. May as well, said Ieuan, following after. He kept about a dozen yards behind them until they were clear of the town, for he had to think of his position as schoolmaster. If the parents of some of the boys under his charge saw him walking through the town with Blind Dick then they might take their boys away from the school which was Ieuan's bread and butter after all.

Dick had to stop to catch his breath about the middle of the rise towards Danygraig Farm. My breath is getting short, he said. I shall have to do more walking and less drinking, Van. I have told you enough, she said. Tell him you, Ieuan. He knows what he is doing without me telling him, said Ieuan. Yes, I know, said Dick. Where are we now? On the middle of the rise to the 'Graig Farm, said Myfanwy. How is it looking about here? said Dick. About the same, said Myfanwy. The same as you remember it this time of year. I'm trying to remember it, said Dick. Is the fire-tip from the Dowlais ironworks much nearer the

Farm than it used to be? It's too near, said Myfanwy. The fire that took my eyes will take the Farm too, said Dick. Not whilst old Ben Watkins lives, said Ieuan. Oh, for my eyes, groaned Dick. You've got my eyes, said Myfanwy. So don't start crying and wet the inside of your mask. Have Mrs Thomas got any more goose-grease for me to put on his face in the night, Ieuan? I expect so, said Ieuan. Call and see when you're passing. If she has not got any of her own no doubt she can get some from the Castle Hotel. Come on now that I have caught my breath, said Dick.

Now that Ieuan has mentioned the Castle Hotel we may as well say all that need be said about it whilst he and Dick and Myfanwy are going up the rise to the farm. We said that there were about two hundred public- and beer-houses in the town and district but we did not mention the hotels, the Bush and Castle hotels in the town of Tydfil the Martyr and the Bush Hotel at Dowlais. These three hotels are not for working people but for the professional men of the town and district and for travellers who can afford to stay a night or two over the week-end in them. The 'big four', the coal-owners and ironmasters who own and control the town and district, have also been known to patronize one or other of these three hotels, which have their own stables, carriage-houses, gardens and hothouses and ever so many other things which the ordinary public-house has not got. In their largest dining-rooms they can serve dinner to a score or more people without any trouble or crowding. The Castle Hotel has a little covered carriage of its own to meet the trains and to take guests who are leaving to the railway station. Two horses drawing this carriage and a footman-porter to assist the coachman, who never gets down off his seat to handle luggage. But he shares the tips. Then the coaches for places to which no railway has yet been laid stop to unload and pick up passengers at these three exclusive hotels. Only after the patrons of these three hotels have been accommodated can ordinary people get what seating there

44

is left on the coaches. Ieuan Ddu, one day when he wanted to go by coach to the Eisteddfod at Abergavenny, could not get a place on the coach which stops outside the Castle Hotel. Ieuan made quite a disturbance and claimed that he was as good and as important as any of those who stayed at the Castle Hotel but that did not get him a place on the coach. So he was glad of a lift on a huckster's flat cart in the end. The three hotels and all facilities inside and out and to and from were strictly reserved for their patrons.

Crawshay of Cyfarthfa Castle and Sir John Guest, M.P., of Dowlais House, both made use of these hotels when they wanted to gather the most influential townspeople together for the furtherance of the interests of these two mighty ironmasters. It was better to give them a feed and plenty to drink and afterwards a talk at the hotels than have mere townspeople at the castle or at Dowlais House. We shall have occasion later on to refer to certain gatherings at these three rather exclusive hotels. Some said it was a good thing to have three such hotels in the town and district.

Whether it was a good thing or no enough has been said for the moment about those three rather exclusive hotels. Blind Dick and Myfanwy and Ieuan Ddu are now in the lane between the two hay-fields of Danygraig Farm and Dick is gasping for breath again. In one of the two fields women and girls are singing as they work and all three standing in the lane are particularly struck by the voice of the leading singer. That woman can sing whoever she is, said Dick. It's Betty Parry, said Ieuan. Lovely voice and she knows how to use it. Let's go nearer, into the field, where's the gate? said Dick. Just here where you are standing, said Myfanwy. You'll have to climb over for there's a chain from the gate to the post. I'll go first to see that you land safe on the other side, said Ieuan.

He was climbing over the gate when old Ben Watkins came riding down the lane and shouted at him. Hoy, where do you think you're going? Get down off my gate. Ieuan got down on the inside and waited there for old Ben, who when he rode down to where all three were waiting cried: Oh, I didn't know you, Ieuan. Why climb the gate when you can open it? Hullo, Dick, you're out of bounds, aren't you? Your little gel is growing – but let me tell you that you're trying to get into the wrong field. Those working in that field are the tea and small-beer people, the strict chapel people. All those who like a drop of real beer are working in this other field. Got to separate them on towards the end of the day when the thirst grows – I expect you can do with a drink after walking up the rise so come and have one in this other field. I've got better beer than you can get anywhere down in the town. It was to smell the hay my father came up here – thank you all the same, Mr Watkins, said Myfanwy. I'll be glad of a drink, said Dick. Then you shall have one. Come on, said old Watkins, turning his horse about. We shall get these two fields in before dark.

You are right, Mr Watkins, Dick was saying a couple of minutes later. This is good beer. Remember that the time is going on, said Myfanwy, sipping small-beer. He's got to go and sing till stop-tap at the Eagle or the Three Salmons, Mr Watkins, she explained. I haven't *got* to go, said Dick. Now that I am up here out of the town let me stay and don't nag me, Van. If I go to sing for Davies the Eagle I shall 'front Jenkins the Three Salmons, and if I go to sing for him I shall have a bad name with Davies the Eagle. You must sing for one or the other for me to collect enough money to keep us over the Sunday, sing for them or along the gutters of the High Street, said Myfanwy. If it's the few shillings then he shall earn them easier up here where he is, said Ben Watkins. We will have a Noson Lawen when all the hay is off these two fields and on the stacks. Three shillings I will pay you to stay where you are for the night, Dick. I'm staying, said Dick. Then give me the money to go down town to get food for Sunday before the shops close, said Myfanwy. Shops won't close till eleven o'clock, said old Watkins. Food and better food than the shops do sell you shall have to take home from here. So go and help to rake what's left of the hay off the field, good gel – and you're a big fine man Ieuan. Go and do some pitching up on to the stack now that it's got so high. I haven't pitched hay for years and years, said Ieuan. But you have pitched hay in your time? said old Watkins. Well, I was born on a farm in Carmarthenshire, said Ieuan. Then go and help another Carmarthenshire man, Daniel Parry – he's on the top of the stack in the corner of the other field. Off you go. I'll look after Dick.

Ieuan chuckled and Myfanwy smiled as they went together to help to finish getting the hay in. Oh, cried old Watkins, that horse of mine have gone back to the stable. Never mind. He took Dick's arm and said: Come with me over to the corner of the field out of the way, the corner where I keep the drop of beer. But you mustn't drink much now before you sing in the barn after the hay is in. Must you wear that old black thing over your face and head all time? Yes, worse luck, said Dick.

In the other field Ieuan was pitching hay off the wagon up to Daniel Parry, who was up on the haystack. Myfanwy was raking hay inexpertly when a six-year-old boy came near and said: Hullo. Hullo, boy, she said, speaking like a woman. I know you, he said. Do you? she said indifferently. Yes, he said. I heard your father singing one day on the Square in front of the Market House. He's the grandest singer of all for a man but my mother is the grandest singer for a woman in all the world. What's your name? she said. Joseph Parry, he said. I can sing too. I have sung by myself in our chapel. Do you go to chapel? No, she said. Then you'll go to the burning fire for sure, he said. Go from me now before I give you a clout, she said. Where's your father? he said. No odds to you but he's over in the other field with old man Watkins, she said. Do you go to school, boy? No, but I wanted to go to the new school next door to Saint David's Church, he said. My mother it was said no. It is the English Church

47

School and no Welsh speaking to be heard there. All English to make us boys forget our Welsh. I can read Welsh from the Bible and hymn-books, long words and all. Can you? No, but I can read English long words and all, she said. Then where did you have your schooling in English? he said. Nowhere, she said. I have been in and out of Ieuan Ddu's house with the school at the back, and when the boys have gone home he has given me a book and told me first the letters, then the words. I have been there late in the night after putting my father to bed safe. Then it is I can manage the words best with my mind at peace. Ieuan he is writing, words or the music writing, and he leaves me in peace too. I want to learn the music writing, he said. That's neither Welsh nor English, is it? No, she said. Ieuan Ddu told me the music writing is the same the world over. My mother wouldn't let me 'tend Ieuan Ddu's school either, he said. Your mother's very particular, isn't she? she said spitefully. She hasn't got the money to pay for me to go in the first place, he said. If she had the money she would not let me go to Ieuan's school because he goes to the Unitarian Chapel. What is Unitarian? Listen now, good boy, she said, her two hands clasped over the handle of the rake. In a hayfield I am and not before the magistrate asking me questions in the police court, is it? Do I ask people what Unitarian is? Whatever it is and whatever Ieuan Ddu is is good enough for me. If more than that you want to know then there Ieuan is over there with his coat off putting hay up to the man on the stack. The man on the stack is my father and nobody can stack hay like him, said the boy. Nobody can sing like your mother and nobody can stack hay like your father – go now, little boy, before I give you that clout side of your head for sure, she said. Little boys should be seen but not heard. How old are you then? he asked. Older than you are a good bit, she said. I'm nearly six, he said. And I'm gone nine, she said. Joseph's mother struck the note again and led all on the field in the singing of another old Welsh air,

48

one that had to do with harvesting. Her voice and Ieuan Ddu's big bass voice were the top and bottom of the singing and in between all the other voices fitted and blended perfectly. Joseph and Myfanwy stopped talking to join in the singing.

Over in one of the corners of the other field old Watkins was sat talking with Blind Dick, who had a half-pint mug full of home-brewed beer in his hand. I am all right for the night for I slept a couple of hours this afternoon, Watkins was saying. I shall have to have glasses before long. I used to be able to look down on the town from here and I was able to tell by name most of those walking the roads down there. All I can see now is that it is like a fair down there – but what kind of talk is this I'm pouring into the ears of the blind? I do forget, for I am getting on to the hundred mark, see, Dick. And if I am spared to live a hundred years what will I have had? The sorrow of seeing the green earth blackened and men mutilated in the dirt I have fought off from all around me. I have fought the good fight. Man after man who worked for me on this farm have deserted me to go down there to work in the dirt for a few extra shillings a week. Now some of them can't work at all. They are minus hands, arms and legs, like all the maimed men who used to work in the fitting-shop of Penydarren Works down there in the dirt. What good all those people down there scramble in the dirt? For who – and for what? Some day when I have more time I'll tell you. Then perhaps you will be glad you can't see what I see every day from up here on the rise. Now I must go up to the house to see if that housekeeper of mine have got supper ready for all these people. Drink your beer and come you with me now.

The old man grunted as he put a hand on Dick's shoulder to get himself up on his feet. I get stiff after sitting a bit these days. Give me your hand across the field and up to the house for this is strange country to you, no doubt. Hand in hand they went across the field and up to the greystone farmhouse. The housekeeper and her daughter with her now had everything ready for when those in the fields had got all the hay in. She had supper laid in the house for the chapel people who did not touch the old drink, and for those who did she had laid supper in the big barn, where the old harpist with his harp had already had his supper.

Hullo, Shenkin, said old Watkins to the old harpist. Had your supper and ready to start playing as soon as they come, are you? Quite right – and look who I have brought to sing with your harp. Blind Dick and my harp know each other, said old Shenkin. Yes, but he must have supper before they come too, said old Watkins. Come on Dick, sit and eat your bellyful and be ready to start soon as they come from the fields. Come, come, put food for him, he shouted. The housekeeper's daughter waited hand and foot on Dick whilst old Watkins went to the stable for his horse, which he mounted and rode down the lane between the two hayfields, their close-cropped and clean faces now blushing golden-red under the tired eye of the setting sun.

Well done, well done all of you, shouted old Watkins, pressing hard on the stirrups with his feet to half-stand clear of the saddle. A bit of hay we have got for the winter that's coming again. Come now when you like. Supper is waiting and so is Shenkin the harpist. Put all the tools in the wagons and let the children have a ride with them up to the house, good people. He chuckled as his eyes rested on Ieuan, now standing in the shadow of the high haystack mopping his brow with his handkerchief. He had taken off both coat and waistcoat and his shirt was wet with sweat for the first time in years. He perspired rather freely when conducting his choir but never had his shirt been so wet with sweat as it was now.

Old Watkins waited for Ieuan to come, carrying his coat and waistcoat, across the field and through the gateway into the lane. Better put your coat and waistcoat on, Ieuan, he advised. Too fat you are getting. Before long you will have trouble in getting your belly inside your trousers. No wonder. How often do you come up out of that town down there? He turned his horse and Ieuan walked beside it up towards the farmhouse. Not often enough, said Ieuan. I should walk up the rise and a couple of miles across the tops of these hills every day, I know, but there is so much to be done down there in the town. Yes, no doubt, said old Watkins. How you can live and grow fat in the dirt and the stink of the place I don't know. Every man to his taste, said Ieuan. I like living down there in the town. Then you are welcome to for me, said old Watkins. Now go to your place in the barn with the thirsty ones.

What a supper they all had! There were a dozen sizeable families made up of sixty-nine children, twelve men and twelve women. That is ninety-three for a start. Then there were another seven made up of Blind Dick and Myfanwy and Ieuan, the three men-servants and old Shenkin the harpist. That makes a hundred without counting old Watkins and his housekeeper and her daughter. There was beer and small-beer and tea and milk to drink for a start. To eat there were sirloins of beef, roast lamb and pork, boiled ham and pickled onions or cabbage just as you liked. Plenty of potatoes of course. Home-made bread and loaf-cake but no puddings, or anything sloppy. Green peas and broad beans for those who liked them.

Old Watkins did not sit down to eat at any of the tables. With a bite in his hand or a cup of tea or a mug of beer he was one minute with those eating in the biggest room of the farmhouse and the next minute with those eating in the big barn. Come on, eat, eat a bellyful, good people, he kept on saying. In the big barn Shenkin the harpist played whilst the people in there ate and drank, so the people in the barn were luckier in one respect than those who ate and drank in the house, where they could only just hear the voice of Shenkin's harp, which only tantalized them. But they stayed to eat a good supper all the same. After supper the

51

people who had had supper in the house went across to the big barn and all but one stayed for the Noson Lawen. The housekeeper's daughter had promised, come what may, to meet her young man down the town by the shows on the ash-tip between the Taff River and the Glamorganshire Canal. It was on that strip of made ground between the river and the canal the roundabouts and the shows with their wonders were situated during the six best months of the year, and it was down there the housekeeper's daughter hurried after she had done her share of the washing-up.

All the others went to the big barn and never was there a better Noson Lawen at Danygraig Farm than on that night. Never before had there been such talent at a Noson Lawen, which, as we said before, means Night of Gladness – or, if you like, Night of Joy – in English. Just think. First there was John Thomas, better known as Ieuan Ddu, a name you cannot translate correctly into English. In English it could either mean Black Jack or Black John, Dark Jack or Dark John – just as you like. Anyway, his presence, even supposing he did not say a word or sing a note, would make any Noson Lawen memorable. We won't say anything about Shenkin the harpist, for there were plenty of his sort about. But there was only one Ieuan Ddu. Pity he was so fat, but then he had the height on which to carry his fat. He was well over six feet in height and the top part of him, his neck and his head and his face with the whiskers, compelled admiration. There was a light in his eyes which never went out – except when he was asleep, of course. It was obvious to everyone who saw him that the man had something in him.

And what about Blind Dick at his best, as he was this night at the Noson Lawen in the big barn of Danygraig Farm? He and Ieuan Ddu joined their magnificent voices in a tenor and bass duet which thrilled us all. The funny thing was that the blind man was the most sure of the two. Later he stood by the side of the harpist and sang penillion – which in English simply means verses – to a variety of Welsh airs. Whilst he was singing this kind of Welsh singing Ieuan Ddu had his notebook and pencil ready, waiting for something original or unknown until then to come from Dick's mouth. One did come right at the end of the penillion singing and a little gem of an air it was. Sing that again, Dick, shouted Ieuan, and Dick obliged him by singing it again for Ieuan to put it down in the writing of music.

Such a night of joy and gladness as this was in haymaking time in 1846 is now beyond description. Who will ever forget Betty Parry's singing that night? Her children hardly knew her when she sang that duet in Welsh with Blind Dick. Myfanwy sang, but in English, and sang rather defiantly, we thought. If I am not mistaken one of the songs was an Irish song, the words in English, of course. She had a lovely voice, thin, and pure. After she had sung twice Joseph Parry said to his mother: Shall I sing now by myself, mam? Wait till you're asked, she said. He went from her side across to where old Watkins was sitting and said: Will you ask me to sing by myself, Mr Watkins? Certainly, boy, said old Watkins. Joseph sang twice by himself, in Welsh, and it was alto his voice was. He was very sure of himself for six years old. After him all the children wanted to sing by themselves, each child by him or herself, I mean. And most of them did sing by themselves, and their mothers would never have allowed them to sing by themselves in front of such a great musician as Ieuan Ddu had they not been able to sing well.

What else do we remember about that Noson Lawen? I remember that Ieuan Ddu conducted the children in a children's part song which used to be so popular in the town of Tydfil the Martyr – and didn't he conduct their mothers and fathers in something as well? Then I remember that we all had a cup of tea in our hands before leaving. About a dozen of the youngest children were asleep in their mother's arms by then. It was getting on for midnight when they all said thank you and goodnight to old Watkins – no, not all.

The old farmer had persuaded Blind Dick and Myfanwy to stay the night, Dick to sleep on a proper bed and not a bed of straw out in the barn and Myfanwy to sleep with the housekeeper's daughter. There you are, said old Watkins after he had waited with the night-lamp in his hand until Dick was under the clothes of the bed he had ordered to be made ready in the barn for him. You will sleep better there than in that cellar down China. Why do you go on living in that den of thieves and vagabonds and bad women? Why do I go on living at all? sighed Dick. We must all live till we die, mustn't we? said old Watkins. You should think of that little gel of yours. Yes, said Dick. No good you say yes and not alter your ways after, said old Watkins. I like that little gel and I would like her to live here with me. And you can live here too if you like. What do you say now before you go to sleep? You are in your sober senses for once so say now yes or no. Ask Van, said Dick. She's the boss. Then I shall ask her first thing in the morning, said the old man. He could have saved his breath for Myfanwy said no thank you. She was too independent for her good even then.

At the bottom of the rise the dozen families and Ieuan Ddu went their different ways and as the Parry family were crossing Jackson's Bridge Betty Parry said: Well, well ... Before she says any more we may as well say as much as need be said about Jackson's Bridge. For it was the oldest bridge over the River Taff which takes its course through the town of Tydfil the Martyr. Yes, Jackson's Bridge is older than the old Iron Bridge that takes people over the River Taff near the district called China. Jackson's Bridge was erected in 1793, and that was two years before the Glamorganshire Canal came the twenty-five miles from down Cardiff up to Merthyr. Some say that the bridge was named after the man who erected it. Whether or no, whoever it was that built it did a good job.

It was on this bridge, which is only about a hundred yards as a bird would fly from the house in Chapel Row in which the Parry family lived, it was right in the middle of this bridge, getting on for twelve o'clock this memorable Saturday night, that Betty Parry stopped and said: Well, well ... What's the matter? said Daniel, with three-year-old Jane asleep in his arms. That's what comes by hurrying, said Betty. I knew there was something and all day I've been trying to think. Now the water in the river has told me. No water in the house over Sunday, that's what it is, said Ann. That's the first time in my married life for me to forget to get the water on Saturday to last over Sunday, said Betty. Come on home and quick to bed, you children. Your father and me must fetch water before we sleep. I'll come with you, said Ann. Leave it till first thing in the morning for I'm tired, said Daniel. So am I but I am not leaving it till the morning, said Betty. I have never once since I first married you carried water on God's day.

In case anyone may think that Betty is making a lot of old fuss over water perhaps it would be well to explain why water and the Sabbath day meant so much to her. This is haymaking time in 1846 and the River Taff is not a river at all. It is only a thin trickle of dirty and stinking water from one end of the town to the other. It has been partly dried by the needs of Cyfarthfa Castle and Cyfarthfa Works, and the drop left has been polluted if not poisoned by works' refuse of all sorts, not to mention all the dead cats and dogs drowned in it when in flood – and it's no use saying: What a shame! For three-quarters of a century coalowners and ironmasters had made and taken millions of pounds sterling out of the place still without water. There are forty thousand people of the town of Tydfil the Martyr now, in 1846, dependent on twelve public wells for water of extremely poor quality. This bad water from these public wells has to be paid for at so much a bucket, so the poor working-people of the place have to go without or go to distant springs. The people who can afford to pay are just as badly-off during the periods when the wells are on the dry side and the water is thick with what is politely called 'animal matter'. Decayed animal matter which stinks, I mean.

There are several springs at quite a distance from where the mass of the people live near to the works in the town of Tydfil the Martyr. A woman has to spend best part of a day in the summer to get two buckets of water from one of these springs, and two buckets of water is not much for a family's drinking and ablutions, especially when the breadwinner has to cleanse himself of the dirt of the mine or ironworks. Daniel Parry and Betty Parry were clean people who tried hard to keep themselves, their children and their home as clean as a new pin. So one of their main preoccupations was water. Then Betty had made a point of doing as little as possible on Sundays. So she always got water for the week-ends on Saturday, but she had forgotten to get it this Saturday.

So after putting four of the children to bed she and Daniel and their eldest of five, Ann, are off up the Georgetown hill towards the best of the springs they knew of half-way through the first hour of the Sabbath she was breaking for the first time in her married life. Betty was carrying an earthenware pan, which she would fill and carry back on her head, a rolled towel between her head and the pan. Daniel had the two biggest buckets and Ann had the two smallest. I hope the water will be coming up through the spout and out pretty fast for I'm wanting sleep more than ever before in my life, said Daniel. We'll see when we get there, said Betty.

When they got to the first spring, which was about a mile and a half from where they lived, it was only to find the droppings of water coming out of the spout. So they went farther and fared better and still it was nearly four o'clock in the morning when they got back home. I'm tired now if ever I was, said Betty. Daniel was too tired to speak but when he did speak he said: I don't think I'll get up in time to go to chapel this morning, Betty. Daniel, she said, looking at him with her eyes wide open now. Daniel, she said again. I was only thinking, he said apologetically. Never say what you've just said in front of one of your own children again, said Betty. Ann, don't go to sleep by there, go on up to bed. After Ann had gone up to bed Betty told Daniel being tired was no excuse for neglecting his chapel. Better a man neglect his children than his chapel, she said. I'm going to bed, he said.

No doubt it was the years Betty had been servant in the home of the saintly Rev. Methusalem Jones that had made her the most loyal chapel member she was. She felt she owed everything first to God and His Son, next to the memory of the Rev. Methusalem Jones, and last but not least to her chapel, Bethesda Chapel. She had been confined to bed eight times with eight children and in all she had been absent from chapel fifteen Sundays due to child-bearing. But she had not been absent the Sundays of the weeks during which three of her eight children died. It was the Sunday that crowned each week of hard work for her, each week of pinching and saving and scraping. It was at the chapel on Sundays that she renewed her strength and spirit and schooling, for she went to Sunday School as well as to the services morning and evening. They went as a family three times each Sunday to Bethesda Chapel, of which they were all members, most faithful and loyal members. Life without the chapel and all it meant to them would be unthinkable and unbearable even were it thinkable.

Sunday was a great day in the town of Tydfil the Martyr, the day when the host of chapel people asserted themselves. Families took part in what was the next thing to a grand march to their respective chapels. There were eighteen chapels, nineteen with the little chapel on Incline Top, nineteen chapels with a total membership of three thousand, five hundred. Then add regular visitors, godly people but not actual members, and you have an army of at least five thousand marching to the chapels Sunday after Sunday. And what about the Sunday Schools of the chapels where

57

upwards of four thousand scholars had a good two hours' schooling every Sunday afternoon? Of course it has to be remembered that about a third of that number were adults and members of one or other of the chapels. I won't say anything now about the churches, Catholic or Church of England, for at this time they were more or less negligible in the town of Tydfil the Martyr.

Yes, Sunday was a great day, the day when those who went to public- and beer-houses instead of God's houses had to sing low, the day when a militant Nonconformity created an atmosphere which impressed visitors who during the day previous had jumped to the conclusion that the town of Tydfil the Martyr was just another patch of hell upon earth. Nothing of the kind, thank you. Families, after leaving their respective chapels, walked the High Street and Lower High Street, exchanging greetings and comparing notes and their talk was of sermons and the singing of hymns. Most of them were poor but well-dressed and respectable people and it was they that held the roads each and every Sunday evening after chapel. Some of them had to hurry home to go to work in ironworks or at collieries on Sunday nights, but they always took a walk after chapel up and down the High Street before taking a short cut home. They felt it was their bounden duty to be on parade for God on Sunday evenings.

It was just after haymaking time of 1846 that Robert Thompson Crawshay brought his seventeen-year-old bride, Rose Mary, to live with him at Merthyr, at Cyfarthfa Castle. William, Robert Thompson Crawshay's father, had bought himself a seat somewhere in England, a place called Caversham Park, to where he intended going soon to live there for the rest of his days. But first he had to settle Robert and his young bride at Cyfarthfa Castle and let Robert try his hand at managing the Cyfarthfa Works. It was high time for him to assume some of the responsibility. Henry could manage the works at Hirwain and Francis the works at Treforest. The old man was nearly sixty years old and worth eight millions sterling and in need of a rest away from it all. Caversham Park, near Reading, was a lovely place though a bit far away from the source of his millions. He would have to keep an eye on things and return to the place occasionally to see that the boys were following out his instructions. There were a number of things requiring his personal attention and he would have to straighten them out before leaving to take up residence at Caversham Park.

But first things first. Robert and his young wife must have a more spectacular welcome than anyone had ever had in the town of Tydfil the Martyr. He, the great William, would give all his workpeople a holiday with pay on the day that Robert and his seventeen-year-old bride, Rose Mary, were returning from their honeymoon. Cyfarthfa workmen should go miles down the Merthyr valley to meet the carriage and pair, take out the horses and then the men should draw the carriage along the road and through the streets of Merthyr up to Cyfarthfa Castle. The streets of the town, twenty thousand souls of which were almost completely dependent upon him for their living, would have to be lined thick with people ready to cheer when the young couple in the man-drawn carriage came into sight. Two miles of cheering they should have from the entrance to the town right up to the entrance to Cyfarthfa Castle. That would give Sir John Guest, M.P., and his wife, Lady Charlotte Elizabeth, sister of the Earl of Lindsay, a bit of a belly-ache, and the huge ball and banquet to follow would make it worse.

As already stated ironmasters are only human after all, and if they are occasionally a bit rough-tongued, as the greatest of the Crawshays was, it must be put down to the times and its strain upon the nerves and temper. Sir John Guest, M.P., had 'bested', to use William Crawshay's own word, his most formidable rival and competitor more than once or twice. Yes, 'bested' him again and again. Over the

seat in Parliament, when William Crawshay had stuck his
lawyer, the extremely clever and far from scrupulous Mr
Meyrick, up against him. What a hope! William had to
withdraw his candidate and leave the field to his rival and
competitor. Why didn't you stand against Guest yourself?
said one who would have supported him but not his nom-
inee, Mr Meyrick. I want no honours, parliamentary or any
other kind, that's why I did not stand myself, was William's
reply. I was born William Crawshay and I'll die William
Crawshay, he said.

Then there was the Taff Vale Railway, into which Sir
John Guest had put a cool hundred thousand pounds in one
lump – just to best me, said William Crawshay. Then there
were other things too numerous to mention. Competition
for markets for one thing. Never mind, said William. Now
going right down from the great William, by whose grace
the majority of the people of the town of Tydfil the Martyr
lived, let's listen to Daniel Parry, one of his workmen. He
had helped to draw the young couple up into Merthyr from
below Troedyrhiw, where the men had taken the horses out
of the carriage.

She looked a nice young woman, he told Betty. She
looked a bit frightened at first when we were taking the
horses out of the carriage. But Mr Robert put his arm across
her shoulders and no doubt told her it was all right. Why
didn't you go out to the High Street or Brecon Road to see
her passing in the carriage? I had to catch the drop of water
up at the spring, said Betty. Lot of old fuss for nothing, I call
it. If William Crawshay paid his men more and spent less on
his castles and his relations I'd think more of him, church-
man though he is. Oh, fair-play, he pays as well as any of
the other ironmasters, said Daniel. They'll all watch that
they don't pay too much, said Betty. Why don't they try and
get some water to the place? I've spent hours to-day again
trying to catch a couple of buckets of water. Why don't you
send the children to fetch water for you? said Daniel.

Children, indeed, said Betty. Ann was the only one big enough to stand her ground in the crowd around the springs. Now that she's working every day it's no good me sending any of the others.

I'll be taking Henry with me to work in the works next Monday, said Daniel. I've had a word with the manager of the rolling-mill and he told me to bring him as soon as I liked. Where are the boys? Out playing somewhere, said Betty. I was thinking about Joseph, said Daniel. Thinking what? said Betty. He's sharper than Henry and would take schooling better, I think, said Daniel. I was talking to a man to-day whose boy have started in that National School next door to St David's Church. The English School, you mean, said Betty. Perhaps it would not hurt our children if they learnt some things in English, said Daniel. It would make them more English and less Welsh, wouldn't it? said Betty. Would it? said Daniel. Of course it would, said Betty.

Joseph and Henry came in together and Joseph said: Mam, they have made the inside of the engine-house in the works look like a palace – haven't they, Henry? You're to start work in the works next Monday, Henry, said his mother. Am I, dad? said Henry. Didn't you hear what your mother said? said Daniel. And at one end – not this end but the other end – there is a place built in the old engine-house for a band to play on, said Joseph. How do you know it's for a band to play on? said Betty. One of the men working there told me, said Joseph. He said it will be the biggest ball and the best banquet ever to be held in Merthyr. Hundreds of people coming from away, he said. Never you mind, said his mother. Who told you to go anear the engine-house in the first place? Nobody, said Joseph. One man asked who I was and I told him we lived inside the works. If we do, said his mother, it is not for a boy your age to walk all over the works. You are getting to be too much of a roamer not only in the works but over the town of Merthyr as well. Talking to old riff-raff of Irish and English and bringing home

English words to mix with your Welsh. Much more of that and I'll have to tell your father; he must beat you, Joseph. Remember that now. Yes, said Joseph, but the very next day he spent all the afternoon by himself in the town. There was a band of six all told playing strange but lovely music on the Square in front of the Market House and Joseph stood to listen. Had they gone on playing for a week without stopping any longer than was necessary to catch their breath then Joseph would have stayed a week without food or anything.

During the brief intervals between selections the young man who played what Joseph called the 'trumpet' then but learnt later that it was called a 'cornet', the young man who played it came round collecting and Joseph was ashamed not to have as much as a halfpenny to give the young man. Joseph was grateful to those standing around who gave coppers to the young man and he almost hated those who did not. A man half-drunk staggered across from the Market Tavern to tell the musicians to go away with their damned noise but if he did ... The music-lovers standing around turned on him and had he not cleared off when he did he would have got what for, and Joseph would have been the first to kick him on the shins. The musicians themselves were encouraged to go on playing by the attitude of those who wanted to listen towards the man who called their music a damned noise. They did not understand what that meant for they were all foreigners who did not speak a word of Welsh or English. Joseph heard a man say that they were a German band. Whatever they were Joseph loved them and their music and he was sorry when they finished playing and were moving away to go and play somewhere else. He was about to follow them when a voice said: Hullo, boy.

It was Myfanwy. Hullo, he said. What are you doing in the town by yourself? she said. Listening to the music, he said. I wonder have they gone to play on Pontmorlais

Square? Perhaps, she said. Will you come with me to see? he said. No, she said, my father's across the road in the Market Tavern. Perhaps I will hear music tomorrow night too, said Joseph. Where? she said. In the engine-shed not far from where we live in the works, he said. What music can you hear in an engine-shed? she said. Don't you know? he said. She shook her head. Then I'll tell you, he said. Mr Crawshay of the castle is giving a ball with a band and all for his son just married and hundreds are coming from away – the man told me. What man? said Myfanwy. One of the men making place for a band to play in the engine-shed, which they have made like a palace, said Joseph. Oh, yes, Ieuan Ddu said something, said Myfanwy. Only we who live inside the works will be able to hear that music, said Joseph. But I tell you what. It would be no lie if I said it. Said what? Myfanwy asked. Said you were my sister, said Joseph. In the Bible it says we are all God's children. So if you come to the gate in the wall not far from Jackson's Bridge I will take you inside the works and up the bank of the canal to see the engine-shed. You take me, said Myfanwy. Can't I take myself if I want to? Certainly not, said Joseph. You don't live in the works. I can say I am taking food to my father who is working there, said Myfanwy. That will be a lie and everybody knows that your father don't work any more, said Joseph.

Whilst the two children were talking on the Square in front of the Market House half a hundred men were busy transforming the old engine-house into a banqueting hall and ballroom. But before we leave the two children on the Market Square we may as well take a look at the Market House, which is the biggest in Wales, as it should be being as the town of Tydfil the Martyr is by far the biggest town in Wales. The Market House was built, if you remember, in 1834, so it was twelve years old now and the people were getting used to it. I think you will find that it was designed by the same architect who made the design for the castle for

63

William Crawshay, who used to live, remember, at Gwaelodygarth House. He made a present of that house to his lawyer, Mr Meyrick, after Mr Meyrick had pulled something very profitable off for him. I tell you what, he said. I'm going to make you a present of Gwaelodygarth House, Meyrick. Oh, thank you, sir, said Meyrick, fetching pen and ink and paper, the tools of his calling. He wrote on the paper and William Crawshay signed his name to it without hesitation. Didn't even trouble to read it, being so happy at the time because of what his lawyer had pulled off for him. Later he fell out with Meyrick, his lawyer, and said: Get out of my house. Whose house? said Meyrick, producing the paper, deed of gift or whatever they call it. So you've bested me, said William Crawshay, now raging with temper in what he thought was his own house, having forgotten the day of rejoicing years previous on which he had made a present of it to the lawyer who never forgot anything. I'll make you pay for this yet, you ... , said William Crawshay. Mr Meyrick smiled and shrugged his shoulders, feeling quite confident that everything was in order. What a present though! Gwaelodygarth House was probably the finest house in the town of Tydfil the Martyr up to the time it was eclipsed by Cyfarthfa Castle. All that was an old story by this time and it was the Market House we were talking about anyway.

Before the Market House was built and opened for trade most of the trade of the town of Tydfil the Martyr was done on the streets, main streets and side streets. Some trade was also done in the small shops along the main street but that was nothing compared to what was being done outside on the streets. That was all right when the place was little more than a village but by 1834 it was a town larger than any in Wales and, what is more, was the recognized coal and iron capital of the world. Try if you can remember, in the 1830's, any town in the world with as many furnaces and coal-pits, any town in the world that produced half the amount of puddled iron and coal as the town of Tydfil the Martyr did. The coal and the iron was then renowned for its quality the world over. So there you have both quantity and quality. So it was entitled to a big Market House and it got it in 1834. Never mind if it was ugly. It was big, so big that the centre part of it alone once accommodated five thousand people, seated and standing, of course, to enjoy a big musical festival. That was only the centre part, which was flanked by two other similar but smaller – because they were narrower, that's all – market buildings. The Market Hall was above the building on the left and that was where many an artistic event was held, and it was where touring companies of players used to act their plays for a week or a season. As I think I have said before the Market Hall was a cold old hall in the winter, which was the season when the players came to act their plays there. Some of those who patronized them during the winters, particularly the brick-yard girls who filled the seats at the back, used to bring their own fire-buckets. Not buckets with water in them to put fires out but buckets with fires burning in them to keep you warm whilst watching a play of five acts and a farce after-wards for good measure. Many of the players used to take drink during the intervals between the acts, when they used to sneak out with a coat or a cloak over their stage clothes and with their make-up still on their faces to the Market Tavern, which was an integral part of the Market House. So it was very convenient for the players, too convenient for some of them. For some of them who slipped out after the first or second act stayed in the Market Tavern until chucking-out time at eleven p.m., leaving whoever would or could play out the rest of their parts for them. This was not altogether the players' fault. The most to blame were those who paid for drink for them and prevailed upon them to stay with them in the Market Tavern. We could tell of nights when the company was reduced to two and those two had to play as best they could several parts apiece. It is most remarkable what these people can do when they are put to it. One night, we remember, one man and one woman were left to carry on. The woman held the stage and soliloquized whilst the one man came on as four different men – disguised by hook-on whiskers and things, of course – to interrupt her non-stop soliloquy and hold brief conversations with her. He came on first to announce the coming of 'My lord', went off and put on whiskers and a cloak and came on as 'My lord' to embrace the lady who was holding the fort so valiantly. He said he was tired and went to rest, leaving his lady on the stage. He took his whiskers off and came on now with a moustache as the lady's lover and she egged him on to kill her husband. She drove him off the stage to do the deed and he did it off-stage and returned full of remorse to say: ''Tis done.' He went off to get horses, leaving her to soliloquize some more to give him time to disguise himself as the man who would say that he had met and killed the man who had killed her husband and now he was going to kill her, for the other chap before he died had told this chap that it was she egged him on to do it.

Yes, that was how these players managed when they had to – but as I have said it was not altogether the players' fault. The three stone buildings of the Market House, the main building and the narrower buildings right and left of it, with cobbled roads between the buildings, looked just like three of the works' engine-houses from the outside. But when you got inside it looked like the mart of all the world. Long lines of stalls loaded with all sorts of things and the aisles between the stalls cram-jammed with people. Now that we had this fine Market House it was a punishable offence for anyone to set up his standing on the streets outside and try to sell things. Everyone with things for sale had to display them in the window of a proper shop or on a stall in the Market House, which is as it should be in a town of the size and importance of our town. Outside the Market

66

House was the Square on which we left Myfanwy and little Joseph talking about what was to be held in the engine-house in the Cyfarthfa Ironworks the night after the one coming. Before going to see the inside of the engine-house in the Cyfarthfa Ironworks we must say a few words about the old man who is seated in a box with wheels under it just outside the main entrance to the Market House.

I said a man but he is only half a man, and a very old half at that. Every day since the Market House was first opened he has been sitting outside – weather permitting – the main entrance to the Market House. In bad weather he sat just inside the main entrance, where he was even closer to the Market Tavern. Most people have long since forgotten his surname but everyone in the town and district know him personally as Harri Hanner-Dyn, which is the Welsh for Harry Half-a-Man. Both his legs were amputated high up and without an anaesthetic after an accident in a coal-level in 1796. Now, well over seventy years old, he still has a stout body and a strong pair of arms but not a leg to stand on. So he sits in his box which has wheels under it as much the captain of his soul as ever he was. Is the oldest resident of the bigger of the two common lodging-houses in the district called China, from where he drives himself each morning in time to be at his place of business by nine a.m. With his hands working like little engines along the roads and what few pavements there are he pushes his box-car along from his place of residence to his place of business. On arrival there he takes off his cap and places it on the ground beside him. Then he looks rather defiantly at everyone entering the Market House. Some drop a copper in his cap, others do not. When there is twopence in the cap Harry suspends business to spend it in the nearby Market Tavern on a two of rum, which is his favourite drink. Then he goes back to his place of business. The next twopence he pockets with a sigh, for that is twopence towards his lodging-money of fourpence per night. Each alternate twopence received with

67

scant thanks is spent on rum and the rest he reserves for food and lodging. He is not a very nice old man and if it wasn't that he happened to be sitting there as we were passing we would not have troubled to say anything about him.

A cheeky old beggar, that's what he is, and a drunken old beggar into the bargain. Curses people under his breath when they pass without dropping a copper into his cap. To go back less than a week before to a night when Betty Parry was looking everywhere for Joseph. Joseph was 'walking the roads', as Betty and other Welsh mothers of the time used to say. He had been down the High Street and in the Market House seeing the sights all by himself and outside the Market House a man had jumped down off his horse and said: Hold this horse's head a minute, boy. Joseph held the horse's head and the man went into the Market House. Whilst holding the horse's head Joseph looked with sympathy on Harry Half-a-Man, who was swearing out loud this day. He had three-halfpence in the cap and was waiting most impatiently for the other halfpenny to fall. But the people passed him by one after the other until the old man could stand it no longer. He had to let go. He groaned and sighed and then swore out loud. He combed his beard with his fingers and spat. He glared at Joseph and the horse whose head he was holding.

Tell me, boy, he roared in Welsh. Tell me now. Is it only Jews do live in this town of Tydfil the Martyr? No, mostly Welsh for sure, said Joseph. Then Welsh Jews they are for sure, said the old man. Nearly half an hour I have been waiting here for a ha'penny to fall. Several tribes of people have passed me in and out of this Market House and I am not even a ha'penny the better off for their passing. The man whose horse Joseph was in charge of temporarily returned and gave Joseph two halfpennies before mounting and riding away. There you are again, boy, said Harry Half-a-Man. He's gone on his horse and I'm left here on my arse wanting a ha'penny. Here's a ha'penny, said Joseph.

Out of the hands of babes and sucklings – thank you, lovely boy, said Harry. What's your name? Joseph Parry, said Joseph. Then bless you and your house for ever, said Harry. Now go and hold the door of the Market Tavern open for me to drive in without stopping. Joseph held the door open and Harry drove his box on wheels through the open doorway. Joseph let the door go and went to buy toffee with the other halfpenny.

A lot more might be said about old Harry Half-a-Man but not much to his credit. There were days when he saved up throughout the day so as to make a night of it in the Market Tavern that night, and there were nights when he was too drunk to wheel himself to where he slept in a common lodging-house. But as it takes all sorts to make a world and a book we may have to say more about him later. For he is what is called a valuable link with the past and it is only when he is soaked in rum you can get him to bring the past forward. So we may have to go and sit near him one night in the Market Tavern, those of us who do want to know about the town of Tydfil the Martyr and the people who lived there in times past, I mean. Now perhaps we had better go and see how they are getting on in the old engine-house of Cyfarthfa Ironworks.

Joseph was right, it is like a palace. There is a flooring over the rails and dirt we used to see there, a flooring of springy floorboards for people to dance on. Sidewalls all decorated and strings of flags from one side to the other and hanging down from the rafters of the ceiling as well. William Crawshay himself was there when we got there, so the finishing touches were being applied under his personal supervision. There were hundreds of chairs with their backs gilded to look like gold in position along the sides of the ballroom – for we cannot refer to it as the old engine-house any longer. Then at the top end, the end nearest the castle, there were four tables in their length right across the room. Sixty chairs, thirty each side of each table, and counting the

69

chairs at the four tables gives us two hundred and forty. So two hundred and forty people would be able to sit down to food and drink at one and the same time. How many sittings would they have? we wondered. There was the bandstand in the far corner, where it stood about two feet or two feet six at most above the springy floor. What band were they having and how many players would there be in it? Only William Crawshay knew that, but judging from the size of the bandstand it would be a big band of at least thirty players. The room was about fifty to sixty yards long and about fifteen yards wide, so it wasn't so big after all. Yet it looked big. Perhaps that was because there was not a real hall of any size in the town. The wonder is that William Crawshay did not have the main building of the Market House cleared and put down a dancing floor there. Then he could have invited thousands instead of just hundreds. Flowers in pots were now coming in and being arranged around the bandstand. The other flowers for all over the place would no doubt be coming fresh from the Castle Gardens next day. All the rooms in the castle would be occupied that night and all the rooms in the Castle and Bush hotels had been reserved by William Crawshay for some of those he had invited. He was looking pleased with the place when we left.

The place was all lit up the next night with hanging lamps and other lamps fixed to the wall. The carriages came driving down the private road into the works whilst it was still daylight and the ladies and gentlemen got out and went arm-in-arm into the banqueting hall and ballroom. The superintendent and inspector and two sergeants and a half-dozen constables of the recently reorganized police force were on duty to see that no uninvited persons were admitted, and also to see that none of the townspeople or workpeople should poke their noses in. But there were two children who somehow or the other managed to see part of the show before they were spotted by a police-sergeant.

Myfanwy and little Joseph Parry got there early and hid behind two large packing-cases behind the bandstand. From there, a peep at a time, they saw the most wonderful sight of their lives and heard the band play as well. The band was conducted by a man from London and he had brought most of the string section down with him. The other instrumentalists were from the town and district but they were every bit as good as the players from London. Oh, yes.

Between dances William Crawshay walked about bowing and smiling and introducing people to each other. It was with pride that he introduced a protégé of his, Penry Williams, the rising young painter, who had hurried back from Rome to be present at the banquet and ball in honour of his patron's son and daughter-in-law. Penry Williams had, when a boy, worked with his father, a house-painter, and during the time he worked with his father the boy had painted several of the signs outside our public-houses. The Lamb; The Lamb and Flag; The Rising Sun; The Wheatsheaf; The Volunteer and other signs. His work as a sign-painter was brought to the notice of William Crawshay, who arranged for him to go to London to study and work. He did very well, almost too well, in London, where he painted some pictures for Sir John Guest and so annoyed his patron, William Crawshay. An artist honoured by the patronage of an ironmaster worth eight million pounds sterling has to be very careful lest he offend him.

However, he had been forgiven by this time and was again basking in the sunshine of his patron's smile. Behind the packing-cases Myfanwy and little Joseph Parry were almost drunk with delight and getting reckless. During the dances they now stood with their heads above the packing-cases, nodding their heads in time with the band and waving their hands. There were never less than a hundred couples on the floor for the round dances and never less than thirty sets for the square dances – for the tables on which the guests had dined had been taken away. Only one part of one remained against the back wall, where it now served as a huge sideboard from which gentlemen served themselves and their partners with drinks from bottles containing all sorts of liquid refreshment. The smell of the flowers, the sound of the band and the spectacle as a whole was too much for Myfanwy. It went to her head and she lost her head, lost it to the extent that she left her hiding-place behind the packing-case and went and mingled with those who had just finished dancing. I wanted to go closer to some of those lovely women in their lovely clothes, was how she explained her seeming madness to Joseph about a week later. The nine-year-old girl with the smile of a grown-up woman and neatly-dressed and pretty but quite out of place in that brilliant assembly, where she soon attracted attention, in particular the attention of the police-sergeant who had already spotted her and Joseph behind the packing-cases soon after he arrived. He had children of his own and had decided to keep a blind eye in their direction, but now he had to take action. He and William Crawshay were approaching Myfanwy from different directions and the ironmaster got to her first. What are you doing here? he asked. I only came to see, sir, she said. Who are you? he asked. Blind Dick's daughter, she said. And there's a boy behind the bandstand as well, sir, said the police-sergeant. It's a little boy I brought with me, said Myfanwy, though it was the other way round actually. It was Joseph that talked her into coming. How is your father? said William Crawshay, who knew Dick and knew of his plight. He's middling, thank you for asking, said Myfanwy. It's all right, sergeant, said William Crawshay. He put his arm around Myfanwy's shoulder and said: Let's go and find that little boy. He only wanted to see, and to hear the band more than to see, she said. Where is he? the ironmaster asked when he and Myfanwy reached the spot where she had left Joseph. Gone by the look of it, she said. Who is he? he asked. A little boy I brought with me – I forget his name, she replied.

William Crawshay was a hard man but not so hard as all that. Of course he had heard of Blind Dick and had heard him spoken of as a most remarkable singer. And this was his little girl, and a pretty little thing she was, God help her. Would you like something to eat? he said. No, sir, thank you for asking. Will you take this, please? he said, holding out a golden sovereign. We're not short of a shilling, she said, her face hardening. He put the sovereign back in his pocket. Will you bring your father to see me up at the Castle some day? he said. What for? she said. There's nothing you can do for him. He wants for nothing but his eyes and you can't give his eyes back to him. Let's go outside, he said. When they were outside he said: Which way are you going home? I came through the works, she said. I wouldn't go back that way if I were you, you may get hurt, he said. I'll walk up this way to the Brecon Road with you. You needn't trouble, I know the way, she said. It's no trouble, he said, Come along.

The ironmaster worth eight million pounds sterling and the daughter of Blind Dick walked slowly up the road together. It was a lovely night and the strains of the band playing in the ballroom behind and below them could still be heard by them. For the first time in years the ironmaster was at a loss for something to say. I want to help if I can, he said at last. We get all the help we want, she said. From whom? he said. From Ieuan Ddu whenever we want help, which isn't often. My father can still sing if he can't see. Ieuan Ddu, said the ironmaster. Is that the man who now runs Taliesin Williams' school in Lamb Lane? Pity you don't know for sure and Ieuan Ddu the greatest musician and conductor Merthyr has ever had, said Myfanwy. Yes, I should have known for certain, said the ironmaster. Myfanwy waved a hand and said: It's all this, no doubt, your castle and your works, that hide the good of the town from you. There's talk in the public-houses that you're leaving here soon. What do they say about me and about my leaving in the public-houses? the ironmaster asked. Let them have their say, said Myfanwy evasively. You shouldn't go around public-houses, said the ironmaster. Where else will I go with my father like he is? said Myfanwy. It's either the public-houses or the gutters for us. Yet you won't let me help in any way, said the ironmaster. I could arrange through my son, who will be living at the castle when I've gone to live elsewhere, to – You needn't trouble to arrange anything for us, sir, said Myfanwy. We shan't starve. You needn't come any farther, I know my way from here. How old are you? said the ironmaster. I shall be ten next birthday, she said. Goodnight and perhaps I should say thank you for not letting the sergeant of the police make a police court case of it. And I may as well take that sovereign if you still want to give it. He handed her the sovereign and smiled at her. You're a strange child, he said. Am I? she said, putting the sovereign in her purse. If ever you're in need of anything you know where the castle is, he said. You took good care to let all who live in the town of Merthyr know where your castle is, she said. He chuckled but said nothing. Never mind, she said. You'll be going away soon and you're getting old into the bargain. So make the most of the time that's left to you. I wouldn't have taken the sovereign if my father didn't want a suit bad. I have patched his trousers till it's more patch than trousers. But don't you say anything about giving me this sovereign, for if he got to know I had it from you he would throw it in the River Taff. I shan't mention it to a soul, he said. I'll thank you not to, she said. Goodnight to you. Goodnight, my child, he said. Perhaps it's not all your fault after all, she said. I hope not, he said. So I will say thank you as well as goodnight, she said, and off she went down the Brecon Road towards the town of Tydfil the Martyr. She had left her father singing in the long Room of the Old Tanyard Inn and she would have to hurry to be there before stop-tap. The ironmaster walked slowly back to the ballroom, feeling better for the breath of air and better again for the talk with the strange child.

Choirs and Conductors a Penny a Bunch

IN the town of Tydfil the Martyr alone there were four choirs now and in the town and district, which includes Dowlais, there were ten choirs all told. We don't mean chapel choirs but choirs formed irrespective of chapels or denominations to perform a work or compete at eisteddfods, which, as you no doubt know, are competitive musical festivals. There are also literary and poetry competitions at our eisteddfods. The Parry family had two of its members in Rosser Beynon's choir, the two being Henry and Joseph. Henry had been working for more than a year and Joseph would be starting to work in about a year's time, for he will be eight next birthday. Ann was in service at the doctor's house now and she slept there and only came to see her parents and brothers and sisters two evenings a week and again in time for tea at home on Sunday, after which she went to chapel as a member of the family. But after chapel she left the family to walk the High Street with young Robert James, the youngest conductor of singing any chapel in Merthyr had. He conducted the singing at Bethesda Chapel, 'Arweinydd y gan' is the Welsh way of saying 'Conductor of singing' when it is in a chapel. For a conductor of a choir which is not a chapel choir we just say 'Arweinydd' and leave it at that. Now young Robert James was most musical and he had learnt music under Rosser Beynon. Robert James's friends called him 'Ropyn' and the few who did not like him called him 'Ropyn Trwyn',

75

meaning 'Robert Nose', for Robert had a rather big nose.

That did not prevent Ann Parry from falling in love with him, neither did it prevent her parents from liking him. All the family liked him, Joseph in particular. It was he got Rosser Beynon to take Joseph, small as he was, into his famous choir, Rosser Beynon's choir, I mean. That was all right. But Ann had annoyed her mother by sprinkling her Welsh talk with English words since she had gone to service at the doctor's house. This doctor was the works' doctor whom William Crawshay had brought into the place from somewhere in England. Then Ann made matters worse by joining Ieuan Ddu's choir, which was soon to perform the 'Messiah' for the first time in Wales, and in English, if you please.

If it's want to sing in a choir you do, said Betty to Ann when she heard about it, then why not join Rosser Beynon's choir or Moses Davies's Temperance Choir. With either of them you could sing to your heart's content in your own language. Ieuan Ddu said the 'Messiah' as a work is greater than any language, said Ann. Never mind Ieuan Ddu, it's I your own mother that knows best, said Betty. Ieuan Ddu is not a proper Christian in the first place. He goes to chapel, said Ann. Yes, but to what chapel? said Betty. That old Unitarian Chapel, that's where he goes, my gel. He can't be anything bad or they wouldn't let him have the High Street Chapel for the performance of the 'Messiah', said Ann. The High Street chapel is English Baptist and not Welsh, said Betty. No Welsh chapel would let him conduct a work in English – no, nor in Welsh, either, inside their four walls. I have heard, my gel, the English Baptists of High Street will allow anything to be done by anybody inside their chapel. Ach y fi. Wasn't it Robert James that told me that Blind Dick is singing the tenor part in the practices of the 'Messiah' they're having there? Dear me ... Blind Dick and the 'Messiah'. He's only singing the part to help the

76

practice, said Ann. A man is coming from London to sing the tenor part the night of the performance. Whoever the man is from London I don't think he will be any better if as good in the part as Blind Dick is already – and he's got a new suit and all. A new suit don't make him fit to sing the 'Messiah' in a chapel, said Betty. A drunkard and a scamp he is and a drunkard and a scamp he'll always be. Yet you sang with him at the Noson Lawen up at Danygraig Farm, Ann reminded her mother. A Noson Lawen is different, said Betty. Nobody can refuse to do something to make others happy at a Noson Lawen. And it's not true to say that the man will always be a drunkard and a scamp, said Ann. He hasn't touched the drink for months – you ask Robert if you like. He still lives with his little gel among the thieves and bad women down China, doesn't he? said Betty. He can't help that, said Ann. Where would he get a house in Merthyr these days? There's two families living in nearly every house in Merthyr as it is. When Robert and I get married I don't know where we are going to live. As for singing under Ieuan Ddu – well, I may as well tell you first as last, mam. I'm going to sing under him and in English whether you like it or not. To think, said Betty, to think that a daughter of mine should ever – I'm not sure that I wouldn't rather you sing with the Catholics in that church they've opened in Dowlais.

No wonder people said 'y cythraul yn y canu', which said in the English way would be 'the devil in the singing'. There were ever so many complications in the life and work shared by the forty thousand people of the town of Tydfil the Martyr. Die-hard Welsh people like Betty Parry wanted to keep you away from everybody and everything English for a start, away from the English Baptists, the English Wesleyans, the Church of England people and away from the Catholics more than any. Whatever you do keep it clean in Welsh, they said. Now Ieuan Ddu claimed that he was as good a Welshman as any in Wales but he would not be a party to what he described as 'the inbreeding of Welsh culture'. He had, in *The Cambrian Minstrel*, collected quite a number of the best melodies of Cambria, but he had in that fine collection given the words in English and Welsh so that the English would have the opportunity of enjoying them as well as the Welsh.

But the die-hard Welsh said no. If the English want to know about us and our songs then let them learn to speak and read and sing in Welsh. Once we Welsh start pandering to the English it will be all up with us Welsh. When it wasn't this it was something else, rivalry between the choirs and their conductors, between the different Welsh denominations and between sections of one or other of the denominations. The latter difference caused more than one split which resulted in one of the two opposing sections leaving the parent chapel to start a chapel of their own. All this was very sad and may seem rather stupid but it has to be remembered that forty thousand people had few outlets through which to express themselves. For most of them it was just a case of from bed to work and from work to bed. Education was in its infancy and so the artistic life of the place was more or less negligible. The religious side of life, particularly in the case of the Welsh, was strong and passionate and more than a little jealous. There was no public hall of any kind but there were plenty of public-houses and beer-houses, also plenty of chapels. Then choirs and conductors were, as I have already said, a penny a bunch, so to speak. More than half the population of forty thousand were made up of English and Irish, with a sprinkling of Scots and Jews. Less than half the population were Welsh, so racial feeling ran high at times, so high that there were fierce clashes between the Irish and Welsh. But the English section of the population, which included all the employers and most of the professional men, kept themselves above racial strife and went on consolidating their position at the top. Just think of the position. At this time the library of the town of Tydfil the Martyr was just over one year old and all the books in the Merthyr Library were a dozen volumes of Knight's shilling series. A dozen books in the library of a place with a population of forty thousand!

Mr Henry Austin Bruce, the new Stipendiary Magistrate for the town and district, was a learned man who had the interests of the people at heart. He hated the pawnbrokers who battened on the most improvident section of the population as much as he hated those who opposed the general advancement of learning. He was a firm but just magistrate and it was during his years on the Bench and the years during which he afterwards represented the town and district in Parliament that some real progress was made. It was he that was mainly responsible for making the Merthyr Library an institution in the place, for he not only subscribed and gave books but lectured there as well. Take his first two lectures there: 'On Amusements, As the Means of Continuing and Extending the Education of the Working Classes'. The next was on 'The Present Condition and Future Prospects of the Working Population in the Mineral Districts of South Wales'. Henry Austin Bruce was a good man, no doubt about that. He did his best to stamp out the crime which was so rife in the district called China, but after he had left the Bench to go and represent the town and district in Parliament it was nearly as bad as ever again.

In any case Blind Dick is keeping himself sober and tidy these days, though he still lives in that same cellar-dwelling in the district called China. Now that he is keeping himself sober and tidy Myfanwy has a better chance of learning all she can from Ieuan Ddu. She is the youngest soprano in his famous choir and she sees that her father, looking as tidy as any other man in the choir, is at every practice – as she and most other members of the choir called rehearsals – of the 'Messiah'. She was proud of him for the way he sang the tenor solos from memory to link up the choruses for Ieuan Ddu. Of course he still went to sing at club feasts held in public-houses but he did not take any strong drink now. He was better in health and the sore part of his face under the mask gave him very little trouble now.

If ever you are short don't forget now, Ieuan Ddu said more than once to Blind Dick. Why, have you come into a fortune or something? said Blind Dick. No, but I am not short of a few pounds, said Ieuan. The fact was, of course, that Ieuan had been visited late one night the year before by no less a person than William Crawshay, who had left a bag of golden sovereigns, a hundred in all, with him. I am leaving the place very soon, he said, and I want to do something for Blind Dick and that old-fashioned little girl of his. I gather that you are interested in them. They would perhaps take from you what they would not take from me. But you will have to be careful all round. The man himself is bitter – And no wonder, said Ieuan. Wonder or no I am leaving this place and I don't want to have to remember that girl of his in want or driven to bad ways by want, said William Crawshay. I hope I can trust you to see that she isn't? You could have trusted to me to see to that without this money, Mr Crawshay, said Ieuan Ddu. I think I could, said the ironmaster. But the money will help. If you require more, anything up to a hundred pounds a year, then my son up at the castle will let you have it. But that's strictly between you and me, remember. On second thoughts we'll say nothing to my son about it. I shall be coming here from time to time and I shall make a point of seeing you – here, not at the castle. Is your school in a flourishing condition? I haven't as many boys as I had last year but there are still as many as I want, said Ieuan. The opening of the National School must affect you chaps more and more as time goes on. Goodnight, said William Crawshay. Goodnight, said Ieuan.

Crawshay walked back to the Castle Hotel, outside which his carriage and pair was waiting. Ieuan Ddu put the bag of golden sovereigns away safe and then continued his study of the choral structure of Handel's 'Messiah'. But he had to give up and go to bed because he could not get William Crawshay off his mind. Next morning he received an invitation, by hand, inviting him to attend a dinner that evening. It was a dinner that was to be given to mark the departure of Mr William Crawshay from the town he was largely responsible for creating. Whether what he had created was good or bad is another matter, and in any case Ieuan had called a practice for that evening so he could not go if he had wanted to. Had he been free he would have gone, if only to see the last of the man.

The last of the man ... All that day, throughout the town and district, people of all classes were conscious of the fact that they were losing a man in William Crawshay. Yes, and whatever his faults, a man. It took a man to make eight million pounds sterling within the law and to make his initials, W.C., and the combe mark of his iron known the world over. He had himself laboured mightily during the forty years he had been in iron and later in coal as well. He was leaving the place little the better off than when he first saw it, in many respects it was worse off. If it was then he did not consider himself in the least to blame for that. He had made work for people and had attracted people from all parts to come to Merthyr to do the work he had made for them to do. He had started his career as owner-manager of Cyfarthfa Works with only four furnaces and now there were twelve. He had more than doubled the production of iron and bettered its quality no end. There were people who called him a 'close-fisted Yorkshireman', but whether or no he had spared no expense to make his works the greatest and most famous the world over. Now Sir John Guest, M.P., had bested him and so it was time for him to leave the scene of his labours.

William hated being 'bested' by anyone, he himself said so. But when 'that man at Dowlais' got the best of him William had no words with which to express himself. Now

Guest had six more furnaces in blast in his works at Dowlais than William had in his works at Cyfarthfa and the Dowlais works were producing 75,000 tons of iron annually! That was 25,000 tons more than William could produce yearly at his Cyfarthfa works! So he thought it was time he went from the place. But he kept his temper pretty well at the farewell dinner. He reminded his hearers that his grandfather had started with only fifteen pounds got by selling the pony he had loved. Had started making flat-irons and had worked himself up and up. After describing how hard his grandfather had worked William went on to say:

'My grandfather established the ironworks at Merthyr and Cyfarthfa ... and by his benevolence I have succeeded to it. During my time the concern has not diminished, and I pray God it never may diminish; and I hope the rising generation will see that, by industry, integrity and perseverance, wealth and rank in life in the position they have chosen are attainable by everybody who started with humbler prospects than my grandfather. No man in this room is so poor that he cannot command fifteen pounds. I have told you this before, and I am proud of it. Depend on it, any young man who is industrious, honest and persevering, will be respected in any class of life he may move in; and do you think, gentlemen, that there is a man in England prouder than I am at this moment? What is all the world to me unless they know me? And you would not be here to-night unless you thought me entitled to your good-will ...'

Say what you like it was a pretty good after-dinner, farewell speech. He was right in saying that no man at that dinner was so poor that he could not command fifteen pounds. But outside that room, in the town of Tydfil the Martyr, there were many thousands of men who could not command fifteen shillings without handing household goods or clothing worth treble that amount over a pawnbroker's counter. Betty Parry had been saving as hard as she could for nearly three years and still she had only six pounds towards the passage money to America her husband was hoping to get some day. For it was not only the passage money. He would have to have a suit of clothes to go tidy, a big box to take his things in and a few pounds to last him until he got work after he got over the other side. But William Crawshay would not know anything about that. One mistake in what was on the whole a very good after-dinner speech. He was speaking in the town of Tydfil the Martyr which is in Wales. Yet what he said was: '... there is no man in England prouder than I am at this moment ...' Many of the Welsh at the dinner noticed that and must have mentioned it when they got outside, for it spread like wildfire throughout the district. A slip of the tongue, that's all, but what most of the Welsh said was that William Crawshay would talk as though he were in England when he got to hell – very few of the Welsh of Merthyr thought he had a chance of going to the other place.

Anyway, there was loud applause and singing of 'For he's a jolly good fellow', after which several gentlemen were called upon in turn to say what they thought about Mr William Crawshay, the guest of the evening. There is no record of the speeches of those gentlemen, or of the chairman's remarks. There was also a toast-master, and what he said might have been interesting. But the town and district had no newspaper in which to publish reports of local events or any other events. Since the *Utgorn Cymru* and the *Free Press* had died in 1840 the town and district had been without a newspaper of its own for seven long years. I think it was a London paper that published part of the farewell speech made at that dinner given to Mr William Crawshay.

A funny thing. William's son, Robert Thompson Crawshay, started a band as soon as his father had left Merthyr for Caversham Park, near Reading. Yes, he started the famous Cyfarthfa Brass Band, which proved to be more of a boon to the town and district than ever anything else had been. A band upwards of a hundred strong at times; after it had been weeded there were seventy good instrumental-ists left. Seventy good instrumentalists under a good conductor can do things to the people of a town and district, Joseph Parry – we won't call him little Joseph Parry any more for he is starting to work as a miner soon – Joseph Parry could think and talk of nothing but the Cyfarthfa Band. It rehearsed in the long rooms of different public-houses when it was first formed, but the rehearsals in those places did not prove very helpful. There were too many volunteers for a start. Men redeemed trumpets and trombones from pawnshops and presented themselves with their acts of redemption at rehearsals, claiming that they were as good bandsmen as any born. They got dry very soon and found it necessary to wet their whistles and things frequently during rehearsals. They were soon weeded-out and the band had a bandroom into which no intoxicants were carried during rehearsals. Wherever it was rehearsing or playing Joseph Parry was as near to the band as he could get. It played on the lawn in front of the Castle, on the Square in front of the Market House, through the streets and at flower shows and sports.

Funny thing. Once the Cyfarthfa Band was formed we had to organize events for it to play at. Talk about bringing life to a town and district. If Robert Thompson Crawshay never did anything else for the town and district he did enough when he gave us that splendid band. There was not a boy in the town of Tydfil the Martyr who did not bless his name. Some said that it was his wife, Rose Mary, that suggested he should start a band to give pleasure to the people of the town and district. I would not be surprised to learn that that were true for she was a real nice lady. The band played not only in Merthyr and throughout the Principality but in London as well. But it played home most of the time, thank goodness.

No one will believe me now if I tell them what a sensation the Cyfarthfa Brass Band was then. We youngsters of the years sometimes referred to as 'the hungry 'forties' were more hungry for what the Cyfarthfa Band gave us than for food. There was the man who played those cornet solos – who will ever forget him for a start? Or the trombonists? 'Gems of Opera' they played, and 'Gems of Welsh Melody'. Marches that made our blood tingle and waltzes that made us want to dance, which was a wrong thing for us Welsh boys and girls to do. The first time the Cyfarthfa Band played down through the High Street the children all ran out of the National School next door to St David's Church and followed the band down to the Square in front of the Market House and would not go back to school that afternoon. Men came out of the public-houses with pints or half-pints in their hand and followed the band down to the Square in front of the Market House. Tradespeople closed their shops and followed the band, landlords and land-ladies closed their public-houses and followed the band – and if you don't believe me ask anyone who was there that day, that great day for the town of Tydfil the Martyr.

Quiet, boys, shouted Ieuan Ddu. He and the boys listened for three seconds only to the band as it passed the Castle Hotel, which was over a hundred yards away from Ieuan's school. Leave everything and come, he said, running out of school followed by the boys. Ieuan's niece, Gwenny, ran after them across the Glebeland. Ieuan's wife could not run but she walked as fast as she could. In the crowd around the band on the Square in front of the Market House Ieuan saw Blind Dick and Myfanwy and waved his hand to them. After the selection of tunes from a comic opera Ieuan left his boys and shouldered his way through the crowd to where Blind Dick and Myfanwy were standing. I thought you'd be here, he said. Everybody's here by the sound of it, said Blind Dick. Grand band, isn't it? said Myfanwy. A splendid band, said Ieuan. How many in it, Van? said Dick. I haven't counted, but if there's one there's seventy, she said. And how many people are here, said Dick.

Thousands if not more, said Myfanwy. They are cram-jammed from down by the police station up to by here and from by here to against the doors of the Market House. Then the other way from here to Victoria Street and down – Can you see old Harry Half-a-Man in his box by the door of the Market? said Dick. They've lifted him up in his box on to a cart from under foot, said Myfanwy. Dick chuckled and said: He'll be mad if they block his way into the Market Tavern. They are going to start playing again, said Myfanwy.

The crowd simmered down as the bandmaster tapped his music stand and the bandsmen glued their lips to their instruments and off they went. Myfanwy tugged Ieuan's sleeve to ask in a loud whisper: What is that they're playing now? Mozart, said Ieuan quietly. Shush, someone from behind them hissed. Myfanwy turned her head and there was Joseph Parry on his toes glaring at her. She made a face at him and looked to her front again. That was an afternoon if you like. As the crowd broke up they saw Robert Thompson Crawshay and his wife, Rose Mary, seated in their carriage out of sight around the corner by the Market House, the meat market part of it. They both seemed very pleased with the reception their band had got from the crowd.

Here, said Myfanwy to Joseph Parry as he was moving past her to fall in behind the band, which was getting ready to march away. Who were you shushing and squinting your eyes at, boy? Learn to be quiet when our band is playing, said Joseph. Your band, she said. It's Cyfarthfa Band and I live in Cyfarthfa Works, don't I? he said. Then go now and follow your old band before I give you a clout, she said. The band struck up and marched off with a regiment of boys following. Some of the boys nearest the tail of the band were privileged to carry the bandmaster's collapsible music stand and others were equally privileged to carry a case of music sheets. Joseph carried the bandmaster's music stand, and talk about feeling proud ...

Well, we've had something to liven the place up at last, said Ieuan Ddu. Some of his boys were awaiting instructions and Ieuan said: Go on home or follow the band, just as you like, and off they ran to catch up with the band. I want you two to come to tea with me, he said to Dick and Myfanwy. We're always having food at your house, said Dick. And lucky to get it, come on, said Myfanwy. I want to discuss the final rehearsals with you, Dick. The last practice, you mean? said Dick. Yes, said Ieuan. Aren't you satisfied with the way it's going? said Myfanwy. Not quite, said Ieuan. I'll tell you when we get to the house.

Did you ever hear such a lovely band? said Gwenny when they walked into the house just as she was laying the cloth for tea. I couldn't get anear it for the crowd, said Ieuan's wife. And I'm gone I can't push. But you heard it, didn't you? said Ieuan. Oh, yes, I heard but I couldn't see. My legs are gone I can't stand, so I had to sit best I could on the stone outside the window of the coffee tavern. Would you and your father like a boiled egg for your tea, Myfanwy? All I want is a cup of tea, said Dick. And some bread and butter and an egg boiled and cake after, he means, Mrs Thomas, said Myfanwy. I don't like eating nearly every day of the week at other people's expense, said Dick. We all eat at God's expense, don't we? said Ieuan's wife. Where's Ieuan gone now again? Out to the school-room for something, said Gwenny. He is worrying his head about the performance, he is – go and ask him if he wants an egg boiled for his tea, Gwenny, said Mrs Thomas. Gwenny went out to ask and Mrs Thomas said: Ieuan tries to do too much. He's having trouble with that singer coming from London, Ieuan wants him to come the night before to have last practice with the choir, but the man have wrote to say he is singing in Hereford the night before. So he can only come just in time for the performance – and if the old train jumps the rails or something then he won't be here in time. That would give many in Merthyr the laugh over Ieuan – Yes, he'll have two eggs but scrambled not boiled, said Gwenny. You scramble and I'll boil then, said Mrs Thomas. Nice fresh eggs old Watkins sent down from Danygraig this morning.

After tea Ieuan said: Come with me into the schoolroom, Dick. And you, Myfanwy. They followed him out to the schoolroom, leaving Mrs Thomas and Gwenny to clear up and wash up. I don't know what to do, said Ieuan. It's taking a big risk. That tenor from London – Mrs Thomas told us, said Myfanwy. Told you what? said Ieuan. About him not being able to come for the last practice before the performance, said Myfanwy. It's a bit of a jaunt from Hereford to Merthyr and anything might happen, said Ieuan. I could have the law on him for in his letter he agreed to come for one practice with the choir before the performance. No, I don't know what to do. David Jones the printer has printed his name on the posters and tickets. Well, you know best, said Dick. Yes, murmured Ieuan, looking at Dick. I wonder, he said more to himself than anyone else. Tell me, Dick. What? said Dick. If that man from London didn't happen to reach Merthyr in time for the performance, would you let others have the laugh over me? said Ieuan. Not if I could help it, said Dick. They would if the performance had to be postponed or perhaps cancelled altogether, said Ieuan. I've had enough trouble to get High Street Baptist Chapel for the performance as it is. If I had to postpone it now I should never get that or any other chapel in Merthyr to put it on later. You're trying to say something, aren't you? said Myfanwy. I am, said Ieuan, and I may as well say it first as last. Dick, you have memorized the tenor solo part, haven't you? Good enough to help in the practices but not to sing in the performance – for that's what you are coming to, isn't it? said Dick. Yes, said Ieuan. I'm satisfied that you will sing the part as well if not better than that man I thought to have from London.

Dick laughed out loud. Nothing to laugh about, said Myfanwy. Isn't there? said Dick, still laughing. The man's got no more sense than I have sight. The laugh over you, you said they'd have if it was postponed. Why, they'd never stop laughing at you if you were fool enough to dress me up to present me as one of the soloists. And they'd have the laugh over me too, standing in a chapel with this mask over my face singing the holy words with my dirty mouth. Don't they all know me for what I am – For what you were, you mean, said Myfanwy. For what I was, am and will be, what difference? cried Dick. You have already sung the holy words with your mouth, let it be dirty or clean, at the practices, haven't you? said Myfanwy. And ashamed I have felt more than once, said Dick. Now you want me to shame the choir as well. No, no, said Ieuan. Yes, yes, said Dick. Your choir didn't mind me looking like I am at the practices. But how will they feel with me there in front of an audience? The members of my choir will feel more at ease with you there than with that singer from London, said Ieuan.

It's the least you can do for Ieuan – and for yourself as well, said Myfanwy. Listen now the two of you, said Dick. If it was one of my legs or my arms you wanted, Ieuan, then you could have it. In front of an audience I said, remember, an audience of tidy people sitting in a chapel – No better perhaps than the audiences you have sung for in club feasts in the long rooms of public-houses hundreds of times, said Myfanwy. And wait a minute now before you say any more. You will be sober and dressed tidy, won't you? The mask over your poor face nearly all the people who will be at the performance have already seen on you. It's only me that knows you without the mask and have had to put you drunk to bed times out of number. I'm not twitting you, remember, only telling you, that's all. Now I want to see you doing something tidy for once and you talk about shame. What about my shame long before I knew what shame was? Never mind me, I suppose? Now tell Ieuan that you're willing and that you will do your best.

That man from London – didn't you hear Ieuan say that his name is already on the bills and tickets? said Dick. That can easily be explained by whoever presides at the performance, said Ieuan. I am not saying any more, said Myfanwy. Do you as you like now. I might break down and spoil everything, said Dick. You won't, said Ieuan. What do you say, Van? said Dick. I've said that I am not saying any more, said Myfanwy. Right, said Dick. But first you must ask the choir, Ieuan. If they are willing to put up with me I'll do it if that man don't come from London. Now he have come to his senses start drilling him, Ieuan, said Myfanwy. Perhaps it's sorry you have talked me into it the two of you will be, said Dick. No fear, said Ieuan.

At the next practice, which was the last but one before the performance, Ieuan put it to the choir. He had already written to the man in London to tell him that he did not want him to come, and he had explained to Dr Dyke when he went to ask the doctor to preside at the performance. I'd rather not preside, said Dr Dyke. I may have an urgent call which will prevent me from being there in time. Why not ask Harry Bruce, the Stipendiary, to preside? Do you think he will? said Ieuan. I'm sure he will, said Dr Dyke. Then I'll ask him and say that you suggested I should, said Ieuan. Now I must go and talk to the choir and the other soloists about Blind Dick going to sing instead of that man from London.

The members of the choir and three of the four soloists and Hetty Harris, the woman at the hired piano, were all there before Ieuan this night. Blind Dick and Myfanwy waited outside the little Unitarian Chapel for the decision. I don't want to be in there whilst you are talking to them, said Dick. As you like, said Ieuan. I'll be out before long. Ieuan went in and explained the position and asked all present if they were prepared to perform the 'Messiah' under him and with Blind Dick instead of the man from London as the tenor soloist. They all opened their eyes and there was murmuring but no one said yes or no. They looked at each other as much as to say that Ieuan was asking too much of them but none of them would say anything. The first to speak out was the bass soloist, Will Morgan, better known as Will Full-Moon – and if ever a man was a fool to himself then it was Will Full-Moon. That's how he was best known because his father had been landlord of the public-house called the Full-Moon for many years.

But never mind his father, it's Will we are talking about. His bass voice was the talk of a dozen valleys where he had won prizes singing. Lady Charlotte Guest had heard him sing the year she presided at the Fenni Eisteddfod. She had been invited to preside as the first Englishwoman to translate a Welsh book into English, which she did with the help of about a dozen Welshmen. *The Mabinogion* was the name of the book she translated from Welsh into English and it would not be mentioned now but for the fact that it explains why she was presiding at the Fenni Eisteddfod, where she heard Will Full-Moon sing 'The trumpet shall sound' from the 'Messiah'. He won the prize and secured her distinguished patronage. She got her husband, Sir John, to give Will an easy and well-paid job at Dowlais Works, and when there were guests at Dowlais House, Will Full-Moon was requested to put on his best clothes and come and sing to them. He did, perhaps a half-dozen times, then he sent his back-handed compliments to Lady Charlotte Guest and begged to inform her that the drawing-room of Dowlais House was no place for him. That, in effect, was what he said, but the way he really said it to the foreman was the rough way. So he lost his easy and well-paid job – what else could he expect? When the bandmaster of Cyfarthfa Band received a message by hand from one of the servants from the Castle, a message instructing him to hurry up with the bandsmen to play on the lawn outside the Castle, then they had to hurry up, didn't they? Of course they did. No doubt Will Full-Moon thought himself a cut above the bandmaster of Cyfarthfa Band. It is true that he was a magnificent singer, but then again he was only one of many in the town and district at the time. Then he was too fond of his beer for another thing, but, fair play for him, he knew how to conduct himself on stage or platform. It was generally admitted that for a singer he was the best 'stager' of himself in the town and district, meaning that he presented himself first as a man in a way that impressed audiences and adjudicators. The way he stood with his right hand holding the lapel of his coat and smiling confidently before beginning to sing made people think he must be a great singer and he was a great singer. Ask anyone who heard him at his best, as he was about this time, the time when Ieuan Ddu and his choir performed the 'Messiah' in its entirety for the first time in Wales.

So it was Will Full-Moon spoke up and said: If anyone has a right to object to Blind Dick singing the tenor part then surely it is I. If anyone's reputation or character is likely to suffer as a result then it is mine. But I see no danger to either. Dick Llewelyn can't help his face. I regard him as a fellow-artist and as such I shall be proud to sing with him – all in favour please show in the usual manner. Come on, put up your hands, he roared. They all put up their hands and Ieuan went out to fetch Dick and Myfanwy in. When they came in it was Will Full-Moon led the applause.

· That's how it was that night at the Unitarian Chapel. Then the night of the performance at the High Street Baptist Chapel, which was crowded inside and there were at least sixty people standing at the back between the outer door and the two inner doors. The choir and the soloists went round the back way, along the lane and through the back door into the minister's and deacons' rooms. Mr Henry Austin Bruce, the Stipendiary Magistrate, who had kindly consented to preside, went in that way too. But Will Full-Moon did not go in that way. He pushed his way through the crowd and walked down the aisle, smiling right and left and carrying a black bag. You would have thought he was early and not late. Ieuan Ddu was most anxious and when Will Full-Moon came at last Ieuan went close to him to smell his breath. Will Full-Moon shook his head and smiled and said: Not guilty, Ieuan. Then he lowered his voice to a whisper and said: But they'll all be closed by the time we've finished and got out of here, so I brought a few quart bottles in my bag. He opened a little cupboard and moved the hymn-books to make room for the bag. Come on, we're waiting to start, said Ieuan. Mr Bruce is out there ready to speak and the choir's in position. Now it's only you soloists and myself – Do you think the drop of beer for after will be safe here in this cupboard? said Will. Who would come to a performance of the 'Messiah' to steal beer? said Ieuan. Come on quick for us to start. Don't get excited, Ieuan, said Will, closing the cupboard door. It's all to the good to keep an audience waiting a few minutes. How are you feeling, Dick? Dick was sitting, looking rather nervous, on the bench between the two female soloists, Letty Lewis, the soprano, and Rachel Thomas, the contralto. I think I am all right, said Dick. Did I hear you say that you have brought some beer for after? Yes, there's a couple of quarts apiece in my bag – that's if it's left alone till we finish, said Will. Dick will leave it alone then for he's off the beer, said Ieuan. Come now, please. Wait, said Will. These things must be staged properly, Ieuan. First you two ladies same as I said at the last practice. First one and, after the one that goes first have had her applause and sat down, then the other. Then the audience will be asking themselves where we men are, won't they? Yes, yes, we arranged all that last night, said Ieuan impatiently. Yes, but we didn't *time* it all last night, said Will. There will be a longish wait between the appearance of the second and last of these two girls and the appearance of me and Dick. He will make his appearance with his left hand on my right shoulder – Go on, Letty, said Ieuan. Don't hurry, Letty, said Will. Walk slowly and with all the

93

dignity of an artist, remember. We have worked hard for those people out there, so don't walk like if you're saying thank you for coming to them. I won't, said Letty.

Letty went first and Rachel followed after. Dick's hand when he placed it on Will Full-Moon's shoulder was trembling, Will said: Everything's going to be all right, Dick. With your lovely voice you are going to open the eyes of the blind who will not see to the Glory of God. So stop shaking. Are you ready? Yes, said Dick, his hand on Will's shoulder steady now. Then come, said Will. Out of the little room and into the chapel they went. There was a loud intake of breath by as many as were present but no applause when they appeared, the new black mask over the upper part of Dick's face and his bald head. Oh, my God, one woman in the audience said quietly, but her voice sounded loud in the silence. So did Will Full-Moon's voice when he said: There's two steps here up into the big seat, Richard. That's right. He placed his chair for him and they both sat down and still no applause or a sound of any sort. Silence, that's all. The audience found relief in applause when Ieuan came to take his place in front of choir and soloists. He should have waited until Mr Bruce had spoken but he wanted to spare Mr Bruce as much as possible and hoped to do so by breaking the tense and embarrassing silence which followed Dick's appearance. He bowed in acknowledgement of the applause and then sat down. Mr Bruce spoke briefly and to the point and then Ieuan got up and nodded to Hetty Harris at the piano. Dick stood up and waited and then:

'Comfort ye, comfort ye My people, saith your God ...'

Myfanwy in her place in the choir listened with pride and joy to her blind father's singing of the holy words. He sang surely and the effect of his singing upon that audience was more moving than the singing of any man able to see could have been.

It was one of those nights worth remembering but it was

poor Dick's swan-song, as they say. Next day he was in the Market Tavern as drunk as a wheel and the next night he was in the water of the lock of the canal, the lock before you come to the wharf of the canal, if you know where that is. Neither Ieuan nor Myfanwy could do anything with him the day following the performance of the 'Messiah', in which he had been magnificent. But it must have been a great strain for him all the same. It was not holy words he sang in the Market Tavern next day. He got drunk twice that day and late that night he went to the coke-ovens with a bad woman. No doubt it was on his way back down from the coke-ovens that he walked into the lock of the canal. A dozen yards higher up or a dozen yards lower down he could have walked into the canal and he could have walked out again and shook himself. But he walked into the deep lock instead, the narrow lock deep down between black and slimy walls.

Not so long before poor Dick had raised his glorious voice in High Street Baptist Chapel to sing the Recit:

'Thy rebuke hath broken His heart; He is full of heaviness. He looked for some to have pity on Him, but there was no man, neither found He any to comfort Him ...'

Did he deliberately walk into the deep lock? Whether or no, he had a grand funeral. The members of Ieuan's choir were all there to sing from Ieuan's house up to the Thomas Town Cemetery. Some of the rough people from the district called China were at the graveside but they did not walk in the funeral procession. Their clothes were not fit to be seen in a funeral procession. There were about a dozen wreaths to put on the coffin and leave on the grave after it was filled in, one wreath from Mr Bruce, the Stipendiary Magistrate. The coffin was carried in turns by the members of the male section of Ieuan's choir and Myfanwy walked with Ieuan right behind the coffin. She did not cry on the way to the cemetery, at the graveside or on the way back to Ieuan's house. The Rev. Mr Lloyd of the Unitarian Chapel preached and prayed at the graveside. Old Ben Watkins from Danygraig Farm rode down on his horse but did not dismount. Sat on his horse just outside the gates of the cemetery and took his hat off when the coffin was carried past. Then he rode up the rise to his farm.

You're going to live with us from now on, said Ieuan to Myfanwy as on the way down from the cemetery. Not unless you're willing for me to go to work in the brickyard to pay my way, said Myfanwy. No need to go to work in the brickyard, said Ieuan. We'll find you plenty to do in the house and behind the house in the school. You've got Gwenny and Mrs Thomas to do all that, said Myfanwy. Gwenny's getting married and you know Mrs Thomas is far from well, said Ieuan. You can work at your ease and learn a bit with us, but it's hard rough work and nothing else you'll have in the brickyard. So be a good girl and stay with us. And that's how Myfanwy came to live in Ieuan's house until he left Merthyr for Pontypridd. Poor Ieuan. It was not long before he lost Mrs Thomas.

CHAPTER 4

Births, Deaths and Marriages

THE Parry family were one of the lucky families of the town of Tydfil the Martyr in the year 1849, the year the cholera swept the place and took one thousand six hundred and eighty-two to their graves. No, it was one thousand six hundred and eighty-two and a half. For didn't it take old Harry Half-a-Man? It did sure enough. He died of it in the common lodging-house in the district called China. It was from there that Wat Evans who did the slaughtering for Millward the butcher took him in a sack. Wat had known the old man for years and years and had been with him night after night in the Market Tavern, where old Harry had made Wat promise to see that he would not have a pauper's grave. I am not afraid of dying but I am afraid of a pauper's grave, he kept on saying to Wat. I'll see that you're not buried at the expense of the parish, Wat said lightly. So don't worry any more. What Wat meant was: Don't worry *me* any more. But old Harry returned to the subject again and again until at last Wat shouted: Would you like me to promise with my hand on the Bible? Yes, said Harry, I would. What if I die before you? said Wat, taking his empty pint to have it filled again. You won't, said Harry, handing him the small glass called 'a tot'. Get me a two of rum being as you're going to the counter.

The night came when he did make Wat promise with his hand on the Bible supplied for the purpose by the accommodating landlord of the Market Tavern. Now are you satisfied? said Wat. Yes, quite satisfied, said Harry. Give the Bible back to the landlord and ask him to let me have another two of rum till tomorrow. Such people as old Harry are not worth bothering with but Wat Evans was a hard-working chap. Old Harry left him alone after he had got him to promise with his hand on the Bible, so Wat didn't think any more of it until the morning when the landlord of the common lodging-house came into the slaughter-house, as he often did, to buy what he called 'lamb-stones' cheap. These were a sort of perquisite which Wat was entitled by custom to dispose of as he liked. Wat got most of his beer-money by the disposal of these and kindred perquisites.

Yes, you can have half-a-dozen if you want that many, said Wat. Sure I do, said Tim Keeley. I'll pay you for 'em now and call for 'em on the way back from the parish officer. I'm after him to take that upper-part of old Harry out of my place. What's the matter with old Harry? said Wat. Nothing, said Tim Keeley. The cholera must have taken him in the night. One of the other lodgers was telling me he was complaining when he got home last night. He seemed all right when I left him in the Market Tavern, said Wat. He's dead now, anyway, said Tim. I'll be back for those lamb-stones.

Wat Evans was nothing if not conscientious. He was also more than a little superstitious. The last thing he wanted to hear was a voice from the grave, and certainly not old Harry Half-a-Man's voice. Whilst thinking the matter out he grabbed a lamb and stuck it and then held it a minute whilst trying to think out a way of keeping the promise made to old Harry. He called out to inform his helper that he would be back before the day was out, put his knife away and took off his apron, put on his hat and coat and picked up a sack and off he went for Harry without as much as washing the blood of the lambs off his hands.

He could bag him all right but where was he to put him till dark? And where would he put him after dark? He hurried down Victoria Street, passing the Market Tavern on his left, a thing he would never have done had he been free of care and worry. He went under the archway into the district called China and walked straight into the common lodging-house. There was an awful smell and three men and a woman were playing cards on a bed in the room in which there were twelve beds, six each side. What are you after? said one of the men. I can see what I'm after, said Wat, going to the bed in which old Harry lay quiet. He slipped him into the sack and hoisted him up on his shoulder and was taking him out when the woman playing cards said: Is it the parish officer you are? Not the official one, said Wat. The card-players stopped playing and followed Wat out as far as the doorway, where they stood looking after him. Did you ever see the like o' that, said one of the men. That's the cholera, no doubt. They've run short of coffins and they're burying 'em in bags now.

Where am I going to take you? where am I going to take you for a start? Wat behind closed lips asked the half-a-man in the bag he was carrying. Then he remembered that Harry had left that half of himself to perhaps get joined up with the other half of himself elsewhere. Think we'll have rain, Wat? said a man standing on the corner near the Lamb Inn. We might, said Wat. He hurried along and turned left up Castle Lane and rested his load on the gate of Castle Field. Now let's try and think where we can put you for now, he said. He thought first of the culvert through which the Morlais flowed when there was any flow in it to join the River Taff. Then he remembered the rats who were so numerous both ends of the culvert. No, mustn't hide him there. Each and every depository in the way of a building he could think of had its drawbacks, so he was at last forced to take his load down to the slaughter-house.

Did Tim Keeley pay you for the lamb-stones? said his helper. Yes, said Wat. Give me a couple of hooks. What have you got in there? said his helper. Something I'm taking away with me tonight, said Wat. The boss have been here, said his helper. What did he want? said Wat, doubling the ends of the sack over twice not for the hook to rip it when he hung it up out of the way. To say that Ike the drover will be bringing a couple of bullocks in the morning, said his helper. One for us and one for Thomas in Pontmorlais – do you want a hand with that? No, I'll manage, said Wat.

There, it was up out of the way and no one was any the wiser, thank goodness. Now after he and his helper had finished work for the day Wat could take the key home with him and return when it was dark and take Harry's earthly remains and bury them ... bury them – yes, but where? He would have to think. In the Market Tavern that evening he was unusually silent but before he left earlier than usual he had made up his mind. He would bury Harry in the grave-yard of the Parish Church, where it was said that Tydfil the Martyr was killed by the pagans. This graveyard had the advantage of being the nearest to the slaughter-house, so he would first dig the grave and then come back for Harry. It was dark enough now and it was raining as well. He cut the sods carefully so as to be able to put them back in a way which would make it difficult for anyone to see the joints. Wat was a good worker and he worked hard through this night to bury Harry tidy before the morning dawned. He did not forget to say a word over Harry either. Where have you been all night, said his landlady, for Wat was single and in lodgings. With Ike the drover for some cattle from over the Black Mountain, said Wat. You're all mud, she said. I know, he said. After he had had a good breakfast and a bit of a wash he went back down to the slaughter-house and killed the two bullocks Ike had driven in.

That was how the odd half of the thousand six hundred and eighty-two and a half cholera victims was disposed of, and I wonder how many people know that old Harry Half-a-Man is buried in the graveyard of the Parish Church? Some might laugh but it was no laughing matter for the people of the town of Tydfil the Martyr that hot summer of 1849. Every Sunday night in the chapels the 'Gyfeillach', as we call it in Welsh; but so that you may understand, the 'Gyfeillach' is a friendly and informal after-service held after the service proper. It is normally as jolly a gathering as one could wish for in a chapel. The preacher steps down from the pulpit to join his deacons in the Big Seat. From there he invites contributions from the children present, not money or anything like that but contributions of verses from the Bible. Each child rises in turn and recites what he or she has learnt during the week in readiness for Sunday's 'Gyfeillach'. Joseph Parry was always ready to jump up and say his piece from the Bible, he could have learnt a chapter to say if they had wanted it. After all the children had pleased their parents by saying the pieces from the Bible the preacher would say: Very good. Well done all of you. Then he would look the congregation over and express his pleasure on seeing some visitors, friends or relatives of members of his congregation. He rejoiced personally and on behalf of his congregation when a child was born in any of the homes of members of his congregation, referred to approaching marriages, departures from the town and district and lastly to recent deaths, and that was where the cholera came in in 1849. It made the happy 'Gyfeillach' heavy with death. It tried the congregation's faith as it thinned it out week after week. Children who said their verses from the Bible one Sunday had left the earth before the Sunday following. One thousand six hundred and eighty-two, remember. It cast a gloom over the 'Gyfeillach', the friendliest and happiest religious gathering the world over. But, thanks be, the Parry family survived intact. They had lost three long before so they were spared now.

It was in the middle of all this that John Thomas, Ieuan Ddu, as he was better known, decided to get married again, and he also decided to leave the town of Tydfil the Martyr to go and live at Pontypridd. This was a blow to many and to Myfanwy in particular. Will you come to live down Pontypridd with us? he asked her. I don't want to leave Merthyr, she said. You're welcome to come if you want to, he said. I know, she said. I have not had fair play here in Merthyr, he said. No man has worked harder than I have to raise the standard of choral singing but little or no thanks of encouragement have I had here. Your choir have stuck by you, said Myfanwy. But the people of the town have not supported me, said Ieuan. I know, I'm a Unitarian. Music should be above all denominational differences but it never will be in Merthyr. Never is a long time, said Myfanwy. Where will you go to live when I've gone to Pontypridd? he said. Perhaps with your niece, Gwenny, she said. I've got some money belonging to you, he said. When did I give you money? she said. It's money someone gave me for your father, he said. Don't ask me who for I can't tell you. I put it in the Brecon Old Bank for you. You'd better come with me now to have it put in your own name. How much is it? she said. A hundred pounds it was, he said. Perhaps a few pounds more by now. It will be something to fall back on. You have come on well with your bit of schooling and splendid with your music. When your voice gets stronger you will be as good a singer as your father. Come with me across to the Brecon Old Bank. I think I know who gave you the money to give my father, she said. You can think what you like but I am not telling you, he said.

They went across to the Brecon Old Bank and that night they went together up to the house where Ieuan's niece, Gwenny, was living with her husband and her first baby. Myfanwy's wanting to come and live with you when I leave for Pontypridd, said Ieuan. She's welcome, Gwenny said. Yes, indeed, said her husband. She will be going out working by the day to different houses, two days a week at Dr Dyke's house and one for sure at the house of the Stipendiary, said Ieuan. The rest of the week I want her to go on with her music under Rosser Beynon. She's not without money to pay. Then come all of you down to Pontypridd to see how I am getting on when you can manage.

He was at a loss for words now that he was soon to leave them and the town. People went about talking more about him leaving them than they talked about William Crawshay when they heard about him leaving the place. Everybody said: Pity he is going from us. Unitarian or whatever he is he was always on with something. Then he is such a fine-looking man too. Yes, a pity he is going. Anyway, it was no use them talk now. Ieuan had not had the support and appreciation he deserved and never would get it in Merthyr, and it was doubtful whether he would get it in Pontypridd. For like all men who feel they are better than most others around them in any given vocation he was not easy to put up with or work with. Then he was, musically, too far in advance of the other musicians of the town and district, and much too progressive, musically, for the population generally, and particularly the Welsh section of the population. Another thing was the way he walked in and out of public-houses in broad daylight. He went and mixed with the Irish in the public-houses they used to the exclusion of patrons of other nationalities and he would encourage Irishmen newly come over from Ireland to sing old Irish songs for him.

Now that he's gone the least said about that and other things the better. No matter who comes or goes the life of the people of a town must go on. But we should go as far as Pontypridd with Ieuan and his second wife to see what kind of a place it is. Well, well, what a place to leave Merthyr for, is what you would no doubt say after one look down at it from – well, say the canal bank. No, say from up where the rocking-stone is. This is a huge stone which a man told us he used to make rock like a cradle by just touching it with his finger. We couldn't rock it by pushing it. But we had a fine view of the town of Pontypridd from up near the rocking-stone. All it was when Ieuan first went to live there from Merthyr was one long and extremely narrow street and one stone bridge over the river, the River Taff. Then there were some houses terraced and scattered about the hills surrounding the town. There were one or two collieries in sight and the smoke of others could be seen rising in the distance. But it was not half the place that Merthyr, twelve miles higher up the valley, was. There was no sign of an ironworks at Pontypridd. Merthyr, as I have said, had four great ironworks employing I don't know for sure how many men, women and children.

Oh, yes, said the people we met that day at Pontypridd. We know all about Merthyr. But Pontypridd is a coming place, and we from Merthyr had to admit that it was a coming place. For all the valleys running up from Pontypridd were just then being 'developed', as they say. The two Rhondda valleys for a start. Then there was Cilfynydd just outside Pontypridd. Aberdare Junction a little farther up, and farther up again there were the towns around the pits of the Aberdare Valley. All these places sent coal down through Pontypridd and the talk was that Pontypridd would soon be the greatest mining centre in the world. So it undoubtedly was a coming place. As it was then trainload after trainload of coal passed one after the other down through the place, with a few passenger trains in between.

The whole 'coalfield', as they called it, was rapidly being developed, mostly by Englishmen who were more enterprising than us Welsh people. There were a few Welshmen who took an active part in the development of the coalfield but they were very few compared to the Englishmen who came to develop our coalfield for us. Men with names like Nixon, North, Raby, Simons, Parsons, Weaver, Townsend, Smith, Vivian and Insole are only a few of the hundreds of English names connected with the development of the South Wales and West Wales and Monmouthshire – which is Wales whatever anyone may say – coalfield. Here and there amongst them, as I have said, a Welsh name to leaven the English lump. The Welsh made excellent managers and workers but their capacity for ownership and control seems to have been limited in the extreme.

So we Welsh could not blame the English who, about 1850, the year the great musician, Ieuan Ddu, moved down into Pontypridd from Merthyr, no, we couldn't blame the English who descended like a swarm of locusts on the mineral wealth of Wales, with an odd Scot or two to introduce the note of thrift into matters affecting wages. But for them and their enterprise the coalfield might never have been developed. With amazing rapidity pits were sunk one after the other and the railway system was extended to all valleys. This was progress, we were told, but old Williams of the mountain farm on Penrhys between the two Rhondda valleys would not believe it. He saw the wooded hills bared by axe and saw and then blown open here and there to get at the stone to build houses around the pits. The rivers and hillsides were blackened and stringy greystone townships drifted towards each other. That's how it was and that was why Pontypridd, at the mouth or junction of these now roaring valleys, was regarded as a coming place.

Being as we have come so far down from where our people live and work at Merthyr we may as well go on down to Cardiff – but we won't stay there long. We would not go there at all were it not that a man now resident in Cardiff Castle is casting a shadow which reaches up to Dowlais near Merthyr. In brief, this is the man and this is the position in the year Ieuan Ddu left us. Sir John Guest, M.P., wants to renew the lease of his works at Dowlais, and the man living at Cardiff Castle at the moment is considering the matter. The man is John, Marquis of Bute, referred to by the Rev. Bruce Knight as 'this magnificent nobleman', which he was. In addition to being Marquis of Bute was he not Earl of Windsor, Lord Mountstuart de Wortley, Viscount Mount-joy, Earl of Dumfries and Bute, Baron Cardiff, K.T. – whatever that is – etc. etc.? We in the town of Tydfil the Martyr knew him only as the ground landlord of most of our county of Glamorgan and we spoke of him as the Lord of Glamorgan, which may or may not have been an ancient title which his family had dropped. It seemed, however, that he was at this time considering the revision of old leases as they came up for renewal. One such lease was already a matter of general concern in our town and district.

The renewal of the lease of the great Dowlais ironworks was a matter of life and death for ever so many thousands of our people. In a sort of petition which was prepared but not submitted at the time it was stated that four thousand five hundred men, three thousand women, and three thousand children were dependent on these works for subsistence, but we who lived practically inside those works knew that at least another fifteen hundred were dependent on those works, making twelve thousand in all. Then what was all the commotion about? was what we went about asking each other. Some said that Sir John Guest, M.P., whose works it was and whose people they were, was going to retire to some place in England, same as William Crawshay had. Sir John, they said, was not going to pay what the Marquis of Bute was asking for the renewal of the lease. Others said that Sir John was ill, and so he was. He was sixty-five years old, remember, and he had that attack when he and Lady Charlotte were dining with Mr and Mrs Disraeli at their house near Hyde Park in London, the Disraelis' house, I mean. They had watched a military review from there in the afternoon and had stayed to dine, and it was after dinner that Sir John Guest, M.P., had that first bad attack. Before he had properly recovered from this attack he had to return to Dowlais, which was his lock, stock and barrel, body and soul, smoke and dirt and everybody and everything, to deal with matters affecting the renewal of the lease of his great works. He was resting at one of his large estates outside Wales, Canford Manor, enjoying the company of his son and heir, the Hon. Ivor Guest, who was a fine lad of between twelve and thirteen at the time. It was lovely and peaceful and clean at Canford Manor and why don't I stay here and tell Bute he can keep his lease? said Sir John to himself. He had immense wealth, large estates, a son and heir, a fine woman who was an earl's sister for a wife, a seat in Parliament and he would no doubt finish up in the House of Lords if only he looked after himself now that he was sixty-five years old. He was probably worth much more than William Crawshay by this time, for William Crawshay was only worth eight million sterling, remember. Oh, yes, Sir John must have been worth a lot more than that by now. It was hard for him to keep tally on his money as it grew and grew.

Yet he was not willing to pay the rental the Marquis of Bute was now demanding before he would renew the lease of the Dowlais Works. Up to now all the Marquis of Bute and his father before him had been receiving from the Dowlais Works was a beggarly £100 a year! This through the years during which Sir John Guest and those associated with him had made millions and millions and millions! This could not go on, the Marquis of Bute told his estate agent, whose name, if I remember rightly, was Mr Beaumont. We must have a yearly rental more adequate to the worth of that estate at Dowlais, Mr Beaumont, said the Marquis. And now that I am here at Cardiff we may as well go into the question of all our old leases and applications for new leases. The whole of my county is being developed industrially and is yielding rich harvests to everyone but me, it seems. Yes, my lord, said Mr Beaumont – though I am not quite certain that that was the name of the man who was estate agent for the Marquis of Bute at the time. But what I do know for certain is that what the Marquis said about the county of Glamorgan – which he spoke of as 'my county' – yielding rich harvests to everyone but himself was true up to a point. Hundreds of millions had already been made on his land and from what came up from under his land throughout the county. So when leases came up for renewal he was preparing now to give the applicants the shock of their lives. He certainly, through his agent – what was that man's name? – gave Sir John Guest, M.P., the shock of his life when he said £50,000 a year. Preposterous! cried Sir John.

However, it was during these negotiations that the people of our town and district went about wringing their hands and saying that the Dowlais Works were going to be closed down and then God help us all. But, thanks be, the new lease was granted for £30,000, and when that was settled to the satisfaction of all concerned Joseph Parry started work down Roblins' Pit, where he earned two shillings and sixpence per week, which works out at fivepence per day. One halfpenny per hour, you could say, for he was down the pit at least fifty-six hours a week. Walking-time on top of that, not to mention washing-time, and you can judge what a long and hard week it was for a boy of nine years old.

But he kept on singing in Rosser Beynon's choir on week-nights and on Sundays in the Bethesda Chapel Choir under the conductorship of Robert James, who was courting Joseph's sister, Ann. They would have been married had they been able to find a house to go and live in. But there were no houses to be had and there was no room for them to live as married people in the Parry home or in the home of Robert's parents. The housing problem was very serious and some said it was partly responsible for the increase in the number of illegitimate children born throughout the town and district at this time. No, no, said others, it's the old drink and the sinfulness of the young people that disgraces our town by bringing their children of shame into it. Ignorance is the cause of the rise in illegitimacy, said others again, and as people became more educated then the percentage of illegitimate children would decrease. There were now several schools to further the education of the children of the place. There was the National School known as St David's and the British School, then there was the Cyfarthfa National School and the School and Library which Sir John and his wife, Lady Charlotte Guest, had started at Dowlais. Yes, there were more schools but no more houses or water and we still had to feel our way about after dark – or carry our own light, of course. There was talk that the gas-works down at the lower end of the town would soon begin lighting the streets and the sooner the better, we said. But things like that take time and it was no use us saying that as they were they were a disgrace to civilization and to the biggest town in Wales, which was also the coal and iron capital of the world. We might not be able to say that for much longer the way things were going, for whilst our two greatest ironworks were growing and growing, that is the Dowlais and Cyfarthfa works, the two smallest, the Penydarren and the Plymouth ironworks, were not. The Penydarren works was practically at a standstill about this time, now that competition was keener. Then our town and district was farther away from the growing port of Cardiff and the other ports than any of the other iron and coal districts. Some said the day would come when – but if we had listened to all that was being said and predicted it is off our heads we would have gone.

Our worse trouble was the shortage of water, I think. Oh, it was awful during the long and fine summers we used to have. For we were such a dirty people – not in our ways, remember. Oh, no, but our work was dirty and there was no water to clean ourselves properly with. About twenty thousand of us working in the ironworks and pits, didn't I say before? Then about another twenty thousand women and children who, though not working in the ironworks and pits, had to have water to drink and make tea with and keep themselves clean, didn't they? Funny thing. There was never any shortage of beer, no, not even in the driest summer I remember. But there was a terrible shortage of water most summers. No doubt the brewers managed somehow to save water during the hard winters, but few of the forty thousand people of the place could save water. I knew people who had up-ended barrels open at the top to catch rain-water, a couple or three out of every thousand, perhaps, had barrels to catch and hold a drop of rain-water.

Some of you who visited the place during one of our dry summers will remember the stink of the place from one end to the other and no doubt you wondered how we could go on living there. Well, born and bred there we had got used to the stink. You can get used to anything, can't you? It was the cholera we were most afraid of, for that did not give us any chance to get used to it. It cut us down and few of us were lucky to get up again. Yet after it had passed over us the town and district seemed as full of people as ever. For every one of the thousand six hundred and eighty-two the cholera took two came from elsewhere to take their place. Yes, the population kept on growing – and singing, of course.

Take Rosser Beynon's choir for a start, the choir which Joseph Parry and Myfanwy Llewelyn were members of, Joseph still singing alto and Myfanwy soprano. On practice nights Joseph hurried as fast as he could home from the pit to wash all over and eat his taters and meat before going to choir practice. More than once he had to go to practice just as he was, before he had washed all over or had his taters and meat. Those were the nights the man he was working with down Roblins' Pit kept him down later than he should. So Joseph went more than once to singing-practice in his pit-clothes and blacker than any sweep. Robert James, who was courting Joseph's sister, Ann, was a former pupil of Rosser Beynon's and it was Robert played the piano as the official accompanist of Rosser Beynon's choir. So Robert was disgusted when Joseph came there straight from the pit one night. Boy, boy, he said, go home and wash the dirt of the pit off your face and hands if no more. Your mother will die of shame when I tell her in chapel on Sunday. Too late it is to go home and wash, said Joseph, for if I do our mam will make me eat my taters and meat too before letting me go. Then no singing-practice will I have. Well, well, mad on singing you must be, said Robert.

Then Myfanwy poked her nose in. Well, well, she said. What a state to come here to practise with people who are clean. Easy for you to talk, said Joseph. You don't have to work down the pit like us men. Listen to the man, she said. You leave me alone, he said, his dirty and dusty pit-cap in his right hand. If you don't I will soon change the look of your face with this cap of mine. Let the boy alone, Van, said Rosser Beynon, who was keeping his promise, the promise made to Ieuan Ddu. He was keeping Myfanwy at her music and singing lessons three evenings a week and she was his most promising pupil. Better say a word about Rosser before we forget. His bardic title was 'Asaph Glan Taf', but as we are not going to refer to him by that title we will not stop now to explain its meaning in English. All our conductors and singers of note had bardic titles or nick-names – take 'Ieuan Gwyllt' for a start. I would translate that famous musician's nickname as 'Wild Jack' and would you be much the wiser? No. Then we won't bother about Rosser Beynon's bardic title either. What matters is that he was a good musician and conductor, and like most good musicians and conductors he was little good in or for anything else. Have I said that Rosser learnt music with Ieuan Ddu? Anyway, he did, and from that time on he has not been good for anything but music. But he was musically inclined and learning as best he could himself for years before he ever knew Ieuan Ddu in the first place.

Rosser had little schooling before he started working underground at the age of eight. But, like Joseph Parry is now, Rosser was mad about singing and music. He worked hard as a miner for a quarter of a century and then gave himself entirely to music. And what a gift he was to music! He was living in Quarry Row, off Bethesda Street, at the time, and Quarry Row at that time was not, believe me, the best place in which to start a musical career. Oh, no. More than half the houses if not three-fourths of the houses in Quarry Row were occupied by wild Irish families who drank as hard as they worked and started free fights most Saturday nights. No doubt it was that that made Rosser Beynon the strong temperance advocate he was all his life.

From now on he taught music, lectured and wrote on music, composed music and conducted choirs and also conducted the singing in Zoar Chapel. Yet, good though he was, he failed to make anything like a living at music and out of music. Time and again he was forced to return to the mines for spells of work and wages and once he started a business, a bookseller's business, in the High Street. What a hope! He was not cut out for business of any sort. Some of you may have gone into that shop of his and you may still remember that tall young man with a deceptive delicate look about him that was sitting with his back to the counter writing. Yes, that was him. He was too busy writing music to get up and sell you that penny copybook you wanted to make some notes on. When he did turn his head and see you and at last gathered what you wanted all he no doubt said was: There were some here somewhere. You had to find the copybook yourself and then he said: Thank you very much. I knew there were some here somewhere.

'Flat-shot', that was how his venture into business was described by miners who were friends of Rosser's. Meaning something which did not come or go off, as blasting-powder did not go off in shots—or holes bored into coal—did not go off sometimes underground. They were 'flat-shots', a waste of time and energy. Same with Rosser's venture into business, except that in this case it was little time or energy he gave to the business. So he had to go back down the mine to work again in order to earn money to pay off the debt the business and his unfitness for same had landed him into. Never mind, he said cheerfully. We'll get over that again. He had a fine tenor voice and he took to singing at concerts to earn a little extra money with which to pay the debt the business had landed him into. He went farther afield to teach and lecture. He also spoke on Temperance. In his case again the town of Tydfil the Martyr failed to give him the encouragement he deserved, with the result that he was down on his uppers more often than not. Yet he refused patronage – Lady Charlotte Guest, knowing his plight, more than once pressed him to take over the choir of the Dowlais Church, which her husband had built. But Rosser was a staunch Nonconformist, a Welsh 'independent' and conductor of the singing at Zoar Chapel, Merthyr. No, thank you, my lady, he said each and every time she asked him to take on the choir of Dowlais Church. His reputation as a musician was such by the time that he could have had £40 a year, with a light job at which he could have earned twice that amount each year, and house and coal free, had he been willing to leave Merthyr for a town in Monmouthshire. But he stuck to Merthyr all his life, which was more than Ieuan Ddu did.

The old saying about prophets not being without honour except in their own place and among their own people was proved true in Rosser Beynon's case, but he did not complain. And so we find him at this time with three choirs to conduct. The Big Choir, the Temperance Choir and the choir of Zoar Chapel. Some of his choristers sang in all three choirs, others in two and others again in one. Myfanwy sang in two of the choirs, and so did Joseph Parry, but neither of them went to Zoar Chapel to sing in that chapel's choir.

A lot more could be said about Rosser Beynon and his work as a musician in the town of Tydfil the Martyr and throughout the Principality of Wales. The life of the soul of the place was partly if not mainly the creation of men like Rosser Beynon, Ieuan Ddu and Moses Davies, to name but three musicians of many. Then there were a dozen preachers of the Gospel who also laboured to make the life of the soul more abundant in the dark and the dirt and under the smoke heavy and constant over the town of Tydfil the Martyr. Those who were referred to as 'impractical men' kept the soul of the place alive and were content to let whoever wanted riches and honours go on gathering those things. Come cholera, explosions in the mines, burnings and maiming in the ironworks, come want and disease and still the body of the place maintained its productive and procreative capacity, the momentum of the body of the place was no longer subject to arrest by the sum-total of bodily ills. But the soul of the place as yet had little momentum beyond what the preachers and poets, musicians and others referred to as 'impractical men' gave it. This is, we know, a mystery of sorts, something about which it is not seemly to be too positive. It is a thing of feeling, of the spirit, and such comparisons as I have made may be worthless. Yet when we remember how things were in those days, those days of immense wealth and productivity on the one hand and mass poverty and stinking conditions on the other, we must try to discover who it was that brought the mass of the people out of that dirt and darkness into whatever light there is in these days.

I could refer to those days in Merthyr as 'the good old days' and leave it at that, for in some ways they were good, as these days are good in some ways. But that does not alter the fact that a great and terrible crime was committed on the body of mankind in those days. The image of God was undoubtedly debased by ... by who? Well, say by man himself in the first place and by the great industrialists of the times in the second degree. Perhaps I have already said too much about all the millions of pounds sterling made out of the place and about the people of the place having no water supply other than wells and springs that dried up in summer, and stank most of the time. I have also said enough and perhaps too much about the decayed animal matter in the water of the dozen wells on which upwards of forty thousand people were mainly dependent for water for all purposes. I do not want to rub this in. But I respectfully suggest that no man of any greatness whatsoever would or should leave, after having made millions of pounds sterling, these people before he had spent some of his millions in providing them with at least a supply of water for all purposes. But they left us without water, without a hospital in which to be patched up after we had been broken and torn and burnt in their service. Not a hall in which to meet or hold any sort of local event. Nothing worthy the name of sanitation – and I could go on. Those who were often referred to as 'our great benefactors' just took what paid out of the pay-dirt and left the dirt to us. Still, we had the Cyfarthfa Brass Band.

Our real benefactors were those who laboured mightily to keep the soul of the place alive, and Rosser Beynon was one of the foremost of those. This night he is smiling as he looks at Joseph Parry, who has worked down the mine twelve hours for which he will receive fivepence, after his twelve hours' work in his pit-clothes wanting to sing. Let the boy alone, Van, said Rosser Beynon to Myfanwy. Only one with music in his soul would want to sing more than eat after twelve hours down the pit. Go to your place in the choir, my boy. Lend him my spare copy, Robert James. But he will dirty it, Rosser Beynon, unless he goes out to one of the houses to wash his hands first, said Robert James. Let him dirty it, said Rosser Beynon. Come on now, all of you. There was the usual coughing and scraping of throats and Rosser said: I hope you all sing as good as you cough. Now, do your best, please. We'll take it right through from beginning to end and see how it goes. Then we can treat the weak spots afterwards. Right, Robert. Robert James played the introduction on the piano and Rosser beating time with his baton until he brought the choir into it. They sang the piece entitled 'Teyrnasoedd y Ddaear', which I would translate into English as 'The Kingdoms of the Earth'. And Joseph Parry, in his pit-clothes and his stomach feeling empty, after having worked hard for twelve hours to earn fivepence, sang of 'The Kingdoms of the Earth'.

CHAPTER 5

A Daniel leaves for America

THE children at the Gyfeillach, which, as I said before, is the informal, friendly and happy after-meeting held after the service proper in our Welsh chapels, and is one of the most pleasant features in the life of the chapels of our denomination, the Welsh Independents, the children present at the evening service at Bethesda Chapel on the second Sunday in January, 1853, were disappointed with the after-service, which some of the older children said was as sad as any Gyfeillach held during the year of the cholera. They felt they were being 'rushed' by the preacher so as he could get to the subject which took up most of the time of the after-service. In fact, it was little more than a farewell service for Daniel Parry.

The years of waiting were over and he was to leave the town of Tydfil the Martyr the morning of the Tuesday following, perhaps never to return. Enough money had been saved and now he was off to America, leaving Betty and the children until he had made a home for them on the other side of the water. He had not long before managed to find a job for Joseph up out of the pit. He could not have gone to America with an easy mind had he not found work for Joseph in the Cyfarthfa Ironworks. So Joseph was no longer a miner but an ironworker. He and Henry between them would now have to work to keep the home until the time came for the family to follow the father across the water.

The Parry family all sat together this Sunday night. Ann was now Mrs James, the wife of Robert James, who conducted the singing at Bethesda Chapel and played the piano to accompany Rosser Beynon's choir. But this Sunday evening she left her husband's side to sit with her parents and her brothers and sisters during the Gyfeillach.

Tonight, said the preacher, we have to say farewell to our dear brother, Daniel Parry. A faithful member from the days of the saintly founder of our chapel, the late Rev. Methusalem Jones. I think I can say, without in any way reflecting upon the members individually or the membership as a whole, that Daniel Parry and his dear wife and our dear sister, have been pillars of this chapel through the years. There they are, sitting all together by there, as holy a family as any on this earth. Our hearts are with them this night, and we shall remember Daniel in our prayers. Yes, Daniel, when you are in the ship on the mighty waters, we of Bethesda Chapel will be praying for you. When, God willing, you reach the new world, we shall still be praying for you. You are leaving your dear wife and children behind. Whatever happens they shall not want, Daniel. We of Bethesda Chapel will look after our own.

Jane, the youngest of the Parry family, started to cry and so made Elizabeth cry. The preacher had charged the atmosphere with intense feeling and many present were on the verge of tears. It did not take much to make Welsh people cry in those days. Now, now, said Betty to her two daughters. Mustn't cry, good girls. Be quiet now. The two girls sighed and sniffed a bit and regained control of themselves. The preacher continued: What more can I say to Daniel Parry? or about Daniel Parry? You all know him, some of you have known him for longer than I have, and no doubt some of you would like to say a word before we give him and ourselves to the Lord in prayer.

Old Ben Watkins, who wasn't far short of a hundred years old by now, had his work cut out to rise from his place in the deacons' big seat. He groaned as he straightened up, groaned aloud under the weight of years. I do go stiff after sitting, he explained. So will some of you long before you are my age. He spoke with his hands resting on the little table in the big seat, the table with flowers in a vase in the centre of it. He was leaning heavily on this little table and he made a face at the flowers. He picked up the vase and handed it to a fellow-deacon. It's in the way, he said. Yes, he said, I have known Daniel Parry longer than any of you. I have known him and everybody worth knowing in this county for nearly a hundred years. Yes, nearly a hundred years, and if I can't ride my horse any more I can still stand on my own two legs. That's through living up on top of the rise in Danygraig Farm and not down here in the dirt. That's one thing on which I differed from the late Reverend Methusalem Jones. Good man, mind you, yes, very good man. But why did he insist on having this chapel built down here in the dirt – and in a hole in the dirt? I told him plenty then. Perhaps there are some still here who can bear me out?

He looked to see if there were. No, he said, they're all dead. Many of them no doubt died before their time owing to the damp of this chapel down in the hole. I do always get stiffer sitting here in this chapel than I do sitting anywhere else – the preacher coughed and smiled and nodded his head as much as to say: Please come to the point, Mr Watkins. But the old man, taking full advantage of his age and his long connexion with the chapel, rambled on. Listen to our preacher coughing, he said. No doubt that's the damp – and the dirt. Damp and dirt are no respecters of persons. They kill high and low before their proper time. Look last year – and him not living as low down as we are here now. But he died. Yes, Sir John Guest died, didn't he. Now that woman of his is boss up there in Dowlais. But she will have to look out or the dirt will kill her too. Oh, yes. I don't know where you are going to in 'Merica, Daniel Parry, but wherever you go try to keep out of the dirt. If it's to get out of the dirt you are going to 'Merica then I don't blame you. Let's see what time it is.

He took about a minute to get his big watch out of his waistcoat pocket. Then before looking at it he put it to his ear. I wonder have it stopped? he said. The time, Mr Watkins, said the preacher, the time now is just a minute after half-past eight. The old man looked at his watch and said: Your watch is slow. One minute short of twenty-five minutes to nine by me. He took about a minute to replace his watch in his waistcoat pocket. Enough old talk, he said. Daniel Parry have come to help me with the hay all through the years. Good man with the scythe. None better. Splendid man on a haystack. There again, none better. So better than any more old talk from me he shall have something in his pocket to go. What day are you going, Daniel? I take the train Tuesday morning, said Daniel. The ship goes out with the tide Wednesday morning. Then come up the farm to-morrow morning and bring all the family with you to have one good day together out of the dirt before you go, said Watkins. Don't send your boys to work to-morrow, Betty. Bring them all up to me and we will have a Noson Lawen to-morrow night. No crying but singing. Remember now –

118

where's my hat? One of his fellow-deacons handed it to him. I must go now, said old Watkins. Too long already I have been down in the dirt. My man is waiting with the horse and trap. Come for me to put my hand on your shoulder up the trip to the road, Daniel. Daniel went forward from his place to steady the old man out and up the 'trip', a slight incline of about ten yards up from the chapel to the road. Before the old man left the chapel he said: One minute, Daniel. Listen all of you. Don't stay too long after I have gone to pray and preach at this man. He is a good man and not an aunt sally to throw a lot of old softness at. Remember that now. Goodnight to you all. Remember, Betty. Up to the farm as early as you like all of you.

Then he went out leaning most of his weight on Daniel's shoulder. His man was waiting to help him up into the trap and to drive him home. You'll be all right now, said Daniel. Wait a minute, said old Watkins. Between you and me, remember. Don't be 'shamed to take it, Daniel, please. You haven't got too much. I have. What's a few sovereigns to me? I don't think Betty would be willing for me to take money from you, said Daniel. Take it now and leave me talk to Betty when you come up the farm tomorrow, said Watkins. I am not sure that we will be able to come up to the farm tomorrow, said Daniel. You must, said old Watkins. *Must*, do you hear. Your Betty is a good woman but she is too fond of prayer meetings at her age. If you stay down here in the dirt tomorrow it's prayer meetings you will have in every house you go to to say farewell. So will you be a man and come up to the farm like I am telling you? Yes, I will, said Daniel. And all the family, remember, said Watkins. Yes, all of us, said Daniel. Goodnight, said Watkins. Goodnight and thank you, said Daniel.

Old Watkins had made it too difficult for anyone in the chapel to change the atmosphere after he had left. Those who spoke after him spoke sincerely but briefly and the prayer at the end was also brief. There was no more crying.

Are we going up the farm tomorrow, mam? said Joseph as the Parry family, now without Ann, were on their way home. Ann had gone Penydarren way to her own home with her husband, Robert James. I don't see how we can all go and spend the day at the 'Graig Farm tomorrow, do you, Daniel? said Betty. Yes, said Daniel. My box is packed. Yes, said Betty, but – But nothing, my gel, said Daniel. I have said we will all be up there early, I told Robert James not to go to work and to bring Ann up the farm early. He's giving us a Noson Lawen for ourselves. Will he have a harpist to play and all? said Joseph. Sure to, said Daniel. That will be grand, said Joseph. After supper and after the children had gone to bed Daniel said: Old Watkins gave me five golden sovereigns. You should not have taken them from him, said Betty. Why not? said Daniel. We must manage without help from anybody, said Betty. Well, I am keeping the money, said Daniel. You must do as you think best, said Betty. As long as you know, that's all, said Daniel. But we must not tell anyone about it. Didn't he tell the chapel full of people? said Betty. He said you should have something in your pocket to go, didn't he? Yes, so he did, said Daniel. But what odds if he did? Time for bed. Yes, said Betty.

We were reminded by old Watkins of the passing of Sir John Guest, M.P., and we should have said something about it at the time. But he only died during the last week of last November and this is only the second Sunday in January, remember. So it is barely six weeks since he died and there was Christmas in between. And what more can we say about him than was said at the time? Read the funeral sermon the Rev. Canon Jenkins preached over him and the obituary notice in the *Gentleman's Magazine* and you've got him as a man, an employer and Member of Parliament. He built a school and a church and, wrote another man, 'left behind him immense wealth. Dowlais was his. He held also large estates, chief of which was Canford Manor'.

There it is. His son became Sir Ivor and in course of time Lady Charlotte married again. The same man wrote: 'With her departure from the scene of her husband's greatness, and finally her marriage to Charles Schreiber, Esq., M.P., the connexion between her ladyship and Dowlais seems to have been nearly severed.' Now I wish that old Watkins had not reminded us of Sir John's passing, for it is not easy to have to mark the passing of a man with a black mark. But 'the scene of her husband's greatness' is too much for any Welshman to stomach, especially if like ourselves he was born in the town or district in which this scene was set. Lady Charlotte herself described it perhaps better than I can when she called Dowlais a 'cinder-hole'. But it was something even worse than that when Sir John died at the age of sixty-seven and it was no better when her ladyship left the place for good to marry Charlie Schreiber. She was one of the richest widows in Britain, if not *the* richest widow in Britain, when she took herself and her money away from our place in the 'cinder-hole'. So Charlie Schreiber did heaps better for himself than Disraeli did, for they both married rich widows whose money came out of our 'cinder-hole'. It is needless to say that none of the money taken out by these two rich widows ever came back to the 'cinder-hole'.

We did not blame Lady Charlotte Guest for clearing out when she did or for marrying Charlie Schreiber. All we had to complain about was the state of the place in which she left us, the scene of her late husband's 'greatness', as that chap wrote. Some of you may have forgotten that scene as it was then. The writer I have already quoted from said: 'It will be long before Dowlais becomes lovable ...' By damn, the chap who wrote that must have been a bit of a wag. For the place was not only a 'cinder-hole' but a hell-hole into the bargain and beyond redemption at the time. The half-dozen or so chapels and the one church notwithstanding. You remember it, don't you? A hotch-potch of little houses inextricably tied up to and mixed up with the huge works.

The works was the thing. It spawned huge and fiery ash and clinker-tips to burn without end and these surrounded the small houses of the place, often sending streams of fiery ash or clinker down on to the very doorsteps of the houses. Some people had to move out and their houses were cremated by the irresistible flow of fire from some of the tips. Other houses were built for the dispossessed on tips in which the fires had died down, keeping them still within the orbit of the eye of the works. Merthyr crept up and Dowlais crept down and between them created Penydarren, made a joint, so to speak, between the two largest hell-holes, and soon this joint, this in-between place called Penydarren, was also closely backed by huge and fiery ash and clinker-tips. You will remember how those blessings, those tips which were an integral part of the 'greatness' of Sir John Guest which the writer referred to, you will remember how those tips spewed fiery ash and clinker to block roads and the Morlais Brook at several points. So we had all the dirt and smoke and sulphurous fumes and fire and ash and clinker and everything of that sort but no water in this scene of 'greatness'.

Never mind. Life went on. Early Monday morning the Parry family went up to the patch of green and brown that was Danygraig Farm. Old Watkins was there to greet them and to welcome them. It was a nice day but too mild for the time of the year, said old Watkins. Come on, breakfast is ready for you, he said. We have had breakfast, said Betty. Yes, but you have walked up out of the dirt and you must have second breakfast, said Watkins. Must have it now my housekeeper have put it. So they all had another breakfast of eggs, and home-cured bacon. Eat, eat full of your bellies, all good food, nothing from the shops on my table, said Watkins. Oh, what a grand day they all had that day up at Danygraig Farm! The boys had rides on the horse old Watkins was no longer able to ride and the girls tried their hands at making butter and cheese.

Old Watkins went to bed for the afternoon so as to be fresh for the Noson Lawen, about which he was uncommunicative in the extreme. Joseph wanted to know if there was to be a harpist and if so who the harpist would be? I'll tell you that much but no more, said Watkins. The same harpist as have been coming for years. Now don't ask me any more questions to make me tell old lies. Robert James, who was there as one of the Parry family now that he was married to Ann, seemed to be the only one who knew something of the old farmer's plans regarding that night of joy and gladness which we Welsh call Noson Lawen. For Robert, just when it was getting dark, after inspecting the big barn with old Watkins, told Ann, his wife, that he was going down as far as the Temperance Hall. What for? she said. I won't be long, he said.

And now that he's gone we may as well say something about the Temperance Hall, which had just been opened. It was the first public hall to be built in the town and district – never mind the Market Hall, for that is part of the Market House and not much of a hall anyway. The Temperance Hall is different and I should have mentioned it as soon as they started building it, but it is hard to keep track of everything. Now it was open and concerts and things were being held there – and temperance gatherings, of course, with Rosser Beynon's augmented Temperance Choir singing. It was the Temperance movement that could claim the most credit for the building of the Temperance Hall, but everybody was welcome there all the same. Oh, it was a grand hall, the Temperance Hall. It could accommodate two hundred people sitting down and perhaps another hundred standing about upstairs and down. It was the talk of the place when it first opened.

Some people, people who are never satisfied whatever you do, said: Why didn't they build a bigger hall whilst they were about it? What good is a hall holding only two hundred for a place with forty thousand people? Never mind,

Rosser Beynon was delighted with it. Yes, delighted. And why wouldn't he be? It was he and his Temperance Choir that were the inspiration behind the building of it in the first place. Now he had a place in which to rehearse and to hold concerts or lectures or eisteddfods without going on his bended knees to preachers and deacons of chapels. The boy, Joseph Parry, spoke of the Temperance Hall as though he owned the place. I was rehearsing with the choir at the Temperance Hall last night, he would one day tell the boys among whom he worked in the ironworks at Cyfarthfa. Next day it would be: I was singing last night at the concert at our Hall. Your Hall? the boys would say. It's the Temperance Hall and I sing alto in the Temperance Choir, don't I? said Joseph. We know, said the other boys. Then there you are, said Joseph.

Yes, the Temperance Hall ... I was passing the little place only the other day. Time had reduced its size and significance in the eyes of many now passing it by as though it were not there at all. But we who remembered it when it was first opened and when it was the talk of the place stopped to look and think a minute. For more than half a century it was the social centre, as you might say, of the coal and iron capital of the world.

Anyway, it was there Robert James went that January night in 1853, leaving the Parry family in Danygraig Farm to wonder what he had gone down to the Temperance Hall for. You will soon know, said old Watkins, their host. You will soon know when it's time to go across to the big barn. Can't we go to the barn now? said Joseph. No, said Watkins. We must wait till Robert James comes back. They waited, Joseph most impatiently, until at last Robert James came, and when he came all he did was to nod his head and look at old Watkins. Right then, said Watkins. Light those two nightlamps, Daniel, and give one to Robert to carry. Have they lit the lamps in the barn, Robert? Robert nodded his head. Then come all of you across to the barn now with me, said Watkins. You are the guests of the night.

What a surprise it was to them to find the big barn crowded with people and with the right people at that. Rosser Beynon was there with his biggest choir, the non-denominational choir, as you might call it, for the members were of all denominations of Welsh Nonconformity. Will Full-Moon was there to sing and old Shenkin was there to play the harp which he seemed to wrap himself around when playing. Letty Lewis, who had won more prizes for singing than any other soprano in the town and district, was also there to sing. Will Full-Moon was frowned upon for asking, as soon as old Watkins appeared with the Parry family: Where do you keep the drop of beer, Watkins? Not a nice thing to say in front of Rosser Beynon, the conductor of a Temperance Choir and a strict teetotaller all his life. But then Rosser was also a musician who would put up with a lot just to hear Will Full-Moon sing.

You shall have a drop of beer, Will, said Watkins. My tongue is hanging out and I'm spitting sixpenny-bits after walking up that rise, said Will Full-Moon. I was born in a public-house so all you good people will forgive me – where is the beer, Watkins? Come with me to the house, said Watkins. You start, Rosser. I must go with Will to see that he don't take too much. Rosser sighed as they left the barn and said: Never mind. Pity it is but never mind. Noson Lawen it is and we must shut our eyes, we who belong to the Temperance movement, to what we would not overlook at any other time. Joseph went to his place in the choir next to Myfanwy who said: Hullo, boy. Rosser continued: Daniel Parry, who is starting on the way to America in the morning, has been a strict teetotaller all his life, and it is for him and his family we have come from the Temperance Hall up here to sing. We must send him on his way with a song in his heart, mustn't we? Welsh songs in his heart will perhaps be better than money in his pocket over there in America. So let us put Welsh songs in his heart in a way that will keep them there all his days. Now, please. No piano for Robert James to help us with tonight but we have got Shenkin to help us with the harp. Quiet, please. You've all got copies of the new piece we are going to try for the first time later on? Say now if you have not? Right. No more talking then.

The choir began to sing and whilst they were singing old Watkins and Will Full-Moon returned to the barn. There you are, Will Full-Moon whispered to old Watkins. Didn't I tell you. Sing sad to break the hearts of the man and his family they will. But you let me have fair play with that lovely drop of beer and 'tis I will make them laugh with my songs. You shall have a drop of beer, said Watkins. Will did his best but the night ended in tears all the same. The choir finished up with a song of farewell that was enough to crack not only hearts but the rocking-stone down Pontypridd into the bargain. Will Full-Moon himself broke down and wept and licked his tears as though they were drops of beer as they ran down his face. Oh, it was a night. Will Full-Moon did not leave the farm that night but all the others did.

Next morning there were more tears shed in the home of the Parry family in Chapel Row, but Daniel Parry himself did not shed a single tear this morning. He was saying to himself: At last. He comforted his wife and children with the assurance that they would all be together again before another year was out. He did not want them or anyone else to accompany him down to the railway station, from where he would take a train for the first time in his life. Then when he got to Cardiff he would board a ship for the first time in his life. Have no fear for me, for I am not afraid, he said. Neither be sad for me for I am not sad either. I am happy for I am going to a better place than this. I hope so, said Betty. It cannot be much worse of a place if no better, said Daniel. We have been very happy here in Merthyr, said Betty. We have tried to make ourselves content but happy we have never been, my gel, said Daniel. No place for real happiness there has been in Merthyr. Over where I am now going with a light heart I am sure it will be better. I can hear the man coming with the barrow for your box, said Joseph.

Daniel went to the doorway and looked left. Yes, Lewis the roller is coming with the barrow before he have washed all over after his night's work. Now, don't cry any more, good children. Robert, he said to Robert James, his son-in-law, remember what I have asked you. To you and God I am leaving them for now, remember. I will remember, said Robert James. Daniel embraced Betty his wife and said: God is good, remember. He embraced and kissed his five children one after the other and Robert James helped Lewis the roller who worked nights in the rolling-mill to carry Daniel's big box with his things in out of the house and on to the barrow. Betty helped Daniel to put his greatcoat on and handed him his hard hat, then gave him the straw bag with the bit of food and the bottle of small-beer in it. With it in his hand he walked out of the house to where Lewis the roller was standing beside his barrow on the canal bank. Right, Lewis, he said.

Lewis the roller wheeled the barrow and Daniel Parry walked beside it down the canal bank, and he did not look back once. His wife and children stood on the canal bank looking after him, Robert James with them. Their neighbours both sides came out of their houses on to the canal bank to look after Daniel Parry and Lewis the roller and the barrow with the box on it that Lewis was wheeling. Lewis wheeled the barrow off the canal bank on to the path left of it and along the path out on to the big road. They were gone. Dad's gone, cried little Jane, and the neighbours right and left of the Parry home in Chapel Row looked sympathetically towards them. Such scenes were not uncommon about this time.

Daniel Parry was a good man and he was gone from Merthyr, and that was what they said about Mr Henry Austin

Bruce, our Stipendiary Magistrate. But he was not gone to America – as a matter of fact he had delivered a lecture at the Merthyr Library not so long before, a lecture in which he had referred to what Daniel Parry had helped to prove this very morning. In the lecture, Mr Bruce, who was a first-class speaker and lecturer, said:

In discussing the chances of the Iron Trade we must also not forget that the field of coal and iron in the United States of America is far larger than the whole area of the British Isles, and that as their population increases, and their capital accumulates, we may look forward in them to rivals as energetic and skilful as ourselves. We ourselves are contributing to this unwelcome result, as numbers of our best workmen are daily emigrating to America, where they find their experience and skill in great request, and I have frequently seen letters from Welsh emigrants employed in the Ironworks of Pennsylvania, describing in glowing terms the comforts and advantages of their new home ...

It is a pity that that lecture delivered by Mr Bruce at the Merthyr Library was not drummed into the minds of all classes of the population of the town and district at that time. Had the advice contained in that lecture been taken and acted upon by employers and employees things would have been much better for all concerned and Mr Bruce would not have had to deplore the fact that numbers of our *best* workmen are daily emigrating to America –

But this was what I was going to say. After the death of Sir John Guest, M.P., Mr Bruce left the Bench to represent us in Parliament, where he would no doubt do more good for the town and district than he was able to do on the Bench. Up to now it was very little help we had had from Parliament – I am speaking of the time up to January, 1853, remember. Our coal and iron was going somewhere all the time but very little was coming back to us in return for it. So we were hoping now that Mr Henry Austin Bruce was our member in Parliament that we would be having more than we had had up to then in return for our great contribution to the industrial might of Britain. For our contribution was a great one – let there be no mistake about that. Mr Bruce himself, in the lecture I have quoted from, describes our town as 'the centre of a population of seventy thousand souls'. What a place it was half-way through the nineteenth century! We had forty-seven blast furnaces all told going at the time. And do you want figures to show you how much coal we were getting up from under the earth and sending the world over? No, never mind the figures. Every valley in our coalfield had been opened up and coal going down to the waiting ships from every one of them. Yes, plenty going down and out but damn little coming up and back in return. So we were hoping that Mr Bruce, who was a fine speaker, would tell those English gentlemen in the British House of Commons about us. All we wanted was fair play all round.

Poor old Ben Watkins ... Talk about a link with the past and you would think of him at once. Only two years short of a hundred years old, according to him, when he died. A life spanning nearly a century and lived to the full right up to the end. And the funeral he had. Upwards of three thousand people following him to his grave in Thomas Town cemetery and the singing was unforgettable. He left a hundred pounds to Bethesda Chapel, a hundred pounds a year for life to his housekeeper, two hundred pounds in one lump to Myfanwy, the late Blind Dick's daughter, a year's wages to each of the three men who worked on the farm, his gold watch to the preacher of Bethesda Chapel and the farm and the stock and whatever money there was left between his sons who were farming somewhere in Breconshire. There is talk that they are going to sell the farm now. Old Watkins died peacefully in his sleep – oh, I forgot. He left a hundred pounds in one lump to Will Full-Moon, who, by the way, is singing better than ever. So old Ben Watkins of Danygraig Farm is gone, Yes, he's gone but it will be long before he is forgotten. We must try and keep his memory as green as he kept his few fields with the dirt all around him and his farm and the smoke over all. He fought the good fight against forty-seven furnaces all told, remember, to say nothing of the slag of coal-levels, coal-drifts and coal-pits. He's out of the dirt and smoke now anyway.

In a town and district like ours it's no good you try to keep track of everybody. So many strangers coming here all the time. Down town on a Saturday or Sunday night we don't know half the people passing us on the streets. Same if we turn into a public-house. More and more English being spoken in the place and there is more drinking too. I like a pint of beer and a bit of good company but such drunkenness as there is in the place now turns my stomach. 'Superfluous earnings are misspent in intoxication and debauchery,' said Mr Bruce, and that was only too true, worse luck. It was almost as bad when there were no 'superfluous earnings', during fluctuations in trade when wages were low the drinking went on as bad as ever.

Great pity, no doubt, but what else is there for us to do after our work? said many. Shall we just sit in the house till it is time to go to bed? If we go out where else is there to go but the public-house? Not one in a hundred of those who drank themselves drunk could read and if you told them to take a walk of a night after their long day's work they would laugh at you. When Merthyr was the centre of a population of seventy thousand souls there was no savings bank or anything like that. What saving was done was done at home. Fair play for Mr Bruce, he tried to tackle this grave problem. Amusements and education, he said, would withdraw our people from the public-houses, and he tried his best to further our education. He did not mention Religion in his lecture, only stressed the need for more saving, more healthy amusement and more education.

Still, Religion as far as our chapels were concerned could speak for itself. Whatever decency was won and maintained in our way of life at that time was won and maintained by the chapels. They were Puritanical in the extreme – they had to be in face of the half that was drunken and debauched, God help them, to the extreme. The chapels and their choirs were the backbone of a militant Temperance movement. The fight was continuous and appeared to be our own judging from the almost criminal indifference of the English gentlemen of the British House of Commons. From behind the Speaker's Chair Henry W. Lucy had viewed them and said: 'A more respectable body of the gentlemen of England it would be difficult to gather together. With the possible exception of one or two political adventurers there is probably not a man in the House who is not well born or at least rich.' And that was still as true as when Henry W. Lucy wrote his opinion of the composition of the British House of Commons, and as true now as when we ourselves quoted Lucy before.

They could not see us, didn't know us, did not care a damn about us. Something was happening but they did not know what it was neither did they care. They only knew that coal and iron in immense quantities was coming from 'somewhere in Wales' and that the late member for one of those places had made lots of money. Our blood and sweat and tears meant damn-all to London or the English gentlemen of the British House of Commons. We could go on praying and singing hymns or drink ourselves to death for all they cared as long as we kept on working. Oh, those English gentlemen of the British House of Commons. I know a Committee of Council on Education instructed a man named Tremenheere to inquire into the state of elementary education in the mining district of South Wales. His report is, in effect, the greatest indictment of the English gentlemen of the House of Commons that could possibly be framed.

Let us forget them even as they forgot us and go to the home of the Parry family in Chapel Row in the town of Tydfil the Martyr, where all are happy this Sunday. For a letter has been received and they now know that Daniel

Parry is safe over the mighty waters and has started work in one of the ironworks of Pennsylvania. At the Gyfeillach after the evening service at Bethesda Chapel there is great rejoicing and parts of the long letter from Daniel are read by the preacher to the congregation. His reading of the letter is punctuated by loud cries of 'Thanks unto God' from one of the deacons in the big seat, and the congregation as a whole say: 'Yes, indeed. Amen.'

In one part of the letter Daniel had said that before long he hoped to send money for them all to come out to join him. On the way home from chapel, and they had to hurry for Joseph had to go to work in the ironworks that Sunday night again, on the way home Joseph surprised his mother by saying: I don't want to go to America, mam. Boy, what are you talking about? she said. I like it here in Merthyr, he said. Plenty of singing here in Merthyr, perhaps no choirs to sing with in America. Don't talk, boy, she said. Didn't your father say in the letter that there is a Welsh chapel with everything in Welsh out there where he is? Our Ann won't be going, will she? said Joseph. Ann is married and must stay with her husband, mustn't she? said Betty. I could live with them, said Joseph. You would rather live with Robert James than with our mam, would you? said Henry. I would rather live in Merthyr than anywhere in America, said Joseph. Don't bother with him, Henry, said Betty. What if dad could only hear you talking like you are, Joseph? said Elizabeth. I am talking the way I feel, said Joseph. Not thinking of dad's feelings, are you? said Jane. Leave him alone to come to his senses all of you, said Betty.

Joseph and Henry took off their Sunday clothes and put on their working-clothes and after a cup of tea and a bit to eat went to their work in the rolling-mill of the ironworks. Joseph was thinking of America as a wild country in which there was little or no scope for musicians, and was he not a musician? Not so long ago he had been present at a performance of Mozart's 'Twelfth Mass', which had been a revelation to him. It was Myfanwy Llewelyn gave him the ticket for the shilling seats at the back of the Temperance Hall, where she sat next to him. He was getting on for thirteen and she must have been seventeen at the time. She still called him 'boy' and he did not like her calling him 'boy'. He was a man, he thought. Had he not been working for four years, first as a miner and now as an ironworker? Then his voice was beginning to change too. When it had finished changing it would be a voice like Will Full-Moon's, he felt – but not if I have to go to America, he said to Myfanwy.

He talked more to her than to anyone, for she was a good listener though a rather indifferent one at times. But she took it all in. She had a certain poise, a sort of sureness of herself which no doubt began to develop when she used to go round the public-houses with her blind father when little more than a baby. Then out of scraps of education she made a better scholar of herself than most boys of her generation who had had proper and continuous schooling. She had taken advantage of her contacts with the wives of professional men, to whose homes she had gone to work for the day, to polish up her English talk. She no longer went out working for she had money, the two hundred pounds left her by old Watkins of Danygraig Farm, and she still had nearly all the hundred and odd pounds Ieuan Ddu had got from someone and put in the Brecon Old Bank for her. Now the two hundred left her by old Watkins was also in the Brecon Old Bank and she was drawing fifteen shillings a week out of the Bank to live on and to pay for her lessons in music and singing with Rosser Beynon. Three times a week, for an hour at a time, she went to him, and the other three nights she sang with one or other of his choirs. He wanted her to compete at eisteddfods so as to get other opinions, the opinions of adjudicators, on her voice and singing. But she said no. Letty Lewis had won ever so many prizes singing at eisteddfods but, said Myfanwy, she have nearly ruined a grand voice by going about singing for prizes at eisteddfods. Perhaps you are right, said Rosser Beynon.

So Myfanwy went on studying and singing in the soprano sections of one or other of Rosser Beynon's choirs. After choir practices she used to let Joseph Parry walk from the Temperance Hall up as far as Pontmorlais Square with her and let him talk to her. He interested her because she felt he had something in him and because he was so confident that some day he would be a great musician. I will sing and I will play the organ and piano and I will compose if only my mother will leave me behind in Merthyr, he said. Myfanwy would nod her head and he would go on talking until they reached Pontmorlais Square. Myfanwy had to go on up to Penydarren, where she still lodged with Ieuan Ddu's niece, Gwenny. Joseph had to turn left off the Square and down Bethesda Street home. They would stand on the Square and he would go on talking until she would say: Go on home now, boy.

CHAPTER 6

Off to Philadelphia in the Morning

THE Cyfarthfa Brass Band was now one of the best bands in Britain, if not in the world. Ask those who heard it about this time if you don't believe me. I would not say as much for it during the time of its first conductor but I will maintain that under its second conductor, Mr Ralph Livsey, it was the best brass band the world over. Mr Livsey came to us from where he was playing the bugle in the band they had at the Vauxhall Gardens in London, and he stayed with us, conducting the Cyfarthfa Brass Band, right up to the time he died. It was under him as conductor that the band first competed at the Crystal Palace in London –

where Mr Dan Godfrey himself said that the Cyfarthfa Brass Band did not get fair play. But never mind.

The band had new uniforms in 1854 – they wore them for the first time to play the old year out and the new year in for the guests and the family at Cyfarthfa Castle. They wore them for the second time at the concert they gave at the Temperance Hall early in 1854 and Myfanwy gave Joseph Parry a ticket for that too. Again they sat next to each other in the shilling seats at the back. Half-way through the concert there was an interval and it was then that Myfanwy saw that Joseph had been crying. What's the matter? she whispered. I must go now, he said and got up and went out. She followed him out and said: After me paying a silver shilling for a ticket for you – I know but I can't stop to listen to any more of the lovely music, he said. Worse it will be for me in the morning if I do. Are you going home straight from by here now? she asked him. No, I'm going to walk the roads of Merthyr for a bit before going home, he said. Then I may as well walk with you, I suppose, she said. I am not much for brass bands anyway. Come if you're coming. I think I would rather the band with fiddles and things in too, said Joseph. But the Cyfarthfa Band is no old circus band, remember. Which way are you going? she said when they had passed the railway station on the left. Any way, he said. Then we'll walk up as far as Pontmorlais Square and back down and around, she said. You must not pine. I shall not pine when I leave Merthyr for good before long. I don't want to leave Merthyr, he said. So you have told me I don't know how many times, she said. It's easy for you to talk, he said. But when you do leave Merthyr you won't be going over the water, will you? No, not yet, anyway, she said. To Cardiff first and perhaps London after. But before I go anywhere I am going on the train down to Pontypridd to ask Ieuan Ddu. It will be the first time for me to go on a train but go I must. For it is Ieuan Ddu that will tell me better than Rosser Beynon. It is no good me wait and wait until my bit of money is all gone, is it? No, said Joseph. How much money are they keeping for you in the Brecon Old Bank? Never you mind, she said. Enough, I hope, for my schooling in music until I start singing to keep myself tidy. That's what I would like too, said Joseph. Not to have to go on the ship to America but stay here and have schooling in music. But I have not got any money in the Brecon Old Bank.

After they had been walking the streets and talking for about an hour she stopped in the middle of Pontmorlais Square and said: Go home, boy. Farewell and thank you for buying me the ticket, he said. Shall I give you a shilling for your pocket? she said. No, he said. Then go home, boy, she said. I'm going, he said. Will you pray for me to get safe over the water? I don't say prayers, she said. Whether or no I like you, he said. Go home and don't talk so soft here in the middle of Pontmorlais Square, she said. I'm going, he said. It will be prayer meeting and crying in our house tonight again. Our Ann is the worst. I wish my mother would take her over the water instead of me. Your mother has got enough to take without taking Ann now that she is going to have a baby, said Myfanwy. Baby? said Joseph. Whose baby? Whose do you think? said Myfanwy. Who is your Ann married to? Robert James, said Joseph. Then there you are, said Myfanwy. What are you waiting for? I don't know, said Joseph. Then I am sure I don't, said Myfanwy. May as well go home, said Joseph. I will say a prayer and ask for you to be taken safe over the water, she said. Go on home now. Farewell, he said, and off home he went. She went home the other way.

My last night in Merthyr, Joseph was thinking as on the way home. I shall never see Merthyr again. No wonder he was thinking that way after a solid week's praying and singing and crying. The Gyfeillach on the Sunday night was more like a funeral service than the happy after-meeting the children of Bethesda Chapel liked and enjoyed. Betty

Parry had meant ever so much more to the congregation of Bethesda Chapel than her husband had, so that last Sunday's services had practically all – the Sunday School as well – been Betty Parry Farewell Services. A Welsh farewell service is most moving and one such service is about all an average person can stand in one day. But three such services in one and the same day was too much, especially for Ann, the wife of Robert James, who was soon to bring her first baby. She had hoped that Betty, her mother, would have been able to stay until the baby, which would be Betty's first grandchild, came. But the man of the shipping company had told Betty that she and those going with her would have to be down Cardiff on the day and there it was. Oh, mam, mam annwyl, cried Ann, now so heavy with child. There, there, said Robert James, Ann's husband. Ann started crying and that started the others crying until they were all crying, and that happened every day during that last week. People came from near and far to say farewell and they cried too. They also prayed over and for the family. The neighbours were in and out throughout the week for they were all very good neighbours. They cried. Betty gave Ann the best bed and bedstead – a lovely feather bed it was and as Robert and the man who came with the cart and horse as far as the spot on the big road nearest the house there was more crying as the bed and bedstead were carried out of the house. Some furniture Betty also gave Ann – take whatever you want and I'll sell the rest, said Betty. The woman who was moving in after Betty and her family moved out bought most of the things and the two upstairs beds and this woman was the only woman who came into the house who did not cry that last week.

No, you are not to go down to the railway station in the morning like you are, Ann, said Robert James. Better not, Ann, said Betty. Robert, don't tell me, said Ann. It is *my* mother and *my* brothers and sisters are going over the water not yours. But you'll only cry down the railway station again, said Robert. If I do it will be with my own two eyes and not yours, said Ann. Leave her alone and let her come as far as the station if she wants to, Robert, said Betty. I am only thinking of the baby on the way, said Robert. And I am thinking more of my mother going than the baby coming, said Ann. There, there, there, don't make yourself ill, good gel, said Robert.

Nearly every woman and child of the congregation of Bethesda Chapel were at the railway station that Tuesday morning to see the last of the Parry family. Ann, God help her, was there in the crowd to say farewell to her mother and her brothers and sisters. The preacher was also at the station and so were two of the eight deacons of Bethesda Chapel. The Parry family had a compartment to themselves – no other passengers could have got anywhere near it if they had wanted to. Ann was as pale as death after crying all night but she was not crying now. Funny thing that. It was she that was the dry-eyed comforter now, the tower of strength, the very fountain of assurance. She stood smiling in the midst and Robert James was proud of her. It was only when the man blew the whistle that she bit her lower lip and those around the door of the compartment made way for her so heavy with child. Give my love to dad, she said, embracing first her mother. Then her two sisters, Elizabeth and Jane. Lastly her two brothers, Henry and Joseph. The engine in front blew its whistle and she stepped back and it was she closed the door of the compartment on her loved ones. She held a tight smile and waved her left hand as the train slowly started on its way to Cardiff.

I should have mentioned the singing of a number of Betty's favourite hymns by those who came in crowds to see her off but that goes without saying anyway. Where the train goes around the bend just outside the town Betty leaned out of the window-space of the compartment and took one look back towards the town of Tydfil the Martyr.

Then she sat down and composed herself. Her four children had a corner seat apiece and before long the novelty of the first train-ride of their lives made them forget some of the pain of the week's leave-taking. Only Joseph was without eyes to see the places they travelled through on the way to Cardiff. His eyes were too full of the town that was in his heart, the town of Tydfil the Martyr. He sniffed when he set foot in Cardiff, from where they were to sail on the good ship *Jane Anderson*. This is not half the town Merthyr is, he said, and he was right. Some Welsh people of the same denomination, the Welsh 'independents', whose home and whose chapel was in Cardiff, were putting them up for the night.

Next morning they went aboard the ship, the sailing-ship, the *Jane Anderson*. Same name as our Jane, mam, said Henry. Yes, said Betty quietly before closing her eyes to pray briefly where she stood, with bag and baggage and children around her. Whilst she prayed silently Joseph looked up at the seagulls that were sweeping, diving and climbing above and about the ship's sails. They never flew inland as far as the town of Tydfil the Martyr, now twenty-five miles away, Joseph thought with regret. Already he was longing for his home-town, longing for it with that intense kind of longing which we Welsh call 'hiraeth'. The sight and smell of the sea, the seagulls crowding the air above the ship, other little ships like the one he was on taking on passengers, coal, iron and merchandise. Sailors hoisting and lowering sails and coiling ropes whilst others went on load-ing and unloading the ships.

Alien sights and smells and sounds to Joseph all forlorn in one of many family groups waiting with their baggage and bedding. Now that they were aboard the children were beginning to dread the prospect of the journey into the unknown but Betty was smiling confidently. She waited patiently with her children and baggage and bedding until a bearded sailor came and picked up the two heaviest of her bundles. Follow me, he said, and they followed him down below where it was dark. Other families were settling themselves in what Joseph called the 'belly' of the ship. The families were mostly Welsh with a sprinkling of Irish and English people. The Captain and his crew were English to a man and Devonshire men at that. The seamen of the West Country of England were the first to realize that Cardiff had a future as a port. They had passed it by contemptuously when it was little more than a creek, but now that it was a port worthy of the name many of them settled there with their families. Many masters of sailing-ships had by this time become shipowners and stayed ashore in little offices smelling of tar and tobacco and rum. Those who sailed their little ships overcrowded with emigrants from Cardiff to Philadelphia were kindly and considerate towards their human cargoes but it was beyond their power to better their conditions, the conditions aboard for the emigrants, I mean. They shipped them across the Atlantic as fast as possible and hoped that they would not have to bury too many during the voyage.

Betty had settled herself and her children in the allotted space in the 'belly' of the little ship, and whilst settling herself and her children she introduces herself to the family groups nearest to her. She and her children are in good hands and they are not unaccustomed to overcrowding, so we will leave them for the moment and return to their point of departure, the town of Tydfil the Martyr, where Mr Fowler, the Stipendiary Magistrate who has recently succeeded Mr Bruce, is listening to the evidence against a man charged with manslaughter. Easier said than done though. The Merthyr train has just this minute gone out and there won't be another until this afternoon, the man told us. Where is that train going to? we asked him. To Pontypridd and the Rhondda Valley, he said. Then I'll go as far as Pontypridd and wait there instead of here for the Merthyr train, I said. Don't you like Cardiff then? he said. No, I said.

So we went as far as Pontypridd with the one train and waited there for the next, went up against the stream of coal that was flowing down to Cardiff almost without a break. Coal-trains like huge black snakes wriggling their way down from the hills to the sea. Two coal-trains to every train of a dozen wagons loaded with pig-iron on the way down to the sea and out to the world. Passengers going up into the hills a negligible factor, shunt them out of the way. We waited on a siding until four coal-trains and one loaded with iron had gone down past one point. At Pontypridd a man on the platform shouted: Change for Aberdare Junction, the Aberdare and Merthyr Valleys. So we got out of the train. Those who were going up into the Rhondda Valley stayed on and presently the train took them up into the Rhondda Valley.

I went down the steps and out of the station and on to the narrow main street of Pontypridd, thinking, now that I was there with a couple of hours to spare, to call and see how Ieuan Ddu was getting on. I only saw his wife, his second wife, I mean, the woman he married in Pontypridd soon after he went there from Merthyr to live. I only knew his first wife. His second wife I now met for the first and last time and she seemed to me to be every bit as tidy a woman as his first wife, but it was not her I wanted to see. John's not home or at the school today, she told me. A girl from Merthyr came here to see him early this morning and he's gone with her to see some man down Cardiff. I have just come up from Cardiff, I said. Pity you did not happen to see him down there, she said. Who shall I say called? One who knew him when he lived up in Merthyr, I said. Is the school he is keeping here a better school than the one he kept in Merthyr? Perhaps not, she said. Will you come in and have a cup of tea and a bit to eat? No, thank you, I said. Only waiting here for the Merthyr train to come up from Cardiff I am. The school here in Pontypridd is not kept by John alone, she said. Do you know Mr MacLucas? No, I said. He keeps the school with John, she said. Oh, I said. Good-day now then. Sure you won't have a cup of tea? she said. Not this time but when I call next perhaps, I said. Who was that gel you said came to see Ieuan from Merthyr? One who used to learn the music with him when he was living in Merthyr, she said. Myfanwy Llewelyn her name was, I think. Do you know a Myfanwy Llewelyn from Merthyr? Yes, I said. Her father was blinded in the ironworks and died in the lock of the canal. Now she wants to go to that place in London where they learn music and nothing else all the time, said Ieuan's second wife. Good-day again, I said, and off back through the narrow street to the railway station I went.

I sat on a two-wheeled trolley which was lying idle on the wooden platform between the two railroads. I watched loaded mineral trains pass me down to Cardiff and longer trains of empty wagons passing me up to one or other of the valleys. I read the names on the wagons and it was the names that made me realize what was happening in all the valleys. Excellent coal and over a million tons of it going down to Cardiff and from there in ships to all parts of the world the year before this one, which was 1854. Next year perhaps a million and a half tons would leave the valleys for Cardiff and from there go in ships all over the world. That was only what was referred to as 'coal for export' and that was nothing compared to what we used at home for making iron and things, and to keep ourselves warm in the winter with, of course.

The names on the wagons told everyone that could read who was responsible for the development of our valleys. There were a few Welsh names on the wagons passing me up and down but for every Welsh name on the wagons there were nine English names. I sat there thinking of all the valleys of the coalfield to the east and west of the Merthyr Valley, and there are at least a score of valleys small and large. They drained the agricultural part of Wales of the rural population until by now some of the mining valleys were densely populated. As the valleys were developed houses appeared on the hillsides, houses that had a frightened look about them. In their terraces, which we called rows at the time, they seemed to be running up the hillsides to get away from something down where the valley was lowest. Then the houses down there where the valley was lowest, there where the pits were open-mouthed all the time, one side of their big mouths spewing coal and the other side swallowing empty trams, the houses down there, four-square around the pit-mouths and under the pit-wheels, the narrow main street strung out both ways to link up with the main streets coming down and up from adjoining villages, those houses down low seemed to be gasping for breath all the time. Their windows, like eyes, looked up to the houses on the hillsides as much as to say: We can't get away from around the mouths of these pits.

As the valleys were rapidly developed houses were thrown up anywhere. The stone was good and the masons were good and they were built upon the rock floor of the valley or on the rocky hills rising both sides of the valleys. Rushed though they were the masons built those houses to last for much longer than they deserved to last. Long strings of little grey stone houses cropped up on every hillside, where they followed the line of and looked down on the narrow and stringy main streets of adjoining villages and townships. Pit-slag spread itself everywhere and robbed the sheep of mountain farmers of their patchy grazing on the hillsides. Pit-slag was allowed to block roads and rivers but not railroads, for they were 'golden miles' along which the coal and iron went out of the valleys and down to the ships that waited for it, or along main lines to London and elsewhere in Britain. New developments attracted new populations and transformed them from human beings into something less than human.

Coal, coal, coal; iron, iron, iron; men, men, men; money, money, money, MONEY. God save our gracious Queen! We sat, that day in 1854, on the platform between two railroads in the mining centre of Pontypridd and watched the trains go by. Then the Merthyr train came up from Cardiff and we got on and went up to Merthyr on it. The town was as crowded as ever and the Parry family did not appear to be missed. What difference could five – six with Daniel gone before – make by taking themselves away from their place in a town that was the coal and iron capital of the world? Not much, but the aggregate of such families, tidy families all and the breadwinners the best workmen we had in Wales at the time, were bound to make a difference quantitative and qualitative on both sides of the Atlantic, and what was Wales's loss was America's gain.

This very year, 1854, scores of little ships overcrowded with Welsh emigrants left the port of Cardiff in Wales for the port of Philadelphia in America. The ships were small but the waters were mighty. Storms raged for days on end and children clung to their parents who tried to calm their fears. Betty and her children in the dark 'belly' of the good ship, *Jane Anderson*, were storm-tossed for several days. There was sickness and great fear when Betty Parry struck the note as surely as she had struck it hundreds of times in Bethesda Chapel to lead the congregation into the hymn. Now she struck it to lead the emigrants in peril on the sea into the hymn so appropriate for people in their situation. Her voice, so clear and steady, was heard above the muffled blows of the waves as they struck the little ship and above the howling wind that was driving the huge waves against and over the little ship. Her two boys and her two girls followed her into the hymn and the rest of the passengers followed them and they all sang themselves into fearlessness and faith.

'Yn y dyfroedd mawr a'r tonnau
Nid oes neb a ddeil fy mhen,
Ond fy anwyl Briod Iesu,
'R hwn fu farw ar y pren;

Cyfaill yw yn afon angau,
Ddeil fy mhen yn uwch na'r don
Golwg arno wna i mi ganu
Yn yr afon ddofn hon.'

A short hymn which they sang over and over again until they had banished fear. Then they sang other Welsh hymns, but each time fear returned they sang the hymn which is the best Welsh hymn for calming all fears. The hymn loses much of its strength in translation. The English words do not seem to mean quite the same or as much as the Welsh words. Here it is for you in the English language:

In the deep and mighty waters,
No one there to hold my head,
But my only Saviour Jesus,
Who was slaughtered in my stead.

Friend He is in Jordan's river,
Holds above the waves my head,
With His smile I'll go rejoicing
Through the region of the dead.

No, it does not seem to mean as much in English as in Welsh, but it will serve to convey something of the spirit of those Welsh people cooped up in the dark below the deck of the little ship called *Jane Anderson*. That short hymn is written indelibly across the hearts of all Welsh-speaking Welsh people and it is theirs alone. No other people sing that hymn in any other language. The English Captain and crew of the *Jane Anderson*, whilst fighting the storm, heard it being sung below by the Welsh passengers, men, women and children, and though the English seamen did not understand what it was all about the spirit of the hymn strengthened them in their long and hard fight against the storm.

Whilst the storm was raging Joseph more than once wondered whether or no Myfanwy Llewelyn had kept her promise to say a prayer to get him safe over the water. When the storm had subsided he felt sure that she had kept her promise and said a prayer for him. Before he reached Philadelphia Myfanwy had gone to London to live and study music and singing. Ieuan Ddu had taken her up to London and had placed her under the care of William Davies, son of Moses Davies, who was a plasterer and conductor and composer at Merthyr until he left and went with his family to London, thinking, no doubt, to better himself. He was a fine musician but self-taught and he conducted two choirs in Merthyr, a Temperance choir and the choir of Pontmorlais chapel. He had side-whiskers but no moustache and whilst at Merthyr he had all he could do to earn enough as a plasterer to keep his family.

So, like many others, he went to London, thinking to better himself. People were all the time leaving Merthyr for elsewhere in the hope of bettering themselves. Some to other valleys, others to Cardiff and others again all the way to London, and then again there were all the people who had gone and were still going across the water to America in the hope of bettering themselves. One could say a lot about people who are all the time going from one place to another in the hope of bettering themselves, but if we did it would be no use. Go they did and go they will no matter what is said. Whether or no Moses Davies did not stay long in London, where he conducted the singing at the Welsh chapel at Jewin Cross on Sundays and worked as a plasterer on week-days. Four years he stayed there before returning to Merthyr. But his eldest son, William, who was also a plasterer, stayed in London, where he married and settled down. William was studying sculpture whilst working as a plasterer and he thought London the best place for him.

It was to William Davies's house in London that Ieuan Ddu took Myfanwy Llewelyn, who wanted to study music and singing under those able to teach her more than Ieuan Ddu and Rosser Beynon could. I want you to look after her, William, said Ieuan Ddu. To be sure I will, said William. She can live here with us as one of the family. I am going to try and arrange for her to spend some time at the Academy, said Ieuan. But I want her to live here with you. To be sure, said William. She has got a bit of money but not too much, said Ieuan. Living here as one of the family she will be able to live cheap, said William. Her voice is lovely, but she must not sing much until she knows better how to use it, said Ieuan. No harm if she sings in Jewin Chapel choir on Sundays just to keep her voice in trim, said William. I don't go to chapel on Sundays, said Myfanwy.

William Davies opened his eyes wide but he did not say anything. It was Ieuan that said: She did not go to chapel in Merthyr where people knew that she was Blind Dick's daughter and where they looked down on her. You know how chapel-people can be if they like. Indeed I do, said William Davies, whose father, Moses Davies, as good a Christian as ever was, was looked down on by the deacons of Pontmorlais Chapel because he had taken his children for a walk in the Big Field on a Sunday. All the same, Myfanwy, you can go to the Welsh chapel here in London, said Ieuan. What for? she said. Because good congregational singing is good for the soul and an important part of a musician's training, said Ieuan. People up here in London won't know about your father, said William Davies. It might be good for them if they were to know, said Myfanwy. Good or bad it is you and not your poor father that is alive and wanting to be a singer out of the ordinary, said Ieuan. So will you do what I tell you and go to Jewin Chapel on Sundays and sing in the choir with Mr and Mrs Davies? The discipline if nothing else will be good for you. A good home you are going to get here with Mr and Mrs Davies and you must be good to deserve it. So remember now, good girl. Will you? Myfanwy nodded. Is it training to be a donkey you are? said Ieuan. Speak with your tongue, good girl. Yes, said Myfanwy. Yes what? said Ieuan. Yes I will go to chapel twice on Sundays with Mr and Mrs Davies, said Myfanwy. Pity Mrs Davies is not here, said William. Perhaps it will be better not for Mrs Davies to come before this girl have come to her senses, said Ieuan. Myfanwy, I don't like the way you said you would go to chapel twice on Sundays with William and his wife. Let Mrs Davies when she comes talk to the girl, Ieuan, said William. I've said I'll go, haven't I? said Myfanwy. Of course you have, said William. How are things in Merthyr these days?

They went on to talk about Merthyr and singing and when Mrs Davies came they all had a cup of tea and a bit to eat. Myfanwy liked Mrs Davies at first sight and Ieuan could see that she did, so he did not say anything more about Myfanwy going to chapel twice on Sundays with Mr and Mrs Davies. Ieuan left for where he was to sleep that night with some friends of the Davieses and next morning he went to the Academy to make arrangements for Myfanwy to study there. Having done that he went back to Pontypridd feeling that Myfanwy was in good hands. Thousands of miles away the *Jane Anderson* was within sight of Philadelphia. Six and a half weeks it had taken her to make the crossing from Cardiff in Wales to Philadelphia in America. Her losses during the voyage were one seaman washed overboard during the great storm, and four passengers, a man and a woman and two children, had died of sickness and had been buried at sea. All things considered it was what you might call a good voyage. The emigrants who had survived were in pretty good shape though a few of them were in need of medical attention, which they would get as soon as they got ashore.

Will dad be waiting for us, mam? said Jane Parry. He said in the letter he might, said Betty. We'll soon know. Dad would not know what day of the week to come and meet us, would he? said Henry. Perhaps not, said Betty. So that's America, said Joseph. I know I won't like it here. Wait until you see the place before talking, said Elizabeth. I've seen enough of it already, said Joseph. How can you see when you have not yet put your foot on the ground of America? said Henry. Be quiet, good children, said Betty. I would not like to be a sailor either, said Joseph as the seamen moved about obeying orders. That man coiling that rope told me that when it's middle day here it's getting on for night in Merthyr. Stop talking about Merthyr, said Betty sharply. She had tried hard to forget Merthyr, to clear her mind of it so as to make place for America. But she could no more forget Merthyr than fly. Same with Joseph. There was little or no excitement among the emigrants as the little ship neared the harbour of the port of Philadelphia. It was a relief to think that within the hour they would be on dry land again after six and a half weeks at sea, but there was no rejoicing. The place of ships and the spread of the city beyond was a sight that gave rise to more uneasiness than joy in the breasts of emigrants from the small and compact island of Britain. They were in hopes that later they would get used to the place and possibly get to like it. But just then, with health and spirit reduced by the weeks of overcrowding and the buffetings of storms, they were in no state to appreciate their good fortune. So they stood, pale and unsmiling, on deck amidst the bags, bundles and baggage of all sorts, including bedding. Those who had lost dear ones during the voyage were crying but not making a fuss. The woman who had lost her husband, the man who had lost his wife and the parents who had lost children during the voyage stood and looked towards the city with tears all the while falling from their eyes. That's how it is, isn't it?

There were relatives and friends to meet and welcome some of the emigrants, but Daniel Parry was not at Philadelphia to meet Betty and his children. But some Welsh

Quakers, whose name was Lloyd and whose home was in Philadelphia, were waiting to see if any of the emigrants needed assistance. So Betty and the children and a Swansea family went with those Welsh Quakers to stay the night with them at their fine house in Philadelphia. This Quaker family, whose name was Lloyd, could not speak Welsh but their grandparents, they said, had been able to speak Welsh. The man's grandfather was that David Lloyd, the lawyer, the Welsh Quaker who had been William Penn's most bitter enemy. It was, these people now told Betty, it was David Lloyd that made most of the laws of the constitution of Pennsylvania. Oh, said Betty. Next morning the man of the fine house asked his guests if they would like to see something of the city and Betty said that she would rather stay where she was in case Daniel came to find her not there.

The Quaker assured her that Daniel when he came down from Danville would wait, for he had sent word to tell him where to call for Betty and the children. The family from Swansea had already been called for by relatives and with them had left for Wilkes-Barre. So there was only Betty and her children left waiting to be called for at the house of the Welsh Quakers named Lloyd. With them they went out of the house to see the sights of Philadelphia, Independence Hall and other places, and when they went back to the house who should be there but Daniel. And he was looking grand, better than Betty had ever seen him look in his life before. He looked taller and broader and everything, and he was laughing all over his face. Then he had to sit down and cry, of course. With his arms around Elizabeth and Jane he cried and cried as happy as could be. After a good meal the good Quakers arranged for conveyances to take them and their baggage down to the railroad station, to where they accompanied them. It is about a hundred miles from Philadelphia to Danville and they travelled on the railroad which was owned and operated by the state.

Wait until you see our house, Daniel kept on saying. He

also said that he had arranged for Henry and Joseph to start work in the ironworks on the Monday of the week following. We have a Welsh chapel in Danville, a bigger one at Wilkes-Barre and a bigger one again at Scranton. Just like Wales – but no Cyfarthfa Castles, thank goodness. Nor no Cyfarthfa Band to play lovely music either, said Joseph. Don't talk whilst your father is talking, good boy, said Betty. Let him talk, for here we are all free to talk as we like, said Daniel. No, my boy, we have not yet got a band same as Robert Crawshay's Cyfarthfa Band – but that will come. Yes, everything is bound to come in this great country. Already we Welsh have formed choirs in our Welsh chapels and outside. Wait until you hear the Pennsylvanians, our male-voice choir, singing as good as ever Rosser Beynon's choir sang over the water in Merthyr. No choir on this side will ever sing as good as Rosser Beynon's choir, said Joseph. It is Merthyr is on the boy's stomach all the time, Betty explained. Naturally, said Daniel. But he will learn. Hiraeth will give way to pride before long.

By 'hiraeth' Daniel meant that intense longing for Wales which, as we have said before perhaps, afflicts us Welshmen when there is water between us and Wales. Daniel Parry was one of the few Welshmen in America who whilst never forgetting Wales had no regrets for having left the land of his fathers. Now that he had Betty and the children with him he was happier than ever he had been in Wales. Betty could not help looking at him with the shine that never went dull in his eyes and a smile with every word he gave her and the children. He, her Daniel, who had when in Wales been such a quiet man, was now most talkative and his talk was not small and modest talk either. It was proud talk, the talk of a man relishing to the full a new and high and wide freedom. His smile and high spirits were infectious and it was only Joseph that seemed immune.

Whilst his father went on talking Joseph looked out of the windowless window-space of the coach next to the engine.

Not as good as the train on which we rode from Merthyr down to Cardiff on the other side of the water, he said to himself. Not half as many places or houses either. This is wild man's country most of the time. Not a tidy-sized town since we left Philadelphia and that place was nothing to Merthyr. Why trouble to come to a place like this from Merthyr where we had everything and knew everybody? Dad is talking as though it is next-door to heaven he is taking us to. I wish I was in Merthyr living with our Ann and Robert James.

He looked again at the other passengers in the coach, some of whom were loudly talking in a language that was neither English nor Welsh. Those speaking the strange language looked like those men of the band he had heard playing that time on the Square in front of the Market House in Merthyr. Someone had said then that it was a German band and perhaps those people talking a language he did not understand or even recognize were Germans. What odds about them anyway. Four men behind where Joseph was sitting around the family baggage with his father and mother and brother and sisters were speaking English the way the Irish of Merthyr did, so Joseph understood them. They were speaking about the Russian War, about which Joseph had heard some talk before leaving Merthyr. Now he gathered from what these men in the coach of the American train were saying that the fighting had begun. One of the men said he hoped that England would get licked. Another said he did not care one way or the other and that was how Joseph felt too. Who were the Russians? he asked himself. He had never heard about them in Bethesda Sunday School. Perhaps he would have known who they were had his mother let him go to where English was spoken and taught in St David's School. Now he was thirteen years old it would be work and not schooling he would have for the rest of his life. There would be no one like Rosser Beynon to teach him the music out here where

152

the train went for miles and miles without passing a house. Where do the people live and work here? he asked himself.

What's the matter, Joseph? said his father. Nothing the matter with me, dad, he said. It's no doubt the jerking and jolting of this old train after the tossing he had on the ship, said Betty. Never mind, soon be there now, said Daniel. It is hotter this time of the year on this side than on the Merthyr side of the water, isn't it? said Elizabeth. Yes, but you will soon get used to it, said her father. I will never get used to it or to anything else on this side of the water, said Joseph to himself, then went on hardening his heart against everything and everybody in America. In the late afternoon Daniel said: Before long you will see Danville. When they saw it from the train Joseph said: It's no bigger than Pentrebach below Merthyr. In English 'Pentrebach' is 'Small town', and Danville was a small town with a population of less than five thousand when Joseph first saw it in 1854, when he spoke of it with the contempt of one who had lived and worked in the coal and iron capital of the world and the centre of a population of seventy thousand souls.

There was quite a crowd of people waiting for the train at Danville, and all but a few were waiting to welcome Daniel Parry's family to the place. Counting men, women and children there were more than three hundred Welsh people waiting to welcome them and to escort them first to the house they had helped Daniel to furnish ready for them, and from there to the Welsh chapel of the Welsh independents to have supper early so as to have a thanksgiving service and a hymn-singing festival after. Whilst they were having supper Joseph said in a whisper to Henry: I did not see the ironworks anywhere. We'll see that soon enough, said Henry. The preacher of the Welsh chapel, which had been built four years previous, was walking up and down between the tables talking to one and the other. When he came to where the Parry family were seated at the top table he asked Betty and the children how they liked America. I am sure I shall like to live here, said Betty, and Henry and Elizabeth and Jane smiled and nodded their heads. Joseph did not smile or nod his head. Yes, I am sure you will, for it is a great country, said the preacher. Which of you is Joseph? Me, said Joseph. Oh, you are Joseph, said the preacher. Your father has talked a lot about you and your taking to the music so young. Plenty of chance to learn the music you shall have here. Perhaps you will sing for us after supper. You are right now you have got them here with you, Daniel Parry. Yes, and I am thankful to God for bringing them safe over the water to me, said Daniel.

That was a big night for the Welsh of Danville in Pennsylvania. David Thomas, a Swansea man who had his own ironworks in Pennsylvania, was there that night, too, and he spoke in Welsh as well as when he used to work as a furnaceman at Ynyscedwin near Swansea in Wales. Now he was getting to be a rich man in Pennsylvania, and a big man, too, but he was not too big to come and extend a welcome in Welsh to the Parry family. Not all the Welsh people there that night could speak Welsh, some of them only spoke a mixture of Welsh and English and there were a few of Welsh nationality present who could not speak a word of Welsh, and this in Betty Parry's opinion was a crying shame. She was of the diehard Welsh to whom 'O bydded i'r hen iaith barhau', meaning 'O let the old language be kept alive', was a sacred charge, a commandment never to be forgotten no matter where one was outside Wales. There was another line of the Welsh national anthem which proudly claimed that 'Mae hen iaith y Cymru mor fyw ag eiroed', which claimed that 'The old language of the Welsh is as much alive as ever'. Betty Parry regretted to find that that was not true of the Welsh of Danville in Pennsylvania.

I must be on my guard and on guard over the children all the time, she said to herself in the presence of the backsliders who in America had lost and were losing the language without which no one could rightly claim to be Welsh. It's the children I must guard against what will rob them of their language, she said, feeling that she herself was beyond the power of all alien influences. Two Swedish men who worked in the rolling-mill with Daniel came smiling to talk broken English to him and to her and the children and she had to smile and nod her head. But not a word of English would she try to speak in reply to what they were saying. Daniel spoke in English to them and spoke it well enough to make Betty wish she had not let him go to America by himself. In just over a year without her to keep him to the Welsh language he had picked up more old English than he had all the years of his life before.

Betty was diehard Welsh and proud of it. Others present that night at Danville were not so fanatical. They had surrendered themselves to America and were ready for melting and willing into the bargain. Some of them had allowed their sons and daughters, born in Wales, to marry men and women of half-a-dozen other nationalities, Germans, Swedes, Scots – and even Irish. This was another thing which Betty vowed to guard against. She had two sons and two daughters who would, God willing, no doubt marry some day, and Betty there and then decided that, with the help of God, she would arrange for them to marry Welsh-speaking Welsh men and women.

After supper that first night there was a brief thanksgiving service, after which there was singing until near midnight, and wherever there was singing the Parry family was bound to be in request as soloists. Betty sang without accompaniment 'Hen Feibl Mawr fy Mam', meaning 'My Mother's Old Big Bible'. By now Joseph was feeling more at home, for singing always had the effect of reconciling him to most things in life, irrespective of time or place. So he sang twice by himself and Elizabeth and Jane each sang once. Henry would not sing by himself; Daniel was not asked to. David Thomas, who owned and operated an ironworks, having experimented successfully with anthracite coal for his furnaces, David Thomas sang an old Welsh air and others too numerous to mention also sang by themselves or two in a duet. I forgot to mention that Joseph and his mother sang a duet, his alto blending well with his mother's soprano. I also forgot to mention that 'The Pennsylvanians', the male-voice choir Daniel had told Joseph about, sang three pieces during the evening. Then everybody sang Daniel and Betty and their children home from the chapel, sang in procession Welsh hymns. Then when the Parry family were inside their new home in the new world the crowd outside softly sang an old Welsh lullaby. If you have ever heard one of our old Welsh lullabies sung or played you will be able to judge the effect of this one on the Parry family this night at Danville in Pennsylvania – no, not night, for it was now past midnight so the night was gone. Never mind. A crowd of about three hundred outside the house under the moon. Singing softly that Welsh lullaby as though the Parry family were all babies. Never mind. It was lovely the way they sang it. People not Welsh who were in bed within sound and who were awakened by the sweet singing slept all the better for it afterwards. Oh, it was the sweetest end to a grand night!

Early the following Monday morning Daniel took his two sons, Henry and Joseph, with him to the ironworks, which seemed small after the Cyfarthfa Works to Joseph. Daniel took his two sons to the man not Welsh who was the boss of the rolling-mill. Here they are, said Daniel in English. As I told you they worked in the rolling-mill in the ironworks in the old country. H'm, yah, said the bearded man. Goot. Den dey know someting, yah. Come. Go with him, said Daniel in Welsh, and they followed the big man with the beard who spoke so funny. Henry was practically a man and he knew nearly all there was to know about a rolling-mill and Joseph, though only just gone thirteen years old, knew almost as much about a rolling-mill as

Henry his brother did. So in less than a week they were workers as good as any in Pennsylvania. Well, hadn't they both been born right inside an ironworks?

CHAPTER 7

R.A.M.

OUR M.P., Mr Henry Austin Bruce, the man who was Stipendiary Magistrate for Merthyr and district until he left the Bench and went to represent us in the House of Commons, didn't have to fight in the election of 1855. No, for he was returned M.P. unopposed. So instead of delivering an election speech he spoke on the progress of the Russian War at the Merthyr Library, which was started in one room of a cottage and now had a house to itself in Thomas Town, and a biggish house it was with lecture-room and all. Before I say anything more about the Library or the Lecture on the progress of the Russian War which our Member of Parliament gave there in 1855, let me tell you about Thomas Town – and I may as well tell you about George Town as well. George Town and Thomas Town were only districts of the town of Merthyr really, but they were called towns after Thomas and George. No one that I knew could tell me who the Thomas was but the George after whom George Town was named was of the Crawshay family and dynasty. The district named George Town after him was a working-class district quite near Cyfarthfa Iron-works and it had ash and clinker-tips threatening its streets all the time. It was built mostly on a hill and the hilly road running up through the middle of this working-class district was called the George Town Hill.

But it was Thomas Town I wanted to tell you about, for this was a better-class district. Lawyers and doctors and well-to-do tradesmen and managers of ironworks and collieries lived in Thomas Town, which was also built on rising ground until the houses of the top terrace overlooked the whole town. In Thomas Town there were houses, big houses with as many as four bedrooms, three big ones and one little one, and downstairs there were drawing-rooms as well as dining-rooms. It was the best part of the town of Merthyr and hawkers were not allowed to shout their wares in Thomas Town. Some of the biggest houses had tradesmen's entrances and ever so many warned us to beware of the dog. The houses of some of the streets in Thomas Town had little gardens in front and bigger gardens at the back. It was the most exclusive and best-educated part of Merthyr and it was fitting that the Library should be there now that it had grown to be something worthy of the name of Library.

There were at least a hundred present at the Library to listen to what our M.P. had to say about the progress of the Russian War, now in its second year. He spoke feelingly and with pride of the Battle of Balaclava and the charge of the Light Brigade before going on to speak of the siege of Sebastopol, in which cannon made of our Merthyr iron had played an important part, even as cannon made of our Merthyr iron had played an important part in the Napoleonic Wars. Mr Bruce also referred to the naval operations and other phases of the Russian War, and after listening to him, a great speaker on an important subject, one would have expected to find more interest in the Russian War than was to be found on the streets of Merthyr.

The mass of the people of Merthyr, the centre of a population of full seventy thousand souls, were not interested in the progress of the Russian War. People have to be fairly well educated before they can take an intelligent interest in a war which is being fought in another country. Either that or considerable numbers of their kith and kin have to be away fighting, which was not the case in Merthyr. Of the population of seventy thousand less than two hundred had gone to the Russian War from Merthyr and district. Less than one per cent of the population had heard of the Russians before the Russian War began. It was only now that they learnt about Russia and the Russians, but what little they learnt was not enough to keep them interested in the war that was going on.

Mr Bruce, in his address delivered at the Merthyr Library, referred to the militia-bill and the men of our town who had joined the militia and were now doing garrison duty. He also said that it had been very hard for the men of the regular army during the previous winter and that as they were now entering into another winter of hardship we should send a thought towards them and do everything possible to support them. The hundred people present said: Hear! hear! but the other sixty-nine thousand nine hundred people of the town and district did not hear. It was not what you could call 'a popular war'. It had somehow or the other been made by the well-born and rich English gentlemen of the British House of Commons, where they ruled the roost, and so the people of the town of Merthyr in Wales were not interested. The Russian War had for a time acted as a stimulant to the iron trade of our town and district, but our production was such that we were soon able to meet the demands of the war. Now we were back where we were and the contraction of our export trade due to the war was threatening us with a slump and with a reduction of wages as one of its consequences.

So the war was by no means popular in the town of Merthyr in the winter of 1855-6, when it would have been hard to find a place anywhere in the world where it was popular anyway. Why should a war in which good men were being killed and wounded and bitten to death by frost be popular? What did we in Merthyr know of the diplomacy which had changed things so that we were now fighting side by side with those we had been fighting against for the best part of twenty years during the Napoleonic

Wars? Now we were fighting against those whom we had fought with for a time during those years. Diplomacy moves in a mysterious way its blunders to perform and Merthyr was saying, in effect, let them get on with it. And what Merthyr said in that respect the rest of industrial Wales echoed.

For, war or no war, industrial developments continued until each and every one of our twenty valleys wore its uniform of black. Valleys long and short, broad and narrow, were blackened and smoke-dried. Valleys twenty-five miles long following the line of the rivers flowing to the sea, valleys only a few miles long branching off another valley, valleys with and without flat-lands, all sorts of valleys were invaded by enterprising industrialists who proved them and saw their worth in the black source of power deep down below the fern and the trees and the green grazing patches on which mountain sheep thrived. Sheep now white one week in the year, the week after the shearing. Then they began to turn black and stayed black until shearing-time came again. Tramway lines began to climb the hillsides between rows of terraced houses and the trams full of pit-slag went up as the empty trams came down day after day and night after night until a man-made mountain of pit-slag loomed more and more threateningly above the frightened rows of houses terraced clingingly below. Boys of eight went down the mines to work long days and nights and when they came back up into the daylight those little children stood and gasped. Too tired to play after their work down the mines or in the ironworks, too tired to eat many a night when they returned home, and during summers there was only enough water to wash some of the coal-dust off their face and hands. When they heard their elders talking about the Russian War they asked each other in whispers: What are Russians?

The Russian War was not what you could call 'a people's war', not in industrial Wales, anyway. Never mind. We lived somehow and we kept on singing too. That Christmas, the second Christmas of the Russian War, without peace on earth or goodwill to men, Myfanwy Llewelyn came back to Wales to sing. Not on Christmas Day but on Boxing Day and the day following, on Boxing Day at Pontypridd and the day following at Merthyr. On the posters and the tickets it said: 'Miss Myfanwy Llewelyn, R.A.M.' which stands for Royal Academy of Music. And you should have seen her. Talk about ladylike. She came up to Merthyr from Pontypridd after singing down there the night before with Ieuan Ddu, him wearing a frock-coat and box-hat. We were on the platform of Merthyr railway station waiting for the train that was bringing them, a sort of reception committee composed of the leading musicians of the town and district. There was Mr J. B. Wilkes, the organizer of the concert, he was an Englishman who played the organ at St David's Church, and English though he was he was an excellent musician, perhaps the best in the town and district. Never mind 'perhaps', he was *the* best musician in the town and district. The Churchwardens of St David's would not admit that at first, so they kept Moses Davies, who had left Pont-morlais Chapel to take over the choir of St David's – which many said no true Welshman would have done, anyway – to act as choirmaster while Mr Wilkes only played the organ. So in order to have something to do besides play the organ, Mr Wilkes formed a choir of townspeople and with them presented a series of concerts at the Temperance Hall, and this concert at which Myfanwy Llewelyn is to sing tonight is one of this year's series.

It was this series of concerts organized and presented and conducted by the Englishman, J. B. Wilkes, that made the Churchwardens of St David's and Moses Davies open their eyes. Let him have the Church choir, for he is one of the best drillers of a choir for an Englishman I have ever known. said Moses Davies, who could be as fair and as generous as the next when he liked. So here was Moses now with Mr

Wilkes, waiting for the train on which Ieuan Ddu was bringing Myfanwy up from Pontypridd, where she had been a sensation at the concert held in the big chapel nearest the bridge the night before. Rosser Beynon was also with Mr Wilkes – and that again shows the right spirit. Rosser had not long before had words with Mr Wilkes, who, and we may as well say it, had no great opinion of Welsh conductors, not those he had met in Merthyr anyway. Never mind about that now that the two Welsh conductors are showing that they are above that kind of thing this night if no other. Robert James was also waiting with Mr Wilkes, to whom he was talking in the highest English at his command. Who else was there? Oh, yes, the conductor of the famous Cyfarthfa Brass Band, Mr Ralph Livsey, was there, no doubt to support his fellow-Englishman, Mr J. B. Wilkes. I say 'Mr', you will notice, when speaking of Englishmen, for that was how all our Welsh conductors address Mr Wilkes, emphasizing the 'Mr' in a way that could be taken in more ways than one. The Welsh conductors used each other's Christian names but never an Englishman's Christian name would they use. No, always 'Mr', with emphasis. Now who else was there – but there is the train coming round the bend.

Oh, you should have seen Myfanwy when she took Ieuan Ddu's hand and stepped down from the compartment on to the platform. Thank you, Ieuan, she said in English. She was dressed – but perhaps you can remember better than we can. I remember she had a long coat down to her feet and she had one hand in her muff. She had gloves on too, didn't she? I know that she did not shake hands with any of us when introduced by Ieuan Ddu. Just smiled a little without opening her mouth and bowed her head slightly. Ieuan Ddu was carrying her bag and Mr Wilkes informed him that rooms had been booked for Miss Llewelyn and himself at the Castle Hotel. We followed them up the platform, Myfanwy walking between Ieuan Ddu and Mr

Wilkes, and the rest of us nowhere as you might say. Moses Davies closed up and said on the move: How did you leave Willie and his wife and children in London, Myfanwy? He had spoken in English and she stopped and turned about.

Mr Davies, I am sorry – I never dreamt it was you. It must have been the darkness. I have a message for you here in my muff. Your son and his wife and their children are all well and they send their love. I do not know how I should have endured London without them – this terrible war has made London so depressing. Here is the message. Forgive me if I hurry away now. Of course, my gel, said Moses, taking the envelope from her. We all thought her English very high and her manner most regal, and when she went off in the Castle Hotel carriage without as much as a word to Rosser Beynon, in whose choir she had sung and learnt a lot, to say nothing of the lessons she had had with him, when she went off without saying one word, good or bad, to him, Rosser said: Well, there you are. Fine lady she is. We must hope that she can sing as well as she can talk, that's all.

After the concert she made amends by actually kissing Rosser and by stating, in front of Mr Wilkes, Lord Dynevor, H. A. Bruce, M.P., and ever so many other distinguished people, that it was Rosser Beynon and Ieuan Ddu were the two to whom she owed most. But the concert at the Temperance Hall, before which Myfanwy nearly had words with Mr Wilkes, who was to accompany her on the piano. She had her own ideas of the presentation of herself on the stage of the Temperance Hall and she was explaining them to him when Mr Wilkes told her that he would give the sign to start her singing. Oh, no, Mr Wilkes, I know when to commence singing and I will indicate to you when I want you to start playing my accompaniment. Here are the copies. And where are yours? he said as taking them from her. I do not need a copy, she said. H'm, he said. All I ask, Mr Wilkes, is that you do not start playing until I have got complete silence. Then I shall incline my head slightly in your direction and then you may start playing the accompaniment. How long have you been at the Academy? he asked. Nearly two years – but I don't see that that has any bearing on what we were discussing, she said. It is just that I have adopted a certain method which in my opinion is the best method of presentation. So I hope you will forgive my insistence? Mr Wilkes sighed and said: Very well.

It was Mr Wilkes himself that told Moses Davies and Rosser Beynon about this afterwards. Started drilling me as though I were one of her pupils, he said with a chuckle. If I'm not very much mistaken that young woman will go very far. Whether or no, she very near went too far at that concert in the Temperance Hall. The place was packed, stage and all. For what were called 'platform tickets' were the next in price to the two front rows of the gallery, which were reserved for people wearing evening dress. We cannot remember all those in evening dress who sat in the seats of the two front rows of the gallery that night. There was Lord Dynevor and his lady and their daughter; H. A. Bruce, Esq., M.P., and Mrs. Bruce and their two daughters; Robert Thompson Crawshay, Esq., and Mrs Rose Mary Crawshay; our Stipendiary Magistrate, Mr Fowler, and his wife; W. Thomas, Esq., of The Court; Mr Overton, the lawyer, and his wife, the Rev. J. C. Campbell, M.A., the Rector, and his wife – and who else now? Oh, yes. Mr Evans of the Brecon Old Bank was another in evening dress, but I cannot be sure whether his wife was with him that night. Anyway, the two front rows of the gallery were full of people in evening dress.

No doubt it was that 'R.A.M.' behind Myfanwy's name that had attracted so many to the Temperance Hall that night. There was the choir conducted by Mr Wilkes; the Dowlais Glee and Madrigal Society conducted by Robert George; Mr Davies and his son to play the harp in turns; and then there was Myfanwy to sing two groups of songs and perhaps encores if the audience proved insistent in its demand for same. Too much English there was to suit the diehard Welsh present. They had to be content with the only Welsh song that was sung, 'Glan Meddwdod Mwyn', and the Welsh airs played on the harp by Davies and Son. All the rest was in English, all with the exception of the aria in Italian which Myfanwy sang as an encore and with which she surprised the English people present and shocked all the Welsh people present. It was a bit of cheek on her part when you come to think of it. Everyone present knew that she was the late Blind Dick's daughter and she knew that they knew her as that. No doubt that was the reason for her presumption in face of an audience which was both critical and patronizing.

She nearly hit them out of their seats when she appeared to sing the first song of her first group. She had waited for Mr Wilkes to settle himself at the pianoforte before she walked on and past him to stand looking like a frozen lily with her right hand over her left just above her waistline. There was encouraging applause which she did not deign to acknowledge. Just stood there compelling silence and rather grudging admiration. Lovely she was and her loveliness was enhanced by the dress she wore that night. A white dress it was, with a full outgoing skirt and a tight V-shaped bodice, out of which her neck and head seemed to grow not stand out. Her hair was massed in a way that made her look regal and much older than she actually was. She wore long white gloves to right up above her elbows. I will not try to describe her face. She had her Irish mother's eyes and her Welsh father's mouth and her nose was perfect. Not a smile did she give her audience. Just waited until they were all quieter than mice and then she glanced at Mr Wilkes and nodded her head at the same time. He began playing the piano and she waited until it was time for her to open her mouth and start singing. And when she did ... No, it is no use me trying to describe what she did to that most critical audience. Even Mr Wilkes got up from the piano to applaud and Myfanwy won his gratitude by taking his hand to share the applause with her at the end of her first group of songs and an encore. Oh, it was a grand night. Ask anyone who was there.

It was a night of nights but like all nights it had to end. Carriages called for ten p.m. had to wait until nearly half-past before those in evening dress left their seats in the two front rows of the gallery. Then most of them went around to the door at the back to go up on to the stage to congratulate Myfanwy and they were disappointed to learn that she had slipped away before they got there. You must try and get her for another of your concerts, Mr Wilkes, said Lord Dynevor. I shall, my lord, said Mr Wilkes. But it will have to be soon if at all. She may go to be finished in Italy in a year or so and meanwhile she will find it difficult to get away from London. Her teacher there is not, I gathered, agreeble to her singing overmuch just now. If it is a question of expense, said Lord Dynevor, then all you need do is just let me know. Thank you, my lord, said Mr Wilkes.

In her room at the Castle Hotel Myfanwy had changed her dress and was tidying her hair when Ieuan Ddu came back. He won't come in to have supper with us, he said. Why not? she said. Some old nonsense about not being dressed tidy, said Ieuan. Where is he? she asked. Waiting on the corner at the end of Castle Lane, he said. She put her long coat on over her dress. He'll come for me, she said. We shall have that room downstairs to ourselves for supper, shan't we? Yes, said Ieuan. Downstairs she went and out of the hotel and along to where a man was standing at the bottom end of Castle Lane. It was Will Morgan, better known as Will Full-Moon, but you would hardly know him now that the old drink had brought him low. Do you want me to catch cold? she said. No, he said. Then come with me into the hotel, she said. And shame you now that you are getting on like you are? he said. I only wanted to tell you that I tidied his grave before the bad weather came – and

166

another thing I wanted to tell you. Your mother died over in Tredegar the week before last. She had two children by the man she went away with but they both died before she did. Now you know. Yes, said Myfanwy. Tonight I sang for you and my father, with whom you sang like a brother the night before he walked into the lock of the canal. For you more than anybody I sang tonight and you were not there. Yes, I was there in the shilling seats downstairs at the back, he said. You were sure like your father always was and you were boss of that audience, the big people and the small. Come into the hotel or I shall catch cold, she said. For if you do not come in to have supper with me and Ieuan Ddu then I shall stay out here all night. So come. My clothes, he said, my clothes – Ieuan told me about your clothes, she said, taking his arm. Take me in to supper. Turn me back when he sees me the porter will, he said. Not if I know it, she said. Come now like a good boy.

Together they went up the steps of the Castle Hotel and Ieuan was waiting for them just inside the double-doors. Met your match, have you, Will? chuckled Ieuan. Not dressed fit to be here I am, said Will, who had lost his fine talk as well as his fine clothes. Those of us who knew him in those days when he used to wear evening dress to sing the solos of oratorios and high-class songs at miscellaneous concerts now wondered whatever had come over the man. His clothes were not in rags but they were as shabby as could be and more than his clothes it was the dejected look of the once proud man that cut us to the heart. He used to be the finest singer and the finest 'stager' in Merthyr and district and look at him now. He had gone from bad to worse and down, down, down – and all in a few years. He was black-listed by all the chapels and choral societies after he had gone as full of drink as an egg is of meat to sing the 'Elijah' that time in Blaenavon, where he sang splendidly. His rendering of 'It is enough' almost made that audience of chapel people forgive him for standing there drunk like he was.

First thing he did on arrival at the place outside Merthyr where he was engaged to sing was to ask where the best drop of beer was. There he would go and there he would stay until it was time for him to go to the chapel or hall at which the concert was being held or oratorio performed. There were times when he had to be assisted from the public-house to where he was to sing the holy words and once he had to be wheeled in a barrow from the public-house to sing at a miscellaneous concert in the Rhondda Valley. There he sang leaning his drunken weight against the end of the piano – oh, he was too much of it. For the sake of his glorious voice even the conductors of Temperance choirs gave him chance after chance before giving him up for lost.

And lost he was now. He had pawned his fine clothes and had lost job after job and to cap it all had lost his wife into the bargain. Broke her heart, no doubt. That is what the old drink can do to a man and a splendid singer. Now he was singing in public-houses and, as I said, you would hardly know him if you saw him. Isn't it a pity? Still, whilst there is life there is hope and Will Full-Moon may yet be heard singing the 'Elijah' and the 'Messiah' in our biggest chapels. Those of us who have heard him in the 'Elijah' know that we shall never hear his equal in it. He *was* 'Elijah', and he had our hearts bleeding for him when he sang 'It is enough, O Lord; now take away my life, for I am not better than my fathers!' Never mind. Let them without sin throw stones at Will Full-Moon. Now he is crying again and Myfanwy is comforting him whilst Ieuan Ddu goes on with his supper in a private room of the Castle Hotel. That girl wants her supper after singing, Will, said Ieuan. To be sure she does, Ieuan, said Will. Then stop crying and pitying yourself and give her chance to eat her supper, said Ieuan. That is why I did not want to come in here in the first place, said Will. Instead of an artist it is a drunken scamp I am. Instead of the holy words it is dirty ditties I am singing now in public-houses – but never mind. You are going to sing for me and for your poor blind father wherever he is, lovely gel. Go on with your supper now. I have finished crying – yes, and I have finished with the drink too. You'll see, Ieuan. Get me a chance to sing in one of the big works, 'Elijah', the 'Messiah' or any other great work and you shall see. Down Pontypridd for a start, then here in Merthyr after. I would like to sing at a concert with this girl who is the best singer for a girl this town has heard and the best stager it has seen. But no, I must not appear on the same stage as you, lovely gel. Eat first and talk afterwards, said Ieuan.

Yes, please get on with your supper, said Myfanwy. I want both of you to accompany me as far as the Iron Bridge afterwards. Don't talk nonsense, girl, said Ieuan. It is not safe down that way by day let alone by night. No one in that district will molest me, said Myfanwy confidently. I am going to stand on the Iron Bridge this night if I have to go alone. You shall not go alone, my gel, said Will Full-Moon. Can't you go in the morning before going to catch your train? said Ieuan. It is the nights I remember, said Myfanwy. Going back there to that cellar after the public-houses closed at eleven. The feel of his hand on my shoulder and a moon like to-night and the mask over his poor face –

Will Full-Moon started to cry again and Ieuan got up from the table and said: Is it a funeral supper we are having? Poor old Dick, said Will Full-Moon. Oh, wouldn't he be proud if only he could have got here tonight to hear his lovely gel singing like an angel from heaven. I know what I'll do. I'll join the militia and go to the Russian War out of everybody's way. Finish your supper first, said Ieuan. Yes, I will pitch-in now and finish, said Will Full-Moon. He did. It was after eleven when the three of them left the Castle Hotel to walk down as far as the Iron Bridge just to satisfy Myfanwy. On the way down she said: I remember walking with a boy, that Joseph Parry, one night that seems ages ago. I wonder how he is getting on in America? Robert James, who is married to the boy's sister, told me to-night that the family is getting on well over in America, said Ieuan.

And so they were getting on well, very well indeed. Henry and Joseph were still working in the rolling-mill at the ironworks in Danville, Pennsylvania. So was Daniel, their father, but he was working as a refiner in another part of the ironworks, which was growing. Things do not stand still in America. Neither do people. Joseph had almost lost his life twice since he had been in America, once mainly due to his own absence of mind. For whilst at work in the rolling-mill he was more often than not trying to make music of the rhythm of the work in his head. So one day the bar on the rolls somehow jumped the rolls and but for the presence of mind of the young man next in line to Joseph it would have injured and perhaps killed Joseph, who, whilst not too slow to get out of his own way was more often than not thinking more of music and singing than of his work. It was the melodeon he was learning to play just then that made him more absent-minded than ever. Then there was the day when the driving-wheel broke and a piece of it struck and killed the young man next in line to Joseph.

The young man was of English nationality and he and Joseph had become very friendly. Joseph was learning English on the sly with this young man, so his tragic death was a double blow to Joseph. I say 'on the sly', for Betty was all the time watching that her children should not get too English in speech and thought. But Joseph had by now concluded that a knowledge of English was necessary as a background to the music he was picking up like a sparrow picks up crumbs in a hard winter. So he felt the loss of this young man. Joseph took little interest in what was going on around him now he had a melodeon. After work he would walk out of town with his melodeon in summer and make up little tunes in his head out of the sound of running water or the puff-puff of a railroad engine and then try them out on his melodeon. Wherever there was singing or any sort of music, there you would find Joseph participating to the best of his ability.

All the important developments in Pennsylvania and throughout America were nothing to him for it was his own musical development was all that mattered to him. He heard his father and some men talking on the way home from the ironworks, but what they were talking about was more than he could have told you had you asked him. He did not know that the State railroads and canals had been sold to the Pennsylvania Railroad Company until that company had been operating them for two years, and when John Abel Jones told him, all he said indifferently was: Oh. There was an election for Governor of the State and more than a little excitement, but Joseph went on playing his melodeon and singing and who it was that was elected Governor was more than Joseph knew or wanted to know. All he knew was that Daniel, his father, was what they called a 'Republican', but Joseph was not interested enough to get to know what a Republican was. Outside music and his work at the rolling-mill he was a dumb-bell, a numbskull, an ignoramus and all those things rolled into one. The life of the family in the home passed over him without making any sort of impression. He was the last to see that Henry had a moustache coming, the last to hear that Elizabeth had been walking home from chapel with a young man not approved of by Betty, her mother. The young man's Welsh was not good enough for Betty, and another thing, his English was too good for her liking. Still, he is Welsh, said Daniel. Yes, but for how long will he stay as Welsh as he is? said Betty. Their children if God blesses them with any will be little better than English.

' Dreamy Joseph would not have minded in the least had his two sisters married Germans or Swedes or Irish or men of any other nationality as long as he could go on making music. The racial differences and animosities meant little or nothing to him, yet, strangely enough, he remained the most Welsh of Betty's children. It was of Wales and the Welsh and their songs he was thinking of when he should have been noting the developments that were taking place all around him. Yes, Pennsylvania in 1858 was a most interesting State, perhaps the most interesting State in America. Its mineral wealth beggared the mineral resources of Wales and its industries were rapidly catching up with those in Wales. Yes, America in the 1850's was worthy of more attention than it got from Joseph. Independence was the operative word in Pennsylvania and liberty seemed illimitable to the scores of thousands who had lived hard and narrow lives by the grace of lords, squires and iron kings in Wales and in Britain as a whole. But it had not yet got music and so it stood condemned in Joseph's eyes. Only the Negroes had melodies and plantation songs and only the Welsh of America had hymns that could awake the soul, that was how Joseph summed things musical up. A cell of a prison with music, a cellar-dwelling in Wales with music and under oppression was more acceptable to music-mad Joseph than a continent and all its freedom and possibilities. He shut his eyes to America and kept the eyes of his mind on Wales, little Wales, the soiled Eldorado of English industrialists. In brief, the boy was mad about music, his eyes were in the back of his head, he was a hopeless nostalgic, he was Welsh mutton dressed up as American lamb, yet, at seventeen, he was a man of sorts. What sort? Well, a rare sort of man, one who thought the world well lost for music. Who can turn the soul of a young musical enthusiast inside out? If I could then I would be able to show you what kind of a man Joseph Parry was in 1858. All of us have been young men of seventeen, but how many of us now remember what we ourselves were like at that age?

But this young man of seventeen had been earning his bread for eight years by the time he was seventeen and he had been a tender and sensitive child in the darkness of a coal mine before he was nine years old. Overworked at that age yet even then he found himself in music, drew strength from it, made of it his defence against brutalization. From the mines to the ironworks he took unspotted his musical soul and through nights when heavy work is unnatural for boys it made him impregnable. He was digging himself into the musical life of the town of Tydfil the Martyr when he was taken away – for taken he was and much against his will – across the water to a new and strange and, to him, most unmusical world. There was never any likelihood of his becoming what is called a 'good citizen'. He walked alone with music and when told that the Russian War was over he just said: Oh! When told of the growing industrial might of Pittsburg he said no more than: Oh!

Can't you say anything but 'oh'? said Henry. What do you want me to say, Henry? said Joseph. Anything but 'oh' all the time, said Henry. Leave him alone, Henry, said Betty, their mother, who now and then caught a glimpse of the soul of her youngest son. It was Betty that asked John Abel Jones to take her Joseph and help him. John Abel Jones had come to America and to Danville in Pennsylvania long before the Parry family, long before Daniel had come before the family. John Abel Jones had lived in Merthyr up to the time he left for America when a young man with a good musical grounding. Now he was working in the ironworks at Danville and taking a few pupils to keep his hand in. But they had to be promising pupils, he would not waste time on mothers' pets who wanted to play or sing. If the boy comes he must come for an hour after work on Saturdays with the others, said J. A. Jones. What time, please? said Betty. From three to four with my infant class, said J. A. Infants of seventeen going to music lessons after work on Saturdays! The first Saturday Joseph went to J. A.'s house he took his melodeon. What did you bring that thing for? J. A. asked him. To play the things that have gathered in my head, said Joseph. Indeed you won't, said

173

J. A. Is it come here to learn me you have? No, said Joseph. Then take that thing out of my house. Whatever you have got in your head can come out on to paper when you have learnt the way.

Now here Joseph was found out. He had been singing in Merthyr from as soon as he could walk up to the time he had left for America, and he had been singing with the Male Voice Choir in Danville from the time he arrived in America. Copies of music he had held up before his face hundreds of times and it was only now that John Abel Jones discovered that he could not read one note of music. I see, only in your head, is it? said J. A. In Merthyr under Rosser Beynon I learnt a bit but it went after crossing the water, said Joseph. Never mind, said J. A. I have caught you in time to start you properly. Go and sit other side of the table with those three other boys. J. A. put a little blackboard across the arms of the armchair and felt in his waistcoat pocket for chalk.

To-day, he said, what I will write on my blackboard I only want you to look at and listen to what I say. I want to give you to-day to get used to the sight of the signs of music. No good picking up if you can't put it down after, is it? Next Saturday slates and pencils you must bring. From this blackboard to your head and from your head on to the slate. No time to waste have I got for anybody that won't learn. Work hard in the ironworks I have to and my bit of free time on Saturdays after my work only those who are worth it shall have. Remember that now. The young men of the infants' class across the table from him nodded their heads and he began writing lines and signs on the blackboard and went on to tell them what they meant.

By the quarter-year they paid John Abel Jones and if any of them had failed to satisfy him by the end of the first quarter he would not accept the fee. No, no good me take money from you, he said to the one who had not made satisfactory progress. Keep it to learn something else. No good you come to me any more. So he weeded them out, but not Joseph. By the end of the second quarter Joseph was the pride and joy of John Abel Jones. Come by yourself to-night again, he would say to Joseph, and they had many a private session during which he used to test Joseph all ways. He would write and write on the blackboard and no matter what he wrote Joseph would sing it correctly. Well done, Joseph, John Abel Jones would say.

There was a slump in the iron trade of Pennsylvania in the winter of 1858–9 and many days there was no work for Joseph in the ironworks, or for John Abel Jones either. So they worked together on the music until the iron trade began to revive and John Abel Jones said: You are as good with the music now as I am, Joseph. I am talking to John Price about you and he have said he will try you for a quarter to see if you are as good as I have told him you are. John Price is the best musician of us Welshmen of Pennsylvania and glad you should be that he is taking you after me. You are still carrying that old melodeon about the place with you, I hear. Yes, for I find it helps me, said Joseph. Saves my voice for one thing. I write the music on the slate and then make the melodeon sing it off the slate instead of my voice. Yes, but you will have to watch out, said J. A. Melodeons and concertinas and things like that are the way to the half-way house of music. But John Price will tell you.

Yes, John Price told him. John Price, who had left the Rhymney Valley in Wales for Pennsylvania in America, was getting to be known as a musician and he could have made a living by teaching others music had he wanted to. But he liked the company of his fellow-workmen in the iron-works, no matter whether they were of English or any other nationality. He liked talking to the German-Americans about German musicians and music and he had more books on music in his house than in any other house Joseph had been in. He gave Joseph some of these books to take home to study and Joseph was slowly and painfully working his way through a book on composition by a man named Hamilton when his mother caught him. What book is that you are reading? she said. A book John Price gave me to read, he said. A book in the English? she said. Joseph nodded and said: I must learn to read the English if I am to learn music like Handel, Mozart, and Beethoven and the other great composers, mustn't I? Must you? said Betty. It was John Price said, said Joseph. H'm, said Betty. Well, I suppose he knows best. But I am sure there are books in the Welsh that would help you every bit as much as the books in English. Still, if you must read English as best you can try not to talk it, good boy. Already your two sisters are talking half-Welsh half-English all the time.

Joseph read and read and studied and studied and his bread-and-butter work in the ironworks was something in the nature of a daily dream in which he played with fire-works set to music. He was educating himself on more than one front and he walked to and from work with English-men only. From them he got the meaning of the long English words in the books John Price loaned him one after the other. He went about asking questions and hardly noticed the moustache darkening his upper-lip. But he noticed a girl one night after a concert at which he had played his melo-deon and sang with the male voice-choir and as soloist. Who is that girl? he asked Gomer Thomas, who was also a member of the male-voice choir. My sister, said Gomer. Oh, said Joseph.

There was some excitement in the town one day when he was on his way to John Price's house for a lesson and though some men were throwing their hats into the air and shouting Joseph's head was too full of music to stop and inquire what all the excitement was about. It was John Price that told him and told him that he would have no lesson that even-ing. Go and celebrate, said John Price. Celebrate what? said Joseph. The election of Pennsylvania's first Republican gov-ernor, John Price told him. Yes, I heard my father saying something, said Joseph. It is more than something, said John Price. You are a Republican same as your father and all us Welsh of Pennsylvania. Am I? said Joseph. I have written something for you to see, a little song for small children to sing. I am not looking at anything till you come next time, said John Price. You can leave it there on the dresser and then come with me up the street.

Now it was, through walking the street with John Price and listening to the talk that went on, now it was that Joseph first heard the name of the man who had been elected Governor of the State. His father and his brother Henry had mentioned the name in his presence scores of times but Joseph had not heard for the reason that he did not choose to hear anything political. He did not know what a Republican was neither did he want to know. So the new Governor they were making all this fuss about and the fact that he was a Republican meant nothing to him. But it meant a lot to most other Welshmen in the State and the name of Andrew J. Curtin was on all their lips. So was the name of another man, Abraham Lincoln.

He led the North to war against the South and Joseph's brother Henry was one of the first to volunteer, but Joseph went on with his work and his music. The war acted as a stimulant on the iron trade so there was plenty of work at good wages and Joseph saved enough to go and spend three months during the first year of the war at Geneseo in the State of New York. For three months during which the Civil War was spreading all he could think of was music. During this three months' course of music he met many people who afterwards became well known as singers and musicians on both sides of the Atlantic. The course included singing under Bassini, organ-playing and composition under Professor Cook, and between lectures Joseph talked only English with the lecturers and other pupils. He worked from early morning till late at night and his moustache grew but his mind grew faster. There were some very nice girls among the pupils but Joseph tried hard not to think of them. One whose name was Antoinette, who was later to become famous as Madame Antoinette Sterling, was the one who disturbed Joseph most. But he tried hard not to think of her too.

It is very hard for a young man not to think of young women when his moustache is growing to look like a moustache on his upper lip, and it is harder for those who are intensely musical than for young men who are not. There is something about music that makes young men think about young women, unless, of course, it happens to be the music of an oratorio or our Welsh hymns. They don't make young men think about young women, but most other music does. This is a sort of mystery, no doubt, but there it is and you cannot get away from it. There was a civil war which was spreading all over the land and Joseph was finding it hard not to think of young women.

One afternoon Antoinette sang for him and he played and sang for her, played and sang the first composition to win a prize for him, played it on the organ and sang it at the same time. It was his 'Temperance Vocal March' and she thought it was very good indeed. Thank you, he said, thinking more of her standing there than of his 'Temperance Vocal March'. The time came when all the pupils and their teachers had to say goodbye for now and Joseph went back to Danville feeling it was high time he earned something as a musician to help him to pay for further schooling. So he became organist at the Welsh chapel and that was all right even though it was not a well-paid Sunday job, but when he went to play for more money per Sunday at the English Presbyterian Church of New York his mother thought the end of the world had come. Don't talk to me, good boy, she said to him. I would rather see you in the Army with your brother Henry than playing the organ on Sundays for the English. Hymn-tunes are not English or Welsh but universal, mam, said Joseph. Don't tell me that, she said. Next

178

you will be trying to tell me that our Welsh penhillion are not Welsh but English and universal as well.

It was no use Joseph talking to Betty, his mother, now that he was playing the organ on Sundays at the English Presbyterian Chapel of New York. That was something for which she could not bring herself to forgive him, but when he won prize after prize with compositions sent to the leading Welsh-American eisteddfods she had to admit that he was a good boy and a good musician after all. So when he was called up for the Army she paid the money to the State to keep him home. Twice she paid, three hundred dollars twice she paid not for him to have to go and be a soldier like his brother. What good would Joseph be as a soldier with his head full of music all the time? she said. He is not afraid, mind you, but it is music and not war he wants to make.

Whether or no there was plenty for him to do in the rolling-mill of the ironworks where he was now head-roller. How he came to be head-roller in the rolling-mill of the ironworks is more than he knows himself. He was efficient in an automatic way but he had no head that could make him the rightful head of anything that was not musical. He held himself in a dignified and rather 'bossy' way and perhaps it was that that made the manager make him head-roller. Then so many of the young men had gone away to fight and Joseph's seven-years service in the rolling-mill had given him some sort of seniority claim for the promotion he got. Now he thought he could get married and marry he did. All Betty said when he told her that he wanted to marry Gomer Thomas's sister was: Very well. You know best. What good me talk. Nice gel perhaps but she have got no more Welsh in her mouth than a swallow has in Wales. She will make you English all over. But I have finished trying to keep you children Welsh. Your sisters are no better and what your brother Henry will be when he comes back from the war goodness only knows. When do you want to get married? I thought we would get married on the day when I will be twenty-one, said Joseph. Have you asked your father? said Betty. Not yet, but I will, said Joseph. Have you got a house to go to live in? said Betty. Not yet, said Joseph. Then it's time you started looking for one, said Betty. You won't need to buy a bed, for when you go the bed you have been sleeping in by yourself since Henry went to the war will be idle. So take that if it will be good enough for that gel. Those who talk more English than Welsh want everything new perhaps. I'll ask her, said Joseph. You are leaving *my* house to get married, remember, Joseph, said Betty, and it is to the Welsh chapel to be married in Welsh you will go, remember. After that it is for her to say where you shall go.

So the marriage service was in Welsh and after the wedding-feast Joseph pulled a piece of paper out of his pocket and stood up and cleared his throat. He spoke in English for his wife's benefit. A little song I composed for the occasion, he said. With your permission I would like to sing it now. I have called it 'Cupid's Darts'. Humph, said Betty, his mother. Joseph took no notice of her. With love in his eyes he looked at his young wife and sang in English the song he had composed for her. Betty did not so much as look at him whilst he was singing. That is how it is when a boy leaves his mother and starts his married life by singing a love song in what was a foreign language to his poor old mother. In Danville in Pennsylvania in 1862 and a raiding party of the Confederate forces not so long before in and out of the State. Continuous excitement throughout the land divided against itself and Joseph, regardless of it all, singing 'Cupid's Darts' at the wedding-feast. Every occasion was for him a musical occasion and he would compose and sing for births, marriages and deaths.

It is a funny old world when all is said and done and the people all over the world will go their own way. Some go up and others down and others again go far, far away. The girl we heard singing that night in the Temperance Hall in the town of Tydfil the Martyr is in Italy, in Milan, if you please, where she is calling herself Lina Van Elyn. Her own name is no longer good enough for her, it seems. Myfanwy Llewelyn is a lovely name, but when she went to Italy she had to break it up and make Lina Van Elyn out of it. It is three bits of her own name it is, the 'Van' in the middle being what her late father, Blind Dick, used to call her, remember? Who would believe that that little girl, the girl who used to go about the public-houses with her blind father, and who used to live with him in that cellar-dwelling in the rough district of Merthyr called China, who would believe that that same little girl is now Lina Van Elyn and singing with the best of them in Italy – and in Italian all the time, mind you. No, no, never, people will say. Well, if they do not believe let them go to Pontypridd and ask Ieuan Ddu. Anyone in Pontypridd will tell you where he lives, you'll either find him at the house or at the school, that is if he is not away at some eisteddfod or other. He will tell you.

Another who can tell you is Will Full-Moon, and anyone in Merthyr will tell you where he lives. For he is steady now again and singing better than ever. For Ieuan Ddu did give him that chance he asked for that time and Will Full-Moon made the most of it. Handel's 'Samson' was the work he performed in under Ieuan Ddu at Pontypridd, and although that work does not give Will's voice the same scope as the 'Elijah' does he was magnificent all the same. Ieuan gave him money to get his evening dress out of the pawnshop and bought him a pair of evening shoes to go with it – and a shirt as well he bought him. Will and his voice were both worth saving and Ieuan Ddu left nothing undone to make their salvation sure. He got a music critic from London to come to Pontypridd to listen to the performance of Handel's 'Samson' and it was what that critic wrote about Will Full-Moon's singing that made Merthyr remember him again. Now Will Full-Moon is getting as many engagements as he can fulfil and he is keeping himself tidy and sober and going to chapel most Sunday evenings, but not the mornings, for he is not a chapel member. Who would believe that again? Right.

Leaving singing and going into the political field. You remember Mr Bruce who used to be Stipendiary Magistrate for our town and district? Right. What would you say if I told you that he is now Under-Secretary of State at the Home Office? He is, and he is the only member of our town and district since we first had a member to be a member of the Government. He was always a good man, but we have sent many a good man to the House of Commons without getting anything from the English gentlemen who are full of the place. Now the member for Merthyr is somebody in that House of Commons. That is another of ever so many things hard to believe that I could tell you if only I had the time. Penry Williams, the artist, is again in Rome, and his paintings are winning him more and more fame. The trustees are doing well for Sir Ivor Guest, and those managing Cyfarthfa Works and collieries for Robert Thompson Crawshay are doing well for him too. Yes, things are going on well.

CHAPTER 8

Eisteddfod Genedlaethol Cymru

THE civil war in America was over at last, thank goodness, and Henry Parry was lucky to get back home safe and well after all he had gone through. Thanks be to God, said Betty Parry, and all the Parry family went to the thanksgiving service at the Welsh chapel in Danville in Pennsylvania. The family had grown. Joseph had two little sons, J. Haydn

Parry and D. Mendelssohn Parry, and I put their name like that because it was their middle names that Joseph called them by. The 'D' in front of young Mendelssohn's name was just a courtesy name out of respect to an uncle named David. Then the 'J' in front of young Haydn's name was just the same for his father, Joseph. But they were known as Haydn and Mendelssohn Parry, the sons of Joseph Parry, the rising young Welsh-American musician who had recently turned professional. Yes, he had given up his job as head-roller in the rolling-mill and was now going to live or die as a professional musician.

We will talk about that later. He is not the only Parry – or the only musical Parry, remember. Oh, no. Not by a long way. I have told you about his mother, Betty, and I need say no more about her as a musician. A real feeling for all things musical she had but music on paper meant nothing to her. She could lead a choir and sing by herself without any old music on paper, thank you. We cannot say as much for Daniel, her husband, who was a sort of singing 'trailer', if you know what I mean. His was a backing-up voice and not very good backing at that. No, Daniel was no singer or musician, but he was a grand man all the same. His children all followed their mother in one respect if no other and their singing was a credit to her. Too much talk there has been about Joseph perhaps and not enough about his brothers and sisters. Henry had a grand voice and he was no sooner back from the war than he began to compose under the inspiration of the wife he took back with him from Virginia. Elizabeth, called Betsy rather than Betty to distinguish her from her mother, had a contralto voice like a nice-toned bell and the eldest of her two little girls could already sing by herself. I would say that Jane, the youngest of Betty's children, had the best voice of them all. Soprano she was and it was she that could make the most of the songs that Joseph was now throwing off. Yes, Jane Parry could have made a name for herself as a singer had she gone in for it and stuck to it through thick and thin as Joseph had.

But there, what is singing after all? A singer and nothing but a singer is little more than a performing animal after all. What is a singer at a time when America was holding her wounded, bleeding sides? When America was painfully trying to make itself whole? The Parry family rejoicing whilst the nation mourned not only for Lincoln but also for the fallen in their graves deep and shallow throughout the land. Now forgetting the nation's long agony families got together and rejoiced and gave thanks. In a Welsh chapel in Danville in Pennsylvania the Parry family unto the third, the truly American generation, giving thanks and forgetting as poor human beings must.

With the rest of the congregation the Parry family sang the hymn of thanks. In English I would say the two concluding lines like this: 'Thanks be unto him for remembering the dust of the earth.' But when it is sung and sung again and again in Welsh it adds volumes to those eleven words of thanks. If you happen to be passing a Welsh chapel some Sunday evening and, if that hymn is among those sung that evening, you judge for yourself. This night I am speaking of it thrilled the Welsh who sang it again and again in Danville in Pennsylvania, thrilled those who had sung it hundreds of times in places on both sides of the mighty waters of the Atlantic. Elizabeth's two little girls looked at Joseph's little boys and the mothers smiled and the grandparents settled down now to listen to the sermon. It was a grand Welsh sermon which Joseph's wife had difficulty in following. So she gave it up and tried her best to keep awake. Most of those present listened most intently, as the Welsh always do listen to a sermon. It was a most moving sermon and it evoked fervent responses from many present. It contained several references to the late President Lincoln and to those who had died to unite America. We must never forget them, cried the preacher. Hear! hear! said many.

Joseph was thinking of one of the compositions he was going to send over the water, to Wales, to the Welsh National Eisteddfod, as entries in several of its competitions this year again. He was one Welshman who did not listen intently to sermons. The inside of his head was always a sort of music-room in which there was always something going on, and what was going on inside his head was what he was interested in. There was so much going on there and war or no war it was only the music in his head that mattered. It was during the war that he had made his name famous among the Welsh of America. I am going back for a minute to 1863 – I won't keep you a minute.

As I told you he was working every day in the rolling-mill, where he was head roller, in 1863. He was married and had one child, J. Haydn Parry. Right. Now then. Most nights after work he would be composing at home, or away competing at a Welsh-American Eisteddfod or adjudicating at same. On Sundays he went to play the organ at the English Presbyterian Chapel of New York and travelled back to Danville Sunday nights so as to be at work in the rolling-mill first thing Monday morning. Between everything a most hectic time for him. Having won ever so many prizes at Welsh-American Eisteddfods at Youngstown, Ohio, and elsewhere, he felt himself man enough to compete against the composers of Wales at the National Eisteddfod of Wales, which we call Eisteddfod Genedlaethol Cymru.

But what is this Eisteddfod Genedlaethol Cymru, this National Eisteddfod of Wales? You ought to know but perhaps you don't. So listen. It was and still is the greatest national musical and literary festival the world over. Yes, it is. Then tell me any other nation who from time immemorial has had such an annual national festival as the Eisteddfod Genedlaethol Cymru. Of course you cannot tell me. It lasts for over a week, for over a week each and every year and it is the Mecca of all Welsh poets and musicians.

Welsh preachers and politicians, Welsh singers and composers, writers, playwrights and Welsh everything. To win the bardic crown or chair or a prize of any sort at this annual national festival is the peak of the ambition of poets and musicians and others. To win you have to be good, very good, very, very good. Right then.

In 1863, Joseph Parry skimmed the cream of his compositions and sent them across the Atlantic to Wales, to Swansea, where our National Eisteddfod was being held that year. He just gave his address in Danville in Pennsylvania, but signed himself as 'Bachgen bach o Ferthyr, erioed, erioed', which means 'Little chap from Merthyr, always, always'. That was Joseph all over. Living in Pennsylvania and describing himself as a little chap from Merthyr in Wales. So he was the mystery man of that year's National Eisteddfod, at which his compositions swept the board. Yes, his six entries were placed first and far ahead of all other compositions in their class. A motet, a set of three songs, choruses for male-voice and mixed choirs –

Who is this little chap from Merthyr? all Wales was asking. But when the news got over to America and was spread throughout the land by the Welsh-American newspaper, *Y Drych*, it was for all Welsh-Americans as notable as a great victory of the North over the South in the war then in progress. For a Welsh-American ironworker had 'swept the board' at the National Eisteddfod of Wales. For the first time Welsh-America had straddled the ocean to put its best foot down in Wales, the old country, Hen Wlad fy Nhadau. The news spread from Danville through Pennsylvania and from there to other states to reach all Welsh-American communities. It went over the mountains, along the rivers and coasts and even into the Army – Henry heard it whilst resting and waiting for reinforcements. Welsh-Americans everywhere hailed Joseph as 'Pencerdd America', which in English means Supreme composer of America. So he was head-roller in the rolling-mill and head-composer of America at the same time – in the eyes of all Welsh-Americans anyway.

He sent another half-dozen of his best compositions to the following year's National Eisteddfod of Wales and again they swept the board. So by the time the war in America had ended Joseph was a professional musician and the talk of Wales and of the Welsh of America. He was able to cross the Atlantic to attend the National Eisteddfod of Wales when it was held at Aberystwyth. He had sent his compositions on in advance for adjudication and he was confidently expecting to hear that they had again swept the board as soon as he got there.

Before going to where the National Eisteddfod was being held at Aberystwyth he spent a day and a night at Merthyr, where he was born and where he had lived and worked for the first thirteen years of his life. The place had grown during the dozen years he had been away from it and yet it seemed small to him now. And ever so much dirtier, he thought. He still loved the place, but its shrunken appearance disappointed him. John Abel Jones and John Price, the teachers to whom he owed so much, had crossed the Atlantic with him on the *City of Washington*, which made the crossing in twelve days. All three marvelled at this for it had taken them nearly seven weeks to get to Philadelphia from Cardiff. This time they sailed from New York to Liverpool and all three were eagerly looking forward to seeing their native towns and valleys after an absence of only a dozen years in Joseph's case, and sixteen years in the other two cases. And only to be disappointed.

With his two Welsh-American teachers and friends Joseph went to Chapel Row, to the house in Merthyr in which he was born. He sighed after he had, at the request of the occupant, written this on the margin of an almanack hanging on the wall of the bedroom. 'Ganwyd fi yn yr ystafell hon, Mai 21ain, 1841 – Joseph Parry.' I was born in this room on May 21st, 1841 – Joseph Parry. He stooped to get out of the little house without knocking his head and although neither he nor his two Welsh-American friends were big men they seemed big in the midst of the neighbours who came out on to the canal bank to ask Joseph about his parents and his brother and sisters. He told them that they were all grand when he left them in America a fortnight before and all the neighbours gasped and looked at each other and one said: All the way from where they live over there in America to by here in Merthyr in a fortnight! Dear, dear. Well, well. If it was not Joseph Parry standing by here that said it I would never believe it. No, never. Good job you have stopped fighting each other over there in America, said another. Many of our Welsh people killed in the fighting, Joseph? Not many of us Welsh, but some, said Joseph. I must go now to see Robert James and my sister, Ann. Then I am going over the top to Rhymney with my two friends before going on to Aberystwyth to the Eisteddfod. Yes, but you will be calling here on your way back to the ship, won't you? one said. Goodbye to you all for now, he said. Goodbye for now, they all said, and Joseph walked down the canal bank and past the lock of the canal and along the path on to the big road. 'Oh give me back my childhood's dreams,' he murmured, then stopped for a minute to put that down in English writing on the back of an envelope. Another song have come to your head? said John Price. Joseph nodded and put the envelope back in his pocket. They walked as far as the Bush Hotel in Dowlais and went to the hotel stables and hired a horse and trap and a man to drive them over the top and down to Rhymney, which is John Price's native town and is the biggest town in the Rhymney Valley, the next valley to the Merthyr Valley.

They stopped right up on the top, on the Waun, as they called it, and got off the trap whilst the pony had a bit of a rest. There were many ponies running wild over the Waun, which is the name of about twenty square miles of common land high up above the two valleys. From the Waun they could see the hills and valleys of three counties, Glamorgan, Brecknock and Monmouthshire. It used to be all green up here and the sky full of larks, said John Price. Rough grazing for hundreds of wild ponies, I remember. So do I, said the driver of the trap, who was stinking of beer. But since then the two valleys have been throwing their muck back over their heads and up to by here. No green they will leave if they can help it. Cover it all they will with their dirty shit from the works and the pits. There it is for you as black as your hats from Dowlais Top to down below Pantywaun. The more money our English bosses take away from here the more of the dirty shit from the works and pits they leave for us. They get the money and we get the shit. Is that how it is where you are out in America?

No, said John Abel Jones. Then what damned fools you are to come back here, said the driver. We came over for the Eisteddfod which is starting Monday at Aberystwyth, said John Price. And if you please try to talk cleaner. Then find me a cleaner place to talk in, said the driver. Don't you try to tell me how to talk. I talk as I please. Eisteddfod, you said? Yes, yes, sing and spout poetry. I know. All teetotallers – that is right, isn't it? Quite right, said Joseph. I knew it, said the driver. I knew it as soon as I saw you coming round the back of the hotel into the stable-yard. I am not a tee-totaller remember. We knew that as soon as we saw you too, said John Abel Jones. I've a damned good mind to turn the pony round and let you walk yourselves to Rhymney, said the driver. Now talk sense, said John Price. I am dying to see Rhymney after being over in America sixteen years. And whilst I am waiting in Rhymney to drive you back to Dowlais I am to sit in the sun till I'm dry-cured like a red-herring, no doubt, said the driver. No, you shall have six-pence to do what you like with, said Joseph. Sixpence! said the driver. No, a shilling, said John Price, who was anxious to get to Rhymney to see it again. You must have made your fortunes out in America, said the driver ironically. Sixpence apiece more like. There will be threepence for bread and cheese remember. Very well, eighteenpence you shall have, said John Price. Let us go now for it is very hot up here in the eye of the sun.

They got up into their seats on the trap, John Price with the driver in front to look forward towards Rhymney, and Joseph and John Abel Jones behind looking back towards Dowlais and Merthyr. The pony walked and trotted and the driver went on talking and pointing with his whip. How far is it from by here to America? he said. Thousands of miles, said John Price. So you have come thousands of miles to sing for a week at the National Eisteddfod, said the driver. And after you have had your fill of singing what better off will you be? Would the English come thousands of miles to sing here in Wales? No damned fear. It is for money they come here. Money to take back to England with them. One generation of Englishmen after the other taking money by the million away from here and leaving us Welsh all this – Yes, yes, you told us, said John Price. What good me tell you? said the driver. Sing you will and the English will let you sing for as long as you let them make money for themselves and hell upon earth for us. Look, look, those little wild ponies over by there have got more damned sense than we Welsh have. I have finished talking. Sixteen years since you saw Rhymney, you said. Wait till you see it now.

It certainly was a disappointment for John Price. Rhymney had changed for the worse – or was it he that had changed during sixteen years of more spacious life in America? He had left Rhymney in the hands of the iron and coal king and it was still under his rule. His subjects were still huddled in small houses in and around the ironworks and coal mines and he had hemmed them in more closely with mountainous slag and clinker tips. The ironworks was an offspring of the famous Cyfarthfa Works at Merthyr and was a Crawshay gift to a son-in-law. It went as it grew and prospered from hand to hand, English hands, but its government remained unchanged. From their cradles to their graves the population of Rhymney lived and worked only by the grace of God and 'the Company', lived in Company houses, worked in Company works and mines, bought their provisions in Company shops, drank their beer in Company public-houses – but they worshipped God in the only free houses, the Welsh Nonconformist chapels. The one and only church was 'tied' to the State and to the iron and coal kings, and it was to the Church of England that the English iron and coal kings and their families went patronizingly. Their Welsh slaves were independent of them and their church on Sundays if on no other day of the week.

John Price and Joseph and John Abel Jones, looking strange and as though too big for the place, spent a few hours in Rhymney before returning by trap to Dowlais. The driver after eight pints of strong beer and only twopenny-worth of bread-and-cheese, talked as though inspired as the pony walked at its own pace. John Price was feeling sad and in no mood to listen to the talk of the rough-tongued driver, but listen he had to. I'll say one thing for the place, said the driver. Not a bad drop of beer there. If the talk about Sunday-closing in Merthyr closes the public-houses on the Sabbath then it's over the top and down to Rhymney I shall be coming. Oh, yes, Rhymney is outside our county, thanks be. Nothing against you teetotallers or chapel-people, mind you. But live and let live is my motto.

He went on talking until they got to the Bush Hotel in Dowlais. Here you are safe and sound, he said. Five shillings for the ride there and back and whatever you've a mind to give me on the top of it. We have already given you sixpence apiece, said John Abel Jones. Of course, for refreshment, said the driver. That, like the snow we had last winter, is gone. Come, come now and don't make me think worse of you than I do already. Better give him another sixpence apiece, I suppose, said John Price. So they pulled out their purses and between them made up six shillings in silver and sixpennyworth of copper. I hope you enjoy yourselves at the Eisteddfod, said the driver.

They did not. When they got to Aberystwyth it was only to learn that Joseph's compositions, which had been sent on well in advance for adjudication, had not been received. Talk about a disappointment! Joseph could not believe it. Eight of my best compositions I sent you months ago, he told the Secretary of the National Eisteddfod of Wales. Yes, and I know he did, said John Abel Jones. To be sure he went to New York to put them in the mail there. I went with him to New York. So did I, said John Price. They were sent in the name of 'Bachgen bach o Ferthyr, erioed, erioed', same as his other winning compositions were sent last year and the year before to Llandudno and Swansea. Oh, said the Secretary of that year's National Eisteddfod at Aberystwyth. And this is the young man everyone is talking about. Then I am more sorry than ever. For no compositions under that name have reached us.

Joseph broke down and wept like a child, wept and wept he did, and so would you if you had travelled thousands of miles only to find that the best fruits of nearly a year's hard work had gone on lost. It was not only the expense but the work he had put into those missing compositions. Throughout America all Welsh-American communities would be confidently expecting him to sweep the board this year again. Woe, woe is me, and he would not be comforted. Come with me to see the adjudicators, please, said the Secretary, whose office was in a bell-tent outside the huge marquee in which the National Eisteddfod was being held at Aberystwyth that summer. Leave me alone where I am, said Joseph. No, come to see the adjudicators, Joseph, said John Price. Yes, come, said John Abel Jones. Enough to break your heart we know it is but play the man you must for the sake of the Welsh of America. Come now.

In a minute, said Joseph. Too weak to stand I am for a minute.

Some might laugh to see a grown-up man with a moustache sitting down and crying bitter tears in a bell-tent, but if it had happened to them perhaps they would be crying too. Too good you have been, perhaps, and no doubt jealous of your success some in Wales have been, said John Abel Jones. Thinking, perhaps that we Welsh of America were getting too good for them. Perhaps some of them have destroyed your compositions not for them to sweep the board again. No, no, please, said the Secretary. That is going too far. I don't know indeed, said John Abel Jones. Whether or no, said Joseph, gone they have and the least said the better now. I am ready to go to see the adjudicators now.

The adjudicators had two bell-tents outside the huge marquee which at this time had an audience of about seven thousand inside it. Better say something first about the adjudicators, which we in Welsh call 'y Beirniaid'. They are the worthy and capable and experienced writers and musicians and poets who sit in judgement on the entries submitted for judgement at each and every year's National Eisteddfod. Joseph and John Price and John Abel Jones followed the Secretary across the grass to the bell-tent reserved for the adjudicators of everything musical. Only two of the adjudicators were in the bell-tent when they got there, but before long the other four came from somewhere to see the three men from America and particularly Joseph. Well, well, they said. You are the young man. Well, well. Come for us to introduce you from the platform in the big tent – Just a minute, said the Secretary. There has been ... er – well, the compositions which he sent in advance from America ...

He went on to explain in a way that made Joseph break down again and this was most distressing for all present. The most venerable and famous of the adjudicators said to the Secretary: Go you into the big tent and put a stop to whatever is going on there. This was done and the six adjudicators, some of whom were great in Wales before Joseph was born, escorted him into the big marquee and on to the platform which by this time had been cleared for them. There was only the Llywydd, which means President, in his place. The six adjudicators, three on either side of Joseph, escorted him to where the Llywydd was seated and the most venerable adjudicator presented Joseph to the Llywydd, who rose in his place to welcome Joseph. Then the Master of Ceremonies, which we in Welsh call Arwei-nydd, was instructed to raise his mighty voice and introduce Joseph to the vast audience as Joseph Parry, 'Pencerdd America', which, as I have said but perhaps you have for-gotten, means 'Head of all composers in America'. Some of you may think that that is going a bit too far but we in Wales did not think so at the time. Never mind. It is the scene I wish I could describe for you.

Seven thousand people on their feet applauding and waving their hats and programmes. Have any of you ever been applauded by as many as seven thousand people? If you have then you will know what you felt like and are in a position to judge what Joseph felt like that summer's day long gone. But the applause did not find his lost composi-tions. But the outcome of it all was that everyone at that memorable National Eisteddfod agreed that the young man was worthy of encouragement and support. The National Eisteddfod Committee met and an offer was made to Jo-seph. A bit 'rough' the Committee thought him, so their offer was that he should take a year's general education under Dr Evan Davies at Swansea, then go for a year's polishing at the Royal Academy of Music in London. The National Eisteddfod Committee of that year would pay the fees for both years and see that he would have enough to keep himself during the two years study. Let us know your decision, they said.

Joseph was left with his two Welsh-American friends and teachers, John Abel Jones and John Price. What about Jane and our two children in America? said Joseph. H'm, said John Price, trying to think. John Abel Jones without stopping to think said: When a Welshman from America comes over here and proves he is good bread it is very thin Wales will put butter on him. Here I am not knowing what to do, said Joseph. Thirteen years I lived here in Wales before going to America, and nearly thirteen years I have been there now. At first I did not like it over in America but now my heart is there as much as here. Then you are going back there with me and John Price, said John Abel Jones.

Joseph nodded and they went to thank the Committee and said they were going back to America on the Tuesday of the following week, leaving Merthyr on the Tuesday and sailing from Liverpool on the Wednesday night or the Thursday morning. Well, you know your own business best, said the chairman of the Committee, who thought Joseph was standing in his own light. The three Welsh-Americans thanked the Committee again and left Aberystwyth so clean by the sea to go and spend the rest of their time on this side of the water in such dirty places as Merthyr and Rhymney. For it is Merthyr and not Aberystwyth my mother and father will be asking about when I get back to America, said Joseph. If I do not go three times to Bethesda Chapel next Sunday then my mother will never forgive me. And if I don't go to chapel in Rhymney what will the Rhymney Valley people over in America say? said John Price. So he went to spend the week-end in Rhymney and Joseph and John Abel Jones went to Merthyr for the week-end.

Joseph was putting something down on paper all the time and John Abel Jones said at last: Is it songs out of your head you are putting down on paper all time? No, said Joseph. Not songs but a big song could be made out of what I am putting down not to forget when my mother and father will be asking all about Merthyr and the way it has changed for better or worse. It would take a long time to say all that could be said about that week-end during which Joseph went about meeting people and going to places and noting nearly a baker's dozen years of changes. Here are some of the things he put down – but before I tell you we may as well get the Sunday at Bethesda Chapel out of the way first. You know we have what are called 'Big Meetings' at our Welsh chapels once a year, don't you? Well, there were never bigger meetings in Bethesda Chapel than on this Sunday. It was not only Joseph's Sunday but what you might call a 'Parry Sunday'. As good as five services that Sunday! Morning service and the Gyfeillach afterwards. Sunday School in the afternoon owing to the presence of so many visitors, also a service. Evening service and the Gyfeillach after that again. Talk about singing! Joseph sat in the Big Seat with the deacons and it was from there that the preacher spoke of him with pride as 'a Bethesda boy'. There were many references to the 'Annwyl frodyr a Chwiorydd', the dear brothers and sisters over the water in America, and five times that same Sunday Joseph was unanimously requested to convey the sacred love of all present in the chapel and Welsh independents throughout Wales to his family and all of the denomination in America, where they were better known as 'congregationalists'. For myself I would say that the Sunday, most of which Joseph spent at Bethesda Chapel, was the most memorable day of Joseph's visit to his native town and district. But you can have too much chapel, can't you? Or can you?

Whether or no we are not going to say any more about what went on in Bethesda Chapel that Sunday. Let us now consider some of the changes which Joseph had briefly noted on a piece of paper no larger than your hand. If they are worthy of comment – well, we will see. Here is what he had put down:

Penydarren Ironworks is finished and they say the Plymouth Ironworks will soon finish too.

Water from a waterworks coming to Merthyr now.

Gas-lamps on some streets and in some buildings but not all.

There is a big Drill Hall for drilling the Volunteers and for holding concerts in. It is ten times bigger than the Temperance Hall.

The Cyfarthfa Brass Band is playing better than ever and there is talk of the Volunteers having their own brass band to play in front of them.

A lot more Irish have come from Ireland to Merthyr and Dowlais and a lot more other people have come to the place, they say.

A lot more houses for the big people up in Thomas Town but none that I could see in George Town.

Trains now going to nearly everywhere from Merthyr.

Choirs more than before in Merthyr and Dowlais.

A weekly newspaper for Merthyr and district now.

People and sports are allowed in Penydarren Park now.

Those are some of the changes which Joseph noted so as to be able to tell his mother and father and brother and sisters when he got back to America. You know how it is after being away from a place twelve – nearly thirteen years in Joseph's case. Such changes as he had noted would strike you too. As he said, a big song might be made about them. Oh, yes. Symphony if you like. I am not going to keep you but let you and me think for a minute. Take the Penydarren Works for a start. That works made history and millions of money for somebody into the bargain. The first rail for railroads ever rolled was rolled in the rolling-mill of this works, and it was rails from this works that made the railroad between Liverpool and Manchester in England. Before that the first engine that ever pulled a load started from this works – but you have heard all about Trevithick's High-pressure Tram Engine. Yes, that steamed like a strange monster out of Penydarren Ironworks. Never mind that now.

Penydarren Ironworks was now closed and derelict and parts of it were buried under the clinker-tips which Dowlais

Ironworks is spewing all over the place. Puddlers and rollers and others who had worked all their lives in Penydarren Works have had to go elsewhere to work, to the North of England and to America. The historic ironworks at Penydarren, the mid-way place that connects Merthyr and Dowlais and the Cyfarthfa and Dowlais Ironworks, is no more. Then the Plymouth Ironworks was, as Joseph noted, on its last legs. It was obvious to everyone now that soon it would be only the Crawshays and the Guests at Cyfarthfa and Dowlais Ironworks would be sharing between them all the orders for iron that came to the town and district. Pity in a way for Penydarren and Plymouth Ironworks but that is how it is and, do what we will, you and me cannot alter things.

From work to water – and this is important. Joseph opened his eyes when he saw the water-taps running water into the people's buckets and jugs. This was progress. A water supply at last, though not a plentiful supply. One water-tap for a row of a dozen houses or two for a street of from twenty to thirty houses. Clean filtered water! Well, well, said Joseph. Taste it, said a woman, handing him her jug. He drank and said: Yes, lovely water. Pity there is not more of it, said the woman. They turn it off half the time and then we have to go to the wells or the brooks or the river same as before. Never mind, it will come, said Joseph.

The gas-lighting again. That had come during the time Joseph had been away in America and now he was thrilled by it. Late one night he followed the lamp-lighter around to see him light each gas-lamp with the long thing like a thick fishing-rod with a light that did not go out at the end of it. With it he turned a tap inside the glass covering and lit the lamp as well. It made a faint explosion when it took light. There were only about twenty gas-lamps on street-corners and along the High Street but they changed the look of the place at night. About two hundred yards apart they were along both sides of the High Street, so there were patches of semi-darkness between them.

This is taking longer than we thought and so we must hurry up. The Drill Hall – this is something we must not hurry over. It cost £2,000 to build and it would hold how many? Anything from one to two thousand with those standing at the back, I should say. The Volunteer Movement had grown and the only place the Volunteers had to drill was the Castle Field behind the Castle Hotel. All right in summer, of course, but in the winter and wet weather you simply could not drill the men there. So a subscription list was sent around the town and some gave and others didn't. The total of £2,000 was reached and the job was put in hand. It was not a very good site but it was the best obtainable at the time. The drill-sergeant and his wife were the caretakers of it and it was available for concerts, dances and eisteddfods and travelling companies of players, if they were reputable, as well as for drilling. So it was a great boon to the town and district and it soon put the Temperance Hall in the shade. As I say, you could stuff nearly two thousand people into the place – and Joseph and his two Welsh-American friends were lucky. For on the Monday evening before they were to leave by train on the Tuesday morning there was a concert at the Drill Hall and they were invited to attend by no less a person than Robert Thompson Crawshay himself. It was his band, the famous Cyfarthfa Brass Band, that was giving the concert, assisted by two eminent artists. And who do you think one of them was? Will Full-Moon, who had won his reputation back. He looked a lot thinner in his evening dress than he used to be when he used to take drink, and his glorious bass-baritone voice seemed to lack feeling this night. It had a drier but not a better quality than of old. It was too well controlled if you know what I mean. But we have had enough of singing and concerts already and it was not what I was going to tell you anyway. The other singer was Maggie Watts from

Dowlais and who was in her third year at the Royal Academy of Music. She was a very religious girl and a grand singer and we could say a lot to her credit but we must leave her for now.

The Cyfarthfa Band – you know that the conductor, Ralph Livsey, had died. Joseph did not and he was surprised when Mr Crawshay introduced him to George Livsey, the talented son of Ralph and the present conductor of the band. When did your father die? said Joseph. Let me see, said George. One, two, three – nearly four years ago. Well, well, said Joseph. We in America never heard a word. The band under your father was my life when a boy here in Merthyr. Well, said George, now that you are getting to be known as a composer why don't you write something for the band, an overture or something? Is it as good a band under you as under your father? said Joseph with a smile. That's for you to judge when you hear it, as you will in a minute or so from now, said George.

It was every bit as good if not better and Joseph promised to write an overture for the band when he found time. But that was not what I was going to tell you either. This was the great thing of the evening. Robert Thompson Crawshay took Joseph by the hand and led him up on to the stage and introduced him to that vast audience as 'an old Cyfarthfa boy'. He was born right inside my works and inspired by my band, said Mr Crawshay. Now he is a composer growing in fame on both sides of the Atlantic and I for one am proud of him – as I am sure you all are. He is leaving here in the morning to return to America and on your behalf and my own I wish him a safe voyage and a successful career in the realm of music.

Joseph said a few words but as he was not a very good speaker then we will not repeat what he said. The next thing he had noted was only hearsay, namely, that the Volunteers were trying to form a brass band of their own to march before them through the town. A regimental band, they wanted. Perhaps that will come in time and we will leave that and take up what Joseph had noted about the growth of the population of the town and district. It had grown. Merthyr was by now the centre of a population of eighty thousand souls! There is people, if you like. Three-fourths of the additional ten thousand added during the years Joseph had been in America were made up of Irish, English and a few other nationalities including Jews. So the town and district was growing more and more English-speaking. To get on we will couple this point with what he noted about houses. There were more better-class houses in Thomas Town but no more working-class houses in George Town and few more working-class houses in the other parts of the town of Tydfil the Martyr. So how did that additional ten thousand manage to stuff themselves into the place? Yes, how? Still, they managed somehow.

Joseph had noted the increase in the number of choirs in the town and district but as that is a natural growth in Wales we will pass that. He also noted that Penydarren Park was now more open to the public than ever before. 'The Big Field' is what we called it but better give it its proper name now. It used to be a private park same as Cyfarthfa Park still was, but when the Penydarren Iron-works went slack and soon closed down the owner of same left Penydarren House. I am compressing a lot of its vicissitudes in order to get on with my story. At one time you would be prosecuted for trespassing if you were caught in Penydarren Park at any time but now you could walk there and go to see sports and listen to the band playing there. So the Penydarren Ironworks left something that was good to the people of the town and district.

There are only two more points which he noted. Trains, he said, trains now going to nearly everywhere from Merthyr. Quite right. You could now go north, south, east or west by train from Merthyr. When Joseph was a boy there was only the one way you could go by train from Merthyr and that was down towards the sea at Cardiff, and that rail-road was made not for man but for coal and iron to go down to the sea. Passenger traffic was negligible then but it was far from negligible now. Now, the last thing before we get on with our story.

As I think I told you, we had not had a newspaper of any sort in the district for fifteen years up to 1855. Then the *Merthyr Telegraph* was started and came out once a week. It was something to be sure but not as good as it might have been. We had to wait nearly ten years for the *Merthyr Express*, and it was worth waiting for. David Morgan started a good thing when he started the *Merthyr Express*, which was a good all-round weekly newspaper, and I only mention it here because it gave two columns to Joseph and his work as a composer, and on the front page it gave another column to the story of his lost compositions. Joseph was interviewed by the editor himself and after the interview Joseph asked if it were possible to subscribe for three copies weekly to be sent to America week after week. And three for me as well, said John Abel Jones. Certainly, said the editor. We are the best link between this part of Wales and America. We cover a half-dozen valleys and events great and small. We are eating up the circulation of the *Telegraph* and increasing our own by scores of copies weekly ...

But no doubt you have heard newspaper men talk before so we will leave him too. No doubt newspaper men on the *New York Times* were talking in much the same strain when Joseph landed back in America, but not to Joseph. They knew not Joseph anyway. But he was known for all that, and known throughout America, if only by handfuls of people here and there. Talk about a reception! Danville, Wilkes-Barre, Scranton, Youngstown, Ohio – and even in New York he had a wonderful welcome from the Welsh-Americans resident in that city. Perhaps you will not believe me when I tell you that throughout America at this time there were nearly four hundred Welsh chapels, three hundred and eighty-four to be precise. Services in the Welsh language in all those chapels from coast to coast and inland as far as you could go. The Welsh of America would not allow Joseph, one of their own and a 'lump of genius', as John Griffiths, 'Y Gohebydd', called him, to be beholden to anyone or anybody in the old country. They, the Welsh of America, could look after their own, thank you.

The Welsh of Youngstown in the State of Ohio started the Parry Fund with a donation of one thousand dollars and the Welsh of all the other States also contributed. But not enough. The aim of the 'Parry Fund Committee' was to collect enough money to send Joseph back across the water to London, there to study for three years at the Royal Academy of Music. The first wave of enthusiasm died down and Joseph himself was sent on tour to exhibit himself and collect from the Welsh of America. At one place he would sing, for he was a good bass-baritone by this time, at another he would play or he would adjudicate at an eisteddfod. The end justified the means and after each appearance in one or other of several capacities he would accept the collection for the 'Parry Fund'. Hospitality provided free everywhere. Jane, his wife, who was most ladylike, thought it all most undignified. But each time he returned to her he said that the end justified the means. He left her and the children time after time during the two years he toured and collected for the 'Parry Fund'. He travelled by train and along the mighty rivers in river boats to get to the Welsh-American communities throughout the land, and whilst travelling he read and studied for dear life. He improved his English by reading and by means of conversations with all sorts of people. His name was becoming a household word in Welsh-American homes along the length and across the breadth of America but he was growing to feel more and more nauseated with the job all the same. It takes a lot of money to send a man from America across to London to the Royal Academy and keep him there for three years, and to keep a wife and children at the same time. But now, now that he had set his heart and mind on going there, he would go down to hell itself to collect before giving up.

At last, at long last ... The year 1868 and he returned to Jane and his two children and the family and friends at Danville for a brief rest before leaving them again, this time for London and the Royal Academy. Oh, he was tired, yet both happy and confident. We shall do it now, Jane, he said to his wife. I am sure you will, she said. America as a whole was too busy pulling itself together to take much notice of the ambitious young ironworker who was gathering strength at Danville, Pennsylvania, before going across the water to study at the Academy of Music in the great city of London, a city he had never been to. America was not feeling very well-disposed towards London anyway. During the Civil War a leading London newspaper had sent a big-nosed and malicious Special Correspondent over and he had said things which were not yet forgotten or forgiven in America. London was the lair of the one they had and were still referring to as that 'fat cockney', the man known to his employers, readers and creditors as George Augustus Sala. He had been denounced and abused in the American newspapers but as Joseph did not read newspapers much he knew nothing of the man he might even meet in London. Never mind that. It is to the Welsh chapel in Danville we are going to and it is there we will leave Joseph, for it is a sort of farewell gathering and we have had enough of such gatherings already, haven't we? So we will leave him there and go to London before him.

You may remember London in 1868 better than I do. Charles Dickens was there and George Augustus Sala was there and the Court was there and Society was there and I did not know any of the big people – oh, yes, I knew one. The Home Secretary in 1868 was none other than our Mr Bruce, though he was not our member any longer. I forgot to tell you that our Henry Richard had beaten him in 1866.

Still, it was we of the town of Merthyr and district that started Mr Bruce on his political career and now he was Home Secretary. So I knew him, and though he was now the member for Renfrewshire I am sure that if I went to the Home Office and sent in to tell him that I was from Merthyr that he would have not thought twice before telling the man to go and tell me to come in. But I did not bother him, I went to see William Davies, the sculptor, instead.

You will remember me telling you about William Davies, who learnt his trade as a plasterer with his father, Moses Davies, who was also a great conductor in Merthyr. I did not know that Moses was dead until William his son told me when I went to see him in London. He also told me that there were three Welsh chapels in London now, in 1868, and that ever so many Welsh people had come up to London since I was there last. Some to sell milk and eggs and butter and others to work in shops for other people. We Welsh people are spreading ourselves all over the place, he said. And getting on some of you are in London too, I said. Oh, I am managing pretty well, he said. Then he told me about Myfanwy Llewelyn under her new and foreign name singing in opera at one of the London theatres the year before. Not in English but in Italian, he said. I don't hold with that, do you? She has got her own mind to please, I said. Is she married? No, married, no, said William Davies. I do not think she will ever get married. Afraid of family those people are if they get married. No doubt, I said. Does she stay here with you when she comes to London to sing? Oh, dear, no, said William, chuckling. But she comes to see us, mind you, and leaves tickets for us to go to the opera. No, she has never stayed here with us since she went first to Italy. Too well she has got on, no doubt, I said. No, it is not that, said William. It is their way of life. She has got a manager and a maid and she must have right of way for visitors as well. So she must stay in the big hotels. My little girl thinks the world of her. Already my Mary has decided to be a great singer too.

Is Myfanwy keeping herself tidy? I asked. Yes, very tidy, said William. Men do run after her, no doubt, but I do not think they will ever succeed in making a bad woman of her. What she saw those years she lived down China in Merthyr is something she will never forget. When she used to live here with us she would talk to me sometimes about those years and about the poor women the men, her own father too, used to go up to the coke-ovens with. God help them, I said. Amen, said William. No, Myfanwy will never go that way. Hard and firm-willed she is, except when she is acting and singing on the stage. But that is only acting. I have never heard her sing in opera, I said. When you do you will not know it is her, said William. She nearly stops people breathing before she starts to sing at all, so lovely she is. Then when she starts singing it is truly thankful people are for the pleasure and privilege of hearing her. I am not much for opera but when she is singing I am very much for it. Time to go again, I said. Glad I am to know that you are getting on so well here in London. Yes, I am glad I did not go back to Merthyr with my father that time, he said. My father could not live long out of Wales. There are many like him in that respect, I said. No doubt, but I am not, said William. I like the English of London and I can keep me and mine Welsh here too. Mary, my daughter, speaks Welsh as good as my father used to, and she was born here in London as you know. Is she in? I said. No, she is gone with her mother for her music lesson, said William. Music it is with us Welsh all the time, no matter where we are, I said. Goodbye for now. Mind to call and see us whenever you are passing, said William.

CHAPTER 9

Alone in London

I T was very rough weather for two days out of the ten which the *City of Brussels* took to carry Joseph across the Atlantic. He was down-hearted when he boarded the ship in New York, which is not to be wondered at. For it was one affecting farewell after another during the day previous. He had a letter of transfer recommending him to the Welsh chapel of 'Yr Annibynwyr', the denomination of Welsh independents, but no one in Danville was certain that that denomination had a chapel in London. The preacher was almost but not quite sure that there was a chapel of that denomination in London. Whether or no Joseph had a letter of transfer for a temporary period of three years, a letter which strongly recommended him as one who from a child had been a credit to the denomination. It also stated that he was a musician and able to play the organ well enough for the singing of hymns at any chapel. It concluded by recommending him as a lodger to any tidy and religious family who would earn the thanks of his family and the congregation at Danville, Pennsylvania, if they took him in and looked after him in the city of London. The letter was signed by the preacher and his deacons.

And here was Joseph in London for the first time in his life and not a soul there did he know. It was raining and everyone appeared to be in a hurry and there was Joseph outside the railway station with his things in a leather bag with a broken lock and a strap keeping it shut tight. Oh, if only I had the luck to meet a Welshman now, he was saying to himself. Still, he could speak fairly good English and he had money so he took the bull by the horns or the lion by

207

the tail if you like and took a cab and told the driver to drive him to the Royal Academy of Music. The driver looked at him and nodded and drove off through the rain.

The day's work was over at the Academy but an elderly man who was sweeping a corridor listened to what Joseph had to say and said that if he would wait a few minutes he would take him along to a nearby hotel, where he could stay the night. Is it a place where drink is sold? said Joseph. What if it is? said the man. I will not sleep in any place where drink is sold, said Joseph. Oh, said the man. Very well. There may be room for you at one of the houses that take our students. There was, and a good house it was. The woman of the house looked surprised when Joseph told her that he had come over from America to study at the Academy, for he was twenty-seven years old and looked older. His moustache was thick and his black hair was thick and as abundant as a musician's hair should be. He looked more like a professor than a student of music. After a wash and a meal he felt better and he felt better still next morning after a good night's sleep. A good breakfast and he was ready to face London.

The sun came out as he walked along to the Academy to present himself to Sir William Sterndale Bennett, the Principal, who was a friend of Mendelssohn's. Joseph waited with confidence for the interview. He had not come across the Atlantic to fail, thank you. Sit down, Parry, and tell me something about yourself, said the Principal. Well, as I told you in my letter, sir – you got my letters and those papers, sir, I hope? said Joseph. Oh, yes, said the Principal. Once I sent compositions to our National Eisteddfod and they never got there – that is why I asked, sir, said Joseph. I see, said the Principal, studying Joseph. That was most unfortunate. You mean you competed in your annual musical festival? Yes, sir, said Joseph. As I told you in the letter I won several prizes at – Yes, as you told me in the letter, said the Principal. You understand, of course, that that kind of thing – competing at festivals, I mean, is not permitted whilst you are here with us. Oh, I have finished with all that, sir, Joseph assured him.

After a fairly lengthy talk the Principal came to the conclusion that Joseph had the makings of a good musician. He placed him in the senior composition class, which the Principal himself took, and he put him under Dr Steggall for the organ and Manuel Garcia for voice-training, etc. But Joseph did no work that first day. He found out that there was a Welsh chapel of his denomination in Fetter Lane and he went there with his letter of transfer after tea and had to wait for nearly two hours before the caretaker came along to open the chapel ready for a prayer meeting. The caretaker was Welsh and Joseph thanked God and let his Welsh flow like a river. Presently the preacher came and Joseph handed him his letter of transfer and explained as well. Other members of the congregation came one after the other from all parts of London to pray on a week-night, and the preacher waited until all that were expected had come and then he introduced Joseph and read the letter of transfer. Many present had heard or read about Joseph in newspapers sent them from Wales, so when the preacher said that Joseph wanted tidy lodging as reasonable as possible, three married couples present said it would be a pleasure to have him. Which of you live nearest the Royal Academy of Music? the preacher asked. I think we do, said one of the women. We have no children and he can have a room upstairs to sleep and a room downstairs for study. I don't mind children, I have two of my own, said Joseph. But I would like to be as close as possible to the Academy. Then that's settled, said the preacher. Now which of you brothers or sisters will lead us in prayer?

Some knelt and the others sat with closed eyes and bowed heads and a woman prayed first and others, men and women, followed. They all mentioned Joseph in their prayers and when Joseph said a few words he asked God to watch over his wife and children across the water, and his parents and his brother and sisters and relations and friends. Also all the Welsh-Americans whose generosity and sacrifice had made it possible for him to come to London to study at the Royal Academy of Music. Hear! hear! said several of those present at the prayer meeting. No better start than that prayer meeting could any Welshman hope for in a place like London was in 1868. Prayer is more than pounds or pence and Joseph, indifferent though the musician he was sometimes made him during a sermon or a prayer, knew he was being given the best send-off possible here on earth.

After that he soon settled down to his work at the Academy and it was only his work he thought of and how he loved it too. He had no time for sightseeing or going places. His only break was twice to chapel on Sundays; he did not attend the Sunday School on Sunday afternoons. Neither did he attend any of the week-night services at the chapel. Work, work, work from early morning till late at night. He passed people on the streets as though they were not there at all, and no playbill, however big the lettering, managed to catch his eye. So he did not know that Adah Isaacs Menken, the extraordinary personality who had made her reputation in the role of the Tartar Prince, 'Mazeppa', was giving her farewell performances at the Sadler's Wells Theatre. He knew nothing about the way famous literary men, including Dickens, Thackeray and Swinburne, felt about this woman. Henry Neville was back in London playing in 'The Ticket of Leave Man' and Charles Fechter was drawing all London to the Princess's Theatre, yet Joseph knew nothing about those men either. There were operas grand and comic and Joseph knew nothing about them or about anything but his work and the way to and from the Academy and from his lodging to the chapel in Fetter Lane twice on Sundays. On Sunday afternoons he wrote his weekly letter home and the last was much the same as the first. He said he thought he was doing well and that he was feeling well and that he hoped all at Danville were well. He said he had good lodging with very tidy people and that the Principal of the Academy was as good as any father could be to him. He concluded each letter by telling Jane, his wife, that if only she and the two little boys were in London with him he would be the happiest man alive. That sort of letter and it never varied except when a visiting preacher came to preach at the chapel in Fetter Lane. He wrote the weekly letter more hurriedly as time went on so as to do a little work on the sly before the man and woman of the house came home from Sunday School. Sunday was the Lord's day and he knew he should not work on the Lord's day but he did all the same. He also worked on the sly Sunday nights after the man and woman of the house had gone to bed. He worked late every night on his home-work until his eyes began to fail him. So he had to start wearing glasses for reading and soon he had to wear them all the time.

He surprised all three of his teachers and Manuel Garcia was of the opinion that he was getting 'too good too quick'. There is not much time, was all Joseph could say. He had to prove himself worthy of the confidence and support of the Welsh of America, so he had to work hard. Sir William Sterndale Bennett no longer called him 'Parry', but 'Joseph' now, and one day he said: Joseph, you are driving yourself rather furiously. Am I, sir? said Joseph. You certainly are, said the Principal. Do you ever go anywhere of an evening; theatre, the opera or to a concert? I have not yet been to any, sir, said Joseph. I think you should occasionally, said the Principal. How do you feel about Verdi's work? I only know him by name, sir, said Joseph. Rossini I have studied a little but I have never been to an opera so I cannot say much yet. Wagner I have been studying a little as you know, sir, and I think he is perhaps my man, though I like what little I know about Rossini. Then I think you will like Verdi, said the Principal. Have you evening dress? No, sir, said Joseph. But if you want me to sing at a concert there is a

211

man about my size in the composition class and I am sure he would let me wear his evening dress. You know, sir. Fenwick, I mean. I don't know that it is absolutely necessary that you should wear evening dress, said the Principal. Yet it would make things less embarrassing for you. So see Fenwick and tell him I suggested you should. It is not a concert but a ticket for the opera at the Opera House this evening. 'Rigoletto', and I think this evening's performance should be good. Here you are. I hope you enjoy it. I am sure I will – and thank you sir, said Joseph. Don't mention it, said the Principal. I could not have gone had I wanted to. Remember what I said about driving yourself. Yes, sir. But I cannot help it. It is the way I am, said Joseph. Yes, I suppose it is, said the Principal. We are all rather pleased with your progress and so we do not want you to make yourself ill through overwork. Are those glasses satisfactory? Yes, and they are a great help, sir, said Joseph. Let me know immediately if they prove unsatisfactory as time goes on, said the Principal. Thank you, sir, said Joseph.

Wearing Walter Fenwick's evening clothes Joseph went to the Opera House. In the tail-pocket of his tail-coat he had the key of the front door of the house at which he lodged. For we shall be gone to bed, said Mrs Lloyd. Are you sure now that you know the way to the Opera House? If you are not then I will come and show you the way – no trouble, said Mr Lloyd. I will find it, thank you, said Joseph. You look lovely in those clothes, said Mrs Lloyd. Yes, as much a gentleman as any that will be there tonight, said her husband. It is a pity it is not my own suit I am wearing, said Joseph. Of course it is to help me in my studies the Principal is making me go. As I told you – and you can tell the people of the chapel if they get to hear about me going and do not like it – I have never in my life been inside an opera house or a theatre. But the Principal said it would be good for me if I went. Certainly, it will, said Mrs Lloyd. Nowhere at all have you been all the months you have been living with us.

I will put the bit of supper on the middle of the table and a cloth over it. There will be tea ready in the tea-pot and all you will have to do will be to wet it with water from the kettle. Thank you, said Joseph. As long as you understand, that's all. To learn more about music I am going. Of course, said Mr Lloyd. I wish now I was going with you. I wish you were too, said Joseph. A bit afraid I am by myself. I know, said Mr Lloyd, and I will go with you as far as the Opera House – and it is no good you say no. First time for you to be out by yourself on towards the night and the streets of London are none too safe. Come on. Yes, let Emlyn take you, Joseph, said Mrs Lloyd. Then pay a shilling for a cab to come home after. Yes, I will, said Joseph. That won't be wasting their money, will it? Waste, indeed, said Mrs Lloyd. If nobody wasted more than you do then it is little would be wasted in this old world – have you got a handkerchief? Yes, said Joseph. And have you got the ticket safe? she said. Joseph felt for it and said: Yes.

Then we had better go for it is a good step from here to the Haymarket, said Mr Lloyd. Wait, said Mrs Lloyd. If he walks in those tight shoes he will be too tired to enjoy himself. Go and find a cab and we will pay there and he shall pay to bring himself back home. Go on, Emlyn – you sit down a minute, Joseph. Off Emlyn went to find a cab and soon returned inside a hansom-cab, if you please. There you are now, said Mrs Lloyd. Off Joseph went with Emlyn in the hansom-cab looking as handsome as any in his borrowed clothes and with his top-hat between his hands on his knees. Mr Lloyd could well afford to pay for the ride in the hansom-cab for he was making more selling milk and eggs and butter and things in his shop not far away from the house than Joseph was ever likely to make out of music.

Mr Lloyd was a nice man all the same. He paid the bare fare to the cabman and put Joseph safe inside the Opera House and then walked all the way back home. Joseph felt very lonely in his seat in the Opera House for they had taken his top-hat and his cape-coat away from him and had given him a ticket for them. He had bought a programme with English and Italian on it and he read the English version of the story of the opera. The names of the cast meant little or nothing to him for there was only their names in Italian. He was in the stalls and the people who filled the stalls talked loud and high English.

'Music by Giuseppe Verdi', he read, and some day, he said to himself, I will write the music for an opera in our Welsh language. The orchestra came from somewhere underneath in ones and twos until they were all there and their scraping and the loud talking of the people in the stalls made enough row between them. The conductor came from somewhere and there was faint applause which he acknowledged with a thank-you-for-nothing nod and a smile. Then ... oh, then. Joseph had never heard anything like it before so he was too appreciative and when the orchestra had finished playing the overture he clapped so hard and loud that people turned to look at him. Joseph blushed and put his hands back down on his lap.

Then the singing and ... He thought he knew her as soon as he saw her and when she started singing he was certain that it was her. To make sure he tried to find her on the programme but he could not because the lights of the auditorium were practically out. So he had to wait until the end of the act before he found her on the programme. 'Lina Van Elyn', said the programme. But I am certain that she is Myfanwy Llewelyn, said Joseph. So do not tell me that it is someone else. The one I mean is the soprano who is the hunchback's daughter in the opera. I know that voice – and wait until the end when I go to talk to her.

Now Joseph was impatient for the end though he thought the last act well worth waiting for. But he wanted to make certain if it was her – I am certain, he said again. As soon as the curtain fell at the end of the last act he hurried out without applauding to get his top-hat and cape-coat back.

Another sixpence to get them back but he did not mind. How do I get round to where the stage is, sir? he asked. The man he had addressed as 'sir' looked surprised and he said: Just for that I will take you around meself, and he took him around and introduced him to the stage doorkeeper as a very nice gentleman. Who do you want to see, me lord? said the stage doorkeeper. Joseph pointed to where it said 'Lina Van Elyn' on the programme and said: I would like to see that lady, sir. Can I have your card, me lord? said the stage doorkeeper. I have no card, sir, said Joseph. Tell her a man from Merthyr – no, better tell her a man from the Royal Academy of Music.

The stage doorkeeper hardly knew what to make of Joseph. He looked like a lord and spoke like a foreigner and called him 'sir'. He stood looking at Joseph and as he looked he rubbed his nose, scratched his head and cleared his throat. Wait here, he said. Royal Academy of Music for the prima donna. We'll see. He presently returned and from the top of a short flight of stairs he beckoned Joseph up and conducted him up another short flight of stairs, across a stage which seemed huge to Joseph and then up another short flight of stairs. He knocked at a door and a voice said: Come in. The stage doorkeeper opened the door and said: The gentlemen from the Royal Academy of Music. Now Joseph was doubly certain that it was her. I knew you as soon as I saw you, he said, then noticed that there was a man and an elderly woman in the room with her. How are you, sir – and how are you, madam? he said. Did I understand that you are from the Royal Academy of Music? said Myfanwy – for we may as well call her by her proper name now. Don't you know me? said Joseph, forgetting the fourteen years between. I certainly do not, she said. The man said something in Italian and she shook her head. Then it must be those glasses, said Joseph, taking them off. Now do you know me?

She sighed impatiently and said: If you are from the

Royal Academy will you please be good enough to tell me what you want? Perhaps it is these clothes I am wearing, said Joseph. No, I know. It is my moustache. I did not have a moustache in Merthyr. Merthyr? she said. Yes, he said, in Rosser Beynon's choir – remember the night we left the concert to walk the roads and you said you would say a prayer to take me safe over the water to America? Oh, the boy, the boy, said Myfanwy. She laughed and said: Go home, boy. Joseph laughed and said: Yes, many times you told me that, didn't you. She took Joseph's hand and whilst holding it she explained in Italian to the man. He and the elderly woman now smiled on Joseph. So little Joseph Parry had grown up, said Myfanwy. But what is this about the Royal Academy? I am there studying for the best part of a year already, said Joseph. Then you are not living in America any more? she said. Yes, I am, he said. That is where I left my wife and two children. It is a long story – Wife and two children, she said. Yes, it must be a long story, and we must have a long talk. How is my dear friend Garcia at the Academy? He is grand – why, do you know him? said Joseph. I should know him after three years under him, she said. But I have yet to change. Will you wait outside with this gentleman until I am ready? Then you shall accompany me to my hotel and tell me all about yourself.

No, no, said Joseph. It is very late and I do not know the way back to where I lodge. So I must go quick to find a cab before they will all be gone. I shall send you home in my carriage after supper and a talk, said Myfanwy. It must be nearly fifteen years – yes, it must be fifteen years since I last saw you. She again spoke in Italian to the man. He smiled and opened the door and said: Pleece. I shall not keep you long, said Myfanwy. Only in lodgings I am, remember, said Joseph, leaving the dressing-room. He waited on the landing with the Italian, a middle-aged man with a pointed moustache and a small beard turning grey. Singers in their street-clothes and talking Italian volubly came down from somewhere above to simmer down and bow and murmur respectfully as passing the man with whom Joseph was waiting on the small landing. So Joseph concluded that the man he was with must be the boss of them all but not Myfanwy's boss. Did you enjoy zee op'ra? he surprised Joseph by asking after a spell of silence. Yes, yes, it was grand, said Joseph. Have you got a watch? Wash? said the man. No, watch – you know, watch to tell the time, said Joseph. Myfanwy came out of the dressing-room followed by the elderly woman carrying a bag and said: Please do not worry about the time, Joseph. Come along.

All four went down the flight of stairs and across the stage and out to where a carriage was waiting near the stage-door. It was a roomy closed carriage and a pair of horses driven by a distinguished-looking man with mutton-chop whiskers took them surely through dark streets to a large hotel. Is this your own carriage and pair, Myfanwy? Joseph asked innocently. She replied in the Merthyr way: Ask me no questions and I'll tell you no lies, then laughed. It is my own each time I come to London, she said. So you did not know that I also studied at the Academy – but how could you? You had gone to America. And you have not been to Merthyr since? Yes, I was there two years ago, said Joseph. Now I come to think of it someone did tell me something about you then. I forget what. It is good to forget most of the time, said Myfanwy.

Yet during supper and after supper she asked Joseph all sorts of questions. They were alone in a sort of lounge, part of the suite occupied by Myfanwy. The Italian man and woman had left them but Myfanwy assured him that the carriage was waiting to take Joseph back to his lodging. Then I must go, said Joseph ever so many times but he was still there talking. About his parents, his wife and two children, his brother and sisters, his two Welsh-American friends and teachers, America, his music, how he swept the board at two National Eisteddfods and how his compositions went on lost on the way to the third – but when did you see Ieuan Ddu last? he asked. I have not seen him for – for five years, I think, she said. I do not go to Wales neither does he come to London. We correspond fairly regularly. I fear that he is a very disappointed man and he is also most depressed since the death of his second wife. I shall never forgive Wales for what it has done to Ieuan Ddu – or rather for what Wales has not done for him. Ieuan Ddu was a great musician who is dying broken-hearted through lack of support and encouragement.

Musicians or whatever we are Wales does what it can for us all, said Joseph. I owe nothing to Wales, said Myfanwy. You owe as much to Ieuan Ddu and Rosser Beynon as I do and they are Wales when all is said and done, said Joseph. But I am bound to go now. What time is it? Only two o'clock, said Myfanwy. Dear me, said Joseph. Two o'clock in the morning! Please don't go, said Myfanwy. But what if the tidy people I am lodging with happen to wake up and look at the time what am I going to tell them? said Joseph. You can tell them that you met an old friend, said Myfanwy. What old friend and me a married man at this hour of the night will I say? said Joseph, getting mixed up. She smiled and said: As a good Christian Welshman you should never have come round to see me, should you? I only wanted to make sure it was you, that's all, said Joseph. Now I know it is you I am content to go knowing that you are a credit to Merthyr and to Wales – and to Ireland, she said flippantly. My mother was Irish. The Irish do not sing as a people any more than the Americans do, he said. It is only the Welsh could have given you what you gave to those people in the Opera House to-night. In my excitement I forgot to tell you that you sang lovely, more lovely than any woman I have ever heard, more lovely than my own mother. To-night before I sleep I will say a prayer for you. In Welsh I will say it. I am going to Merthyr over the Christmas-time. Is there anyone there you would like me to see for you?

No, thank you – oh, yes, there is, she said. Will Full-Moon – I heard him singing with the Cyfarthfa Brass Band when I was last in Merthyr, he said. Will Full-Moon is the man for Wagner, for he can make his voice heard above the Cyfarthfa Brass Band. What shall I tell him for you? I would like you to thank him for me, said Myfanwy. He sees to my father's grave. Goodbye, Joseph. Goodbye, Myfanwy, he said. How long will you be here in London? I return to Italy next week, she said. Opera is not appreciated as it should be here in London. Are you sure the carriage is still waiting outside? said Joseph. Shall we go and see if it is? she said with a smile, taking his arm. Joseph, you really do look handsome. It is these clothes, no doubt, he said, dis-engaging himself. I shall remember this night. Riding in a carriage and pair wearing borrowed clothes. You must be getting a lot of money for singing, Myfanwy, he said as they went down the broad stairway. A fair amount, she said. Are you short of money? No, he said. Why? You referred to your clothes as borrowed, she said. So I thought – well, you should have an evening dress-suit of your own. I will in time, he said. I am sure you will, she said. But now, for old times' sake – Yes, the carriage is here, thank goodness, said Joseph. Goodbye. She held his hand and said: If ever you are in need of money then you need not have to take it from me. I shall be writing Ieuan Ddu about you. Someone sends him a hundred pounds a year for me as a sort of conscience-money. You can draw on that at Pontypridd. And why not? You have taken money from those people in America. That is different, Myfanwy, said Joseph. Will this man know the way to my lodging? He knows his way all over London, she said. Just tell him where it is and he will drive you there. Now go home, boy. They both laughed and she surprised him by saying, in Welsh: Pob llwyddiant, and she surprised him even more when she stood on her toes to kiss him before hurrying back into the hotel. Joseph felt his lips and looked at the impassive man with mutton-chop whiskers who had opened the door of the carriage. Well, well, murmured Joseph. She has not forgot all her Welsh after all. In Welsh she wished me every success. The man with his hand to the handle of the carriage door waited patiently.

Right you are, sir, said Joseph, getting into the carriage. The man slammed the door to and Joseph cried: Hoy. Did I tell you where to take me? You did, sir, said the man. And you are sure you know the way there? said Joseph. Quite sure, sir, said the man. And what is the time now? said Joseph. The man sighed as feeling for his watch and moving with it in his hand to hold it under the light of the carriage-lamp. A quarter past three exactly, sir, he said. Y nefoedd mawr! said Joseph, taking the great heavens in vain for the first time in his life. Go, go as quick as you can for me to have some sleep. The man deliberately pocketed his watch, and as deliberately mounted to his place and took up reins and whip. The horses trotted Joseph homeward and their trotting ran so rhythmical along the hard roads of the empty streets that Joseph forgot Myfanwy as he tried to set the horses' trot to music in his head to put down on paper later. Empty streets, trot of horses against background of rumbling wheels all combined to fascinate him. So he was at his lodging before he knew it. He decided to offer the man the shilling he would have had to pay for a cab from the Opera House, but the man respectfully declined to accept it. You are very welcome to it, sir, said Joseph. The man bowed his head and said: Goodnight, sir. Goodnight, sir, said Joseph, feeling for the key of the door in the tail-pocket of his tail-coat. The horses trotted away and Joseph stood with the key in his hand listening and using the key as a baton until the sound of the trot of the horses had quite died away. Then he unlocked the door and went into the house and locked the door again. The lamp on the table with his supper under the cloth was burning low so he blew it out and tip-toed up-stairs to bed.

Did you enjoy the opera, Joseph? the Principal asked him next day. Very much, thank you, sir, said Joseph. He worked all the better for it anyway and he was that year's bronze medallist. He wore it on his watch-chain, the watch-chain he had been unable to wear with evening dress the night he went to the opera, but he wore it and the medal attached to it to go to Merthyr to spend best part of Christmas week there. Before leaving for Merthyr he had written to tell his wife to come with the two little boys as soon as she liked now. He had arranged for them to stay with him in rooms at a bigger house than the one he was lodging at, the bigger house of another member of the Fetter Lane Welsh chapel, a member who was a draper in a fairly big way.

With that settled Joseph felt better. A man without his wife in a place like London was only half a man, and a half a man continually subject to temptation. Women intercepted and accosted students on their way from the Academy to their lodgings and Joseph had been accosted more than once. But behind the frown he put on there was the ghost of desire, so he felt that the sooner he had Jane with him the better and safer he would be. No amount of work, he found, could place him quite beyond reach of the promptings of his healthy body. So he sent for his Jane, his lovely and most desirable Jane, who did not want pressing to leave Danville for London.

Joseph on his way from London to Merthyr, where he had for weeks been advertised to appear as a singer at two concerts and as an adjudicator at the semi-national Eisteddfod at the Drill Hall. It would mean nine guineas and expenses and nine guineas were very acceptable to him just then. He had been advertised as 'JOSEPH PARRY, R.A.M. (Pencerdd America).' He was confident that he would prove himself worth the three fees of three guineas each and he certainly was full value for the money. A year under Manuel Garcia had made his bass-baritone voice something well worth hearing. He used his voice intelligently and sang with just the right feeling. He sang in both Welsh and English and his most popular number was 'Y Bachgen Dewr' (The Noble Boy of Truth). His adjudications at the Eisteddfod held at the Drill Hall on Boxing Day were given in a manner which enhanced the prestige of the Royal Academy of Music in Merthyr and district.

Of course Joseph went to Bethesda Chapel three times on the Sunday of that Christmas week, but we will not say any more about that. Perhaps we have already talked too much about Bethesda Chapel and too little about other places and people. In trying to keep up with Joseph we have had to hurry past many people including his sister, Ann, and her husband, Robert James. We cannot help ourselves. This Christmas-time Joseph saw the hundreds of children on the way to the Ragged School for their Christmas breakfast and an orange apiece to come away with. He also saw hundreds of poor people going to fetch their Christmas dinners from St David's School, where those of the Church of England faith in Merthyr prepared it for them. He wondered why there were so many poor people and ragged children in his native town and district and he was not the only one to wonder.

This is something worthy of comment, for we are not talking about some sleepy little village, remember, or about a place which in itself is poor. Far from it. We are talking about a town which is the centre of a population of full eighty thousand souls, a place which for nearly a hundred years had been the acknowledged coal and iron capital of the world. So when talking or writing, which is just the same in the long run, we cannot by-pass such a place as this was and still is. You must stop and look at the place. Residentially it is not worth considering. The only bit of substantial housing is, as I have said more than once, in the Thomas Town district of Merthyr. There were also a few biggish houses at Gwaelodygarth and a few more here and there about the town where doctors and others lived, and a few more again on the outskirts of districts where ironworks and colliery managers lived.

The rest of the housing was bad, some bad in the extreme. But there should not have been so many poor people or so many ragged children in the town and district, for in addition to the huge profits unto the fourth generation of ironmasters who were also mine-owners, there had been fairly good wages paid to the men, women and children workers during the century of our development and progress. Good wages for the time, I mean. We had to suffer reductions in our wages when there was a slump in the iron trade, of course, but during the century the slumps were few and far between. There were times when men earned as much as thirty shillings a week! The wages question over a hundred years is too long a story for now but we must say a word about the poor and ragged of the town and district, who had been with us from the very beginning of our industrial development.

Now, in the winter of 1868–9, there were many more such people of course, and that was why we had a Ragged School and Christmas dinners coming from God and handed out at St David's School. Take the Ragged Sunday School first. That was only for children without clothes to go tidy to the other Sunday Schools. It was, amongst us Welsh, an unwritten law that made us try to send our children to Sunday School dressed tidy. If we could not send them tidy then we kept them home and out of sight on Sundays. The people of the English Nonconformist chapels were not as particular as we Welsh in this respect – but that was their business, of course. Then what about the couple of thousand ragged children of the town and district? Little boys with no behinds to their trousers and little girls with only a yard of dirty rag around them? That is where the Ragged Sunday School came in and said: Never mind how ragged or how dirty you are, come you to the Ragged Sunday School and qualify for the big treat we give each and every Christmas morning. The Ragged Sunday School did not say that the more ragged you are the better we like you, but they seemed to imply as much. The teachers at the Ragged Sunday School were all good people and the Superintendent always brought some well-born and rich people to see those teachers waiting on those hundreds of ragged children on Christmas morning. Once Lady Charlotte Guest came and said: Yes, a splendid work you are doing. That was the Christmas she left the place for good to get married to Charlie Schreiber, Esq., M.P.

Then the hundreds of poor people lining up for Christmas dinners. Some of those poor people need not have been any the poorer than you or me. Others, such as widows and cripples, of which there were plenty in the town and district, were worthy objects of charity, having been widowed and crippled by the development of our great industries. In receipt of little or no compensation the least we could do was to remember them at Christmas-time, they and the score or so broken veterans of the Russian War were most deserving people. We had two cannon which had served in the Russian War outside St David's Church to remind us of our debt to those broken veterans. But those others who spent their money on drink instead of clothing themselves and feeding themselves and their wives and families – what can we say about them?

Two hundred and odd public-houses and from twenty to thirty pawnbrokers knew something about those people. Mr H. A. Bruce, M.P., in one of his lectures at the Merthyr Library, referred to a book in which some great writer described what pangs in hell some people suffered for what they had done to people whilst on earth, and no doubt some of our pawnbrokers have been frying in hell ever since they left our town and district. Many of the landlords of our public-houses may still be undying frizzlers on the grids of hell, but more sure of hell and all its torments than either our pawnbrokers or landlords are those Welshmen who deliberately extended and deepened the poverty of the people of our town and district. A word about these chaps and then we will get on with our story. They were what you might call 'middle-men' between the employers and the workers. Sub-contractors, gangers, leading-hands – call them what you like. It was they that paid thousands of men their wages, the 'big pay' once a month. For three weeks they gave the workers what you might call 'a sub', then on the fourth Saturday the monthly settlement, the 'big pay'. But the word 'big' was just a bad joke for thousands. Those jovial chaps paid out only in public-houses, in which workers sometimes had to wait an hour or two in their working-clothes and dirt before the jovial paymasters came with the gold in one bag, silver in another and coppers in yet another. By the time they came the workers-in-waiting had been obliged by the most obliging landlord or landlady with about a half-dozen pints of strong beer on the credit system, also an ounce of tobacco, with a new clay pipe free of charge. So they were as happy as could be and as free-and-easy as one could wish by the time the paymasters arrived. The first thing they did on arrival was to call upon everyone present to drink up and have one with them. Is every one served, landlord? Yes, everyone present is served. Then my very best respects to you all, said the paymaster. Listen, landlord. There are no better workmen than these chaps in this or any other valley – drink up, boys.

After a little friendly conversation he would pay them one by one and one by one they would settle-up with the landlord, who, after they had all settled-up with him would insist that they should have another pint with him. Many of them left those public-houses with hardly enough to get their clothes out of the pawnshop let alone keep their wives and children for the week. The paymasters rarely took too much drink for there was another settling-up in private between them and the landlords of the public-houses into which the paymasters herded those workers Saturday after Saturday. Other nights those workers drifted in to the public-houses in ones and twos to find the landlords just as obliging, but the paymasters only appeared there with them on Saturdays, when they insisted on every one of their chaps 'paying-up like men'. Some of those paymasters who paid our workers in public-houses went to chapel and some of them died leaving money behind. But if there is a hell – and the man who wrote the book referred to by Mr Bruce, M.P., said there was, didn't he? – then those paymasters of ours are certainly having a hell of a bad time there now. Pity? No, no pity.

Back to London Joseph went and to London his wife, Jane, came with their two little boys. We have been so busy talking about Joseph that we have said very little about Jane, his wife. Better say something about her for she was a remarkable woman and most ladylike into the bargain. Her father was Gomer Thomas and her brother was named Gomer after his father, and we could say a lot about the two Gomers, for they made their contribution to the development of America, remember. But we must stick to our story and only talk about those more closely related to Joseph. I may have to say something about the contribution of Welsh people to the development of America later but here and now let us consider Jane Parry, Joseph's wife, for a moment. For the first year Joseph was in London she and the two little boys were in Danville in Pennsylvania, where she and her mother-in-law, Betty Parry, had been having words in a nice-nasty way about the two little boys, J. Haydn Parry and D. Mendelssohn Parry. Betty, their grandmother, talking Welsh to them all the time, and Jane, their mother, talking English to them. Not a word of English would Betty talk to the little boys or hear from them, and hardly a word of Welsh did they hear from their mother.

Silly, perhaps, but Betty Parry was funny that way. Still,

she had her way with the two little boys who, when they arrived in London, could speak better Welsh than their mother could. She had barely enough for conversational purposes, a little Welsh thrown into a well of far from pure English as you might say. As such it was acceptable to the Welsh of London, who like the Welsh seasoned with high English words and phrases for conversational purposes. But they want the Welsh pure and undefiled from the London-Welsh and visiting preachers. So Jane Parry got on very well indeed with the London-Welsh. She was a good wife and mother and a good-looking woman into the bargain. She was not amongst the best workers of the women who attended the Welsh chapel in Fetter Lane but she was there twice most Sundays and she sent the two little boys to Sunday School as well. There they built on the Welsh foundation their grandmother had laid in them. After a time Jane took them to Sunday School in a cab and called and took them home in a cab as money became more plentiful. They lived comfortably at the big house of the up-and-coming Welsh draper, whose wife had not brought him any children. So the Parrys had the house to themselves most of the time, Mr and Mrs Evans being away at the shop from early morning during the week. Only on Sundays were they home and in the company of their paying-guests from America. They had a piano which was a great help to Joseph in his studies.

Jane was also a great help to Joseph in another way, giving him lessons in deportment, you might say, and helping him to rid himself of the Welsh way of speaking English, which is on the backward side at times. Joseph was in a metamorphic state, in the throes of a mental transformation from thinking in Welsh to thinking in English, and this is where Jane helped him by talking her best English to him when he came home to her from the Academy at night. Before she came it was Welsh only he heard at night at his lodging and he would start thinking in Welsh again after having been taught in the English all the day. It was confusing for him then but now Jane was continuing each night the English momentum of each day. So she was most helpful and he was getting to speak English very nicely. Then she looked after his clothes and turned him out as well-dressed as any of the other and much younger students at the Academy. She insisted on his buying an evening dress-suit. She also read aloud to him from English books at night when his eyes were tired. She also insisted on his coming home to a proper lunch each day, so, between everything he was, sartorially, physically and mentally, getting to be a credit to her.

Yes, and a credit to everyone concerned. For this year he won the silver medal, which was presented to him by Mrs Gladstone, who was a Welsh woman herself. Miss Glynne she was before she married Mr Gladstone, remember. That was a proud day for Joseph and an even prouder day for Jane, who was told by Mrs Gladstone that she had a husband to be proud of. So now Joseph had two R.A.M. medals on his watch-chain and with them and his wife and two children he went to Merthyr this Christmas-time again to sing and adjudicate at higher fees. Fifteen guineas in all he earned over Christmas-time at Merthyr this year, and he spoke more authoritatively when delivering his adjudications at the Eisteddfod at the Drill Hall. He also sang much better and sang more English than Welsh songs at the two concerts. He took pleasure in taking his wife and two children to the house where he was born and to many of the scenes of his childhood and boyhood, but she was only mildly interested. Men should think twice before taking their wives to the scenes of their childhood and boyhood, particularly when those scenes are on the poverty-stricken side and smelling a bit strong here and there. Wives do not want to see all the places where their husbands went with their mothers. But Jane was very nice about it all.

Back to London they went and after another year's hard

228

work Joseph took his degree of Mus.Bac. at Cambridge. Pretty good, you know, when you come to think of it. Anyway, I must leave it to speak for itself for I have to go to a funeral at Pontypridd. Plenty of talk there was when Charles Dickens passed away on the 9th of June but little talk there was when Ieuan Ddu passed away at Pontypridd the June following. But he was more to us Welsh people than Charles Dickens or any other famous Englishman. For fifty years he laboured for us and for music and little thanks he had from us. But it was he that well and truly laid the foundation of choral singing in Wales. So when next you hear a Welsh choir singing as only a Welsh choir can just think of John Thomas, better known as Ieuan Ddu, will you?

I have seen many a bigger funeral than his but there were quite a number of musical people present. Will Full-Moon was there looking very sad and gone as thin as any lamppost. Nothing like the man he was when he took drink. I was told that he was singing as well as ever but without much of the old fire. Well, I said, the man must be getting on. I remember him singing in Merthyr ... let's see now. Yes, thirty years ago if not before. Myfanwy came from somewhere to Pontypridd, a little over-dressed in black, we thought, but she did not follow the coffin to the Glantaf Cemetery like the rest of us did. She wore a veil so I could not tell whether she was crying or not. She was stood talking to Will Full-Moon whilst we were waiting for the coffin to be brought out of the house and put into the hearse, so I did not have a chance to talk to her. But I had a word with Will Full-Moon as he and I walked together away from the graveside.

That is the end of poor old Ieuan again, I said pleasantly to start the conversation. Yes, great man, said Will, wiping the tears from his eyes. He was great, I said. Wasn't that Myfanwy Llewelyn I saw you talking to whilst we were waiting for the funeral to rise? Yes, he said. I am hurrying to catch the train to go up as far as Merthyr with her. She wants to see her father's grave and the stone I had put at the head of it before going back to London. Is that where she is now then? I said. No, from Paris she came to London and up here for the funeral, he said. In Paris she is singing just now and she has to be back there to sing the night after to-morrow night. That girl is singing all over the world, I said. This place is growing too. I remember when Pontypridd – What would you say if I told you that I am leaving Merthyr to go with an opera company? he said. What opera company are you talking about? I said. The Carl Rosa, he said. Temperance and holy words are killing me. You *have* gone thin, I said. I am gone till I am nothing but skin and bone, he said. Beer is the only thing to build my body up again and beer my body shall have no matter what anyone says. To-night after I put Myfanwy on the last train out of Merthyr I will drink until I am drunk. I am saying that now in my sober senses and after years of most agonizing abstinence. So you will know when you hear that I have broken out. Well, I said, you *have* gone thin. Are you coming up to Merthyr with this train? he said. No, I said. Next train will do me. Remember me to Myfanwy.

He went across the road to the railway station and I went on down Taff Street. Yes, the place was growing and some who lived there said that Pontypridd was now the greatest mining centre the world over. Nonsense, I said, and this man said: Nonsense, is it? Half a minute now – do you take a glass of beer? Yes, but no more than a glass – a pint at most, I said. Then come on in here, he said. Been to a funeral by the look of you. Where do you come from? Merthyr is where I was born, I said. Two pints, he said to the landlord. Oh, Merthyr, is it? Well, there you are. All the coal and iron from Merthyr has to come through here – Drink up. Good health, I said, and after I had drunk I said: Not a bad drop of beer. But leaving Merthyr out, he said. Take the other valleys whose coal and iron comes down through here without touching Merthyr. You in Merthyr will soon be left high and dry. Never, I said. You wait, he said. But as for us in Pontypridd – well, we are able to attract people from half-a-dozen valleys that Merthyr cannot touch. Have you been up in the Rhondda Valley lately? No, I said. And when were you last up through the Aberdare Valley? he said. I have never been through the Valley, I said, but I have walked the mountain from Merthyr to Aberdare. Then how can you know? said the man. Aberdare is only one of a dozen places in the Aberdare Valley and everything produced there comes through Pontypridd. Same with the Rhondda Valley and the places opening up to the west. Pontypridd is the natural centre for all those valleys. Nearly a million tons of coal coming through here every year now, man. I think I will have another half-pint – but you have a pint, of course, I said. I do not drink with men who drink half-pints, he said. Then fill these two pints please, I said to the landlord.

This chap kept on bouncing about Pontypridd which he would have was the greatest mining centre in the world. So I left him in the public-house and went to catch the next train up to Merthyr. The platform of the railway station is up high and from there I could see for myself how the place had grown. There was another bridge across the River Taff, I could now see, and there were houses climbing up the hillsides. Most of the houses were on the hill called 'Y Graig', and I was forced to admit to myself that there was something in what the chap had said about Pontypridd being the greatest mining centre in the world. Whether or no it had done no more for Ieuan Ddu than Merthyr had done. Me and my father before me had bounced about Merthyr being the coal and iron capital of the world, yet it was little Merthyr had done for the great man whose body we had buried this day. At Pontypridd we had buried him, Pontypridd the great mining centre, through which the coal of a half-dozen valleys went day and night, night and day. Yet Pontypridd had failed to honour a great man in John

Thomas, better known as Ieuan Ddu. All he had from all of us was a bit of a stone at the head of his grave in Glantaf Cemetery, and on that stone was written these words:

In Memory of John Thomas (Ieuan Ddu),
Who died June 30th, 1871.   Aged 74.

The stone went on to say to us the stony-hearted and un-appreciative:

Possessed of great and varied abilities, and extensive information upon more than one science, his genius shone pre-eminently as a musical composer and –

Never mind the rest. We were not worthy of him and that is the long and short and the shame of it. It was we, the Welsh, that disappointed and failed him. Now we had only the memory of him and of that we might yet prove worthy. I was fast asleep when the train got to Merthyr and it was a railwayman that woke me up.

CHAPTER 10

Welsh-American Welcome

It has been said by a United States Senator, Senator John Sharp Williams of Mississippi, and the *Congressional Record* will bear me out that he said that no nation in proportion to its size had contributed more to the development of the United States than had the Welsh. That is on record. In-dustry, agriculture, religion, music – and this is where Joseph comes in. For he is on his way back to America, with two Royal Academy medals on his watch-chain and his Cambridge degree in Latin writing. He organizes and sings at two concerts on the ship named *The City of Berlin*, and he speaks both Welsh and English fluently and with authority on matters musical. He and his wife and two boys are very popular with passengers and crew and they sit at the Captain's table for meals. Good weather and the crossing only takes nine days. Joseph is bubbling over all the time except when he simmers down and goes to hide for long enough to put down on paper two little songs that came to his head.

The Welsh of the city of New York wanted him to stay for a great 'Welcome Home' gathering they only wanted twenty-four hours to organize. Yes, do stay for it, said the friends of the English Presbyterian Church of New York. No, but I promise to come back to New York as soon as I have seen my people at Danville, said Joseph. So the New York Welsh had to be satisfied with that promise. A crowd of them accompanied Joseph and his wife and children down to the railway station after the reception at the hotel kept by Eleazar Jones. Jane was presented with flowers and suitable gifts were made to the two little boys. The train left to the accompaniment of singing in Welsh and when the party reached Danville in Pennsylvania they were lifted out of the coach and carried some distance to the first of a line of carriages and conveyances of all sorts. The telegram which Joseph had sent as soon as the ship reached New York had set things moving immediately. The ironworkers asked for and were granted a holiday to meet the one who had worked in the rolling-mill and who was now one of the bachelors of music of one of the two oldest and greatest Universities of Britain. I am the first Welshman to get that degree at Cambridge, said Joseph in the course of his speech at the dinner given in his honour. The first Welsh-*American*, Joseph, John Price said from his place at the top table. I stand corrected, and rightly so, by my friend and one-time teacher, said Joseph. The first Welsh-American. It was the Welsh of America that made it possible for me to study over there in London, and, as soon as it can be arranged, I am going to as many places, to meet as many friends as possible, and to thank them for making me what I am. The credit is more theirs than mine. Seated here with me this evening are my dear parents, my brother and my sisters and my sister-in-law and brothers-in-law – and let me tell you something. I shall have to look to my laurels. My brother Henry is composing – seriously now, is composing music which I would be proud to claim as my own work. He chuckled. Then those two boys of mine. He smiled on them but they did not smile back at him. Sitting one each side of their granny they were very bored with all the talking that they had had to listen to. Yes, those two boys of mine are already thinking of a musical career. So I shall not suffer through lack of competition in my own household – and in my own family. But such joking is out of place at this gathering. I will not try to thank my dear mother or my dear wife. They know what my heart is saying – and so does my dear father. Then what can I say to my two friends and teachers, John Abel Jones and John Price? It goes without saying, my friends. I have spoken in English out of respect to the English friends present and my friends of other nationalities who understand English but not Welsh. I am sure that those friends will now forgive me if I address myself in our ancient language to the friends who are Welsh like myself.

He began all over again in Welsh and his two sons leaned their heads against their granny and sighed audibly. Sit up and listen to your father speaking Welsh for a change, she whispered. It was a grand reunion. A week later Joseph went on tour, a tour which commenced at New York, a concert tour during which he sang and played and spoke at a hundred and three concerts. Through the States of New York, Illinois, Wisconsin, Ohio, Iowa, Minnesota, Tennessee, Kentucky, Virginia and Pennsylvania. He returned thanks to all the friends who had helped to make it possible for him to achieve what he had achieved and he advertised the fact that he was soon to open a Musical Institute in Danville, Pennsylvania. Triumphantly he went through State after State to demonstrate how worthy he had proved himself of

234

the confidence and support of the Welsh of America. His net earnings during that tour were considerable, averaging about twenty dollars per concert. This, of course, was trifling compared to the average per reading of the late Charles Dickens during his farewell tour of America. His readings were not 'penny readings'. Oh, no. The late Mr Dickens averaged about three hundred pounds gross per reading whilst in America, so Joseph, who knew this, did not think he was asking too much when he asked for twenty dollars and expenses per concert.

At a chapel in Youngstown he met an itinerant Welsh preacher who was preaching in Welsh for just enough to keep himself and his boy going. He and his boy stood in dusty clothes listening to Joseph singing. The boy would be about ten or eleven years old and the father anything from forty to fifty. Joseph in his evening dress-suit was acknowledging the loud applause and the preacher and the boy stood listening but not applauding. The preacher and the boy were waiting for the man who had promised to put them up at his house for the night. Judge Lewis had also promised to put Joseph and Jane up for the night after the concert and it was at his house that Joseph was introduced to the itinerant Welsh preacher. Hughes, said Joseph. Have you a brother living in Utica? No, said the preacher. Well, there's a William Hughes who resembles you very much living there, said Joseph, turning to smile on the good-looking but serious boy. And is this your boy? Yes, said the preacher. I have two boys – but not as old as this one, said Joseph. What is your name, my boy? Charles Evans Hughes, said the boy. H'm, Evans after your mother, no doubt – is he musically inclined? Joseph asked the father. He sings alto very well, said Judge Lewis. About the right age to take up music, said Joseph. I am hoping to have a Musical Institute going soon at Danville, Pennsylvania – So you said at the chapel, the preacher reminded him. Yes, said Joseph, and I shall be accepting pupils in voice-training, the organ

235

and advanced pupils in composition. It is what we have been wanting, said Judge Lewis. If you will excuse us we will go to bed, Judge, said the preacher. Certainly, certainly, said the Judge. After the preacher and his boy had left the room Judge Lewis said: Not a very jovial man but a very good preacher. Got no chapel of his own, won't take one. On the tramp everywhere and that boy with him. Very independent too. Did you ever go to the Law Courts when in London? No, said Joseph. For me it was work all the time I was there. This travelling about is very tiring. My wife stands it better than I do. She has only got to sit and listen, said the Judge with a smile. Which does not get easier, Judge, said Jane with a smile. That is one for you, Professor, said the Judge. A little joking and a little talking and then to bed. H'm, Professor, said Joseph as he was getting into bed. What? said Jane. The Judge addressing me as Professor, said Joseph. I like Professor.

So it was 'Professor Parry's Musical Institute' at Danville, and it was a fairly good place for the youngsters who attended there, though Joseph was not yet what can be called a good teacher. How could he be? He went on composing, conducting a choir, playing the organ in chapel and went about to different places adjudicating and performing. He had developed a taste for going about and that is not helpful in the case of the head of a Musical Institute. His lessons were like bran-tubs out of which his students got what they could. There was much that was good in these 'bran-tub' lectures but the students had to do the sorting-out. The students were keen and they were inspired to work hard merely by the physical presence of one who had returned from London with the greatest honour possible after three years' hard work. This Musical Institute started by Joseph might well have developed into the American Academy of Music had it been persevered with, but never mind that now. We will leave it as it is for the moment, for there is a terrible state of affairs at Merthyr across the water.

The ironworkers and miners of Merthyr and district have struck work and they have been idle for two months already and they looked like staying out for another two months. It is no use going into detail or trying to trace the cause of the strike which rendered idle one of the greatest iron- and coal-producing centres the world over. There were ever so many contributing factors, some of which I have mentioned. Two months ago the men just boiled over, that's all, and now they are with their families next-door to starvation. But they are still firm in their demands for better wages and conditions. To see the men on the streets was enough to break your heart and to see the women and children was worse. It was an awful time and '73 will be long remembered in the town and district of Merthyr.

Think what it must have meant for the mass of the people without a penny coming from anywhere. People don't deprive themselves of wages and purchasing-power for the fun of the thing. They certainly were not lazy, but they were certainly bitter. Only about one in a hundred could put into words their grievances but each and every man felt those grievances deep in his heart. The men of coal and iron came together and stuck together for the first time in the hundred and odd years of the industrial history of the town and district. Very few had savings to fall back on and there was no strike pay, but they stuck together in '73. Tidy chapel men side by side with men who had never gone to chapel sticking together. Upwards of twenty thousand workers tightening their belts and women their apron-strings, for there must be an end of brutal exploitation.

We have already said enough about this but who has listened? Men are men and the least we can expect is that they should be treated as such. We were civilized in '73, so they said. Well, then. Live and let live. We were prepared to live in the middle of all the dirt of the works and the pits and make the best of it if only we were allowed to earn enough to live on like human beings should live. True it is that half of us drank beer and spent money on beer, but is that the reason why we should be exploited as we were? Did not the famous Dr Johnson say that he remembered 'when all the *decent* people in Lichfield got drunk every night, and were not the worse thought of. Ale was cheap ...'?

Anyway, the good, bad and indifferent had pooled their bitterness and were standing firm in this third month of the strike. There was a rumour to the effect that the Plymouth Ironworks would never start again but most of us took that with a pinch of salt, as just another bosses' trick which had been played in the hope that it would make us give in. People all over Britain read about our strike in their newspapers and so did the Welsh of America read about it in their own newspaper, *Y Drych*, and in the *Merthyr Express*, which many Welsh-Americans received weekly and only about three weeks late. Betty Parry sighed when she read in the *Merthyr Express* how the women and children were suffering in the bloodless war for bread. We are lucky to be in America, she said to Daniel. Better go and see if Joseph and Jane want anything done before going to bed. I won't be long.

Joseph's two boys were sleeping at their granny's for a week, and perhaps two, and they were enjoying the change, as most boys of their age do when living and sleeping at their granny's. Betty was taking advantage of the opportunity to cram them with Welsh talk without a word of English. The boys had seen the new baby, your little sister, said Joseph. Do you like her? The boys nodded but did not say yes or no. She was there in the big bed with their mother and she did not open her eyes to look at them. So they just looked at her critically until their granny said: Off you go to play now. They did not need to be told twice. They were growing and they were in and out of their father's Musical Institute all the time. For there was a piano as well as the organ there now and there were big boys and girls from a dozen States having schooling in music there. Big boys and girls whose homes were far away and they gave the Professor's two boys candy and things. I can play a tune on the organ, J. Haydn Parry would say on the days when their father was away elsewhere. And I can, said D. Mendelssohn Parry. Then the big boys and girls who had come there from far away would listen to the two Parry boys playing little tunes on the organ and afterwards invited them to try it on the piano. But they could not make the piano play as well as the organ.

They were at the Musical Institute the afternoon the new baby came and it was there their granny found them. Your father is home, she said. He have brought you a little sister. To-night you will sleep in my house. Come there now to have food before your father comes and catches you here at that organ. So the two boys that were growing so quick went with their granny, Betty Parry. She had eight grandchildren in all, nine with this new baby Jane had just brought. Her five children married, one on the Welsh side of the water and four on the American side. To keep half of them Welsh was as much as a woman could do. With five children married a woman had to be careful for when she pleased the one she more often than not offended the others. One son-in-law and one daughter-in-law without a word of Welsh between them – and that was what the world was coming to. What would the world and America in particular be like if everyone in America and the rest of the world left the ancient Welsh language die through want of mouths to talk it? Well, not on her the shame would be. She would take pleasure in doing her duty by her Welsh language to the end.

So she was glad to have Joseph and Jane's two boys with her for the week or two Jane was getting over her confinement. She would give the two boys who heard little Welsh from their mother a short refresher course in the ancient language. If only the Welsh chapels of America, nearly four hundred all told, stood firm against time and space and the Irish and all the other foreigners who were coming from everywhere then the Welsh language would hold its ground and perhaps gain ground in America. But the Welsh chapels were not standing firm, more was the pity. How many times had she protested against the growing Anglicization of Welsh sermons in the Welsh chapels of America? Scores if not hundreds of times. Welsh preachers who ought to know better to their shame pandering to those who had let their Welsh go. Welsh preachers translating parts of their sermons into English for the benefit of the lazy, indifferent and disloyal people of Welsh origin. Next they would be translating our old Welsh hymns into the English and that would be the end, the end of everything as far as Betty Parry was concerned. Then it would be time for her to die and go where Welsh and only Welsh was spoken, in that part of the other and better world where all good Welsh people went to. She had grown to like America and she no longer felt the 'hiraeth', that intense longing for Wales that she used to feel. In Wales itself the Welsh people and the Welsh language would have a harder fight as time went on. And no doubt there would be strike after strike now that the people over there had started to fight for their lives against their English masters. No, she said to Daniel, no, I do not want to go back to Wales ever. Let who will go back there. I am staying the rest of my days here in America. You were right, Daniel. No castles or stinking places here in America – not yet anyway. Place to sleep and good food we have got and plenty of work you have got. But keep Wales in our hearts we must all the time and Welsh talk in our mouths. Not give up like Samuel Roberts in Tennessee or follow Michael Jones to Patagonia. I am content where I am, said Daniel. If only our children and our children's children will stick to their Welsh I shall be more than content, said Betty. Daniel shook his head. I do go to the ironworks to my work every day, he said, and there amongst those I work with it is America and not Wales that is first, Betty. It is no good you or anyone else try to make a Wales that will live here in America. We, the Irish and English, the Germans and

Swedes and all the rest came here to make America, Betty. We can stay Welsh and make America, said Betty obstinately. No, never, said Daniel.

So they talked, talked the way people who are getting on do talk when all their children have left them for homes of their own. People must talk about something when they are getting on and their children all married. Henry was still working at the ironworks and studying at home and at Joseph's Musical Institute. Some nights when Joseph was away adjudicating Henry would take the students and prove himself a better teacher up to a point than Joseph was. Then one day Joseph received a letter which made his heart jump with joy. After he had read it he ran with it to his mother and that evening there was a family conference. Before going there perhaps it would be better to go to where the letter started from, to Aberystwyth in Wales, a clean little place in Cardigan County, a place quite near the sea, which is lovely and clean at Aberystwyth. Now let me tell you.

For years people had been talking about Wales not having a University of any sort in which young Welsh people could get what is called 'higher education'. This is a long story but I will cut it short, come you. England had Universities and Scotland had Universities and Ireland had Universities. Only we in Wales were without one. No good crying shame, better keep on trying to start one, people said. Many English people living in Wales, fair play to them, wanted to help Wales to start a Welsh University. H. A. Bruce, M.P., the Home Secretary up to last year, when he was made Lord Aberdare, was ready and willing to help. But then we were such a small people numerically in Wales, only about two million of us all told left in Wales, and if the truth were known I don't suppose that many more than half of that two million were real Welsh. Never mind, we were as much entitled to a University of our own as any of the other nations of the United Kingdom. We were a nation and a people, remember, the population figures notwithstanding. And we wanted Welshmen trained so that they could teach in our schools as well as any Englishman. But no more of that.

To start a University you must first have a college, and if it is a Welsh University you are starting then the college must be built somewhere about the middle of Wales. That is why our mother college by the sea was put up at Aberystwyth, which is somewhere near the middle of Wales. As I said it is a long story. Many a man now long forgotten worked hard to bring that college into being. Of the hundreds of preachers, educationists and writers and others I will mention only one. Many of us still remember John Griffith, who was an enthusiast for better education for Wales to the end of every hair of his whiskers. He was better known in Wales as 'Y Gohebydd', the London and world correspondent of the *Banner and Times of Wales*. There is a lot which could be said about John and to his credit, but we must get on with our story. He strode along London's streets with Celtic pride and along the corridors of the House of Commons as though he was running the place. His letters and despatches to his paper were widely read throughout Wales and by the London-Welsh and the Welsh of America. He was not a teetotaller.

I said I was going to mention only one in this connexion but I must say something about Henry Richard, M.P., member for Merthyr but regarded as the member for Wales. I may have said that it was he that defeated Mr H. A. Bruce, who was also a good man, in the general election of ... let me think. Was it in 1868? I know it was in the latter part of the 'sixties, for if you remember Mr Bruce went to stand for Renfrewshire and was returned for Renfrewshire about that time. Anyway, since that time Henry Richard, who was the better of the two as far as Wales was concerned, had worked with all his might – and he not in very good health – to have a Welsh University started.

When you come to think of it – having to wait until this time for the first college of the Welsh University is enough to make a man say things. Welshmen had started colleges and Universities in America – I will mention only two of them, Elihu Yale who did most to start the College named after him in New Haven and it was Morgan Edwards who founded Rhode Island College. Yet here were we in Wales without a college until now, on towards the middle of the eighteen-seventies! Still, better late than never, and lo and behold Joseph Parry was invited to leave America and come back to Wales to take charge of the music department of the College – with a capital C now that it is an established fact. Yes, go, said the majority. No, stay, said the minority at the family conference. Betty had not said anything either way so Joseph asked: What do you think, mam? She looked first at him and from him to his wife, then looked around at her other three children, her daughter-in-law and her two sons-in-law and at all their children. All of them looked at her and waited for her to speak.

Well, she said at last, a great honour it is for you no doubt. How long is it since we came here, Daniel? Twenty years and me by myself a year before you, said Daniel. H'm, said Betty. Yes, a long time. Yes, indeed. Well, Joseph, I am of the same mind as your father – I am not, said Jane, in English. So you said before, my gel, but I am talking now, said Betty, in Welsh. You do understand Welsh quick when you have a mind to, Jane. But I am talking now, remember. Say again I will that I am of the same mind as your father, Joseph. You are getting on here in America, where you have been helped to make yourself what you are. You are fond of running about, Joseph. Here in America there is room for you to run, but little room there is in Wales. Three years you have had your Institute here and with Henry to help you something big you will make of it in time. If it is a bigger place and a bigger Institute you want then go to Pittsburg or Philadelphia.

Those you are teaching here will follow you to either of those two places and give you a good start. If I was told I had to give one of you back to Wales then it is you would be the best I could give. But I am afraid for you, Joseph. I am not, said Jane, in English. There you are, said Betty, in Welsh. Now it is for you to do what you yourself think best, Joseph. One word, said Daniel. Our Joseph no doubt is the best man for the music they could find to start the College in Wales. But more musicians there are in Wales than here in America, which is now my country whatever the rest of you think. There are thousands and thousands of miles here without music and millions and millions of people the same. So stay and give your music to the people here, Joseph. Well, said Joseph. Well ... He looked at Jane, his wife. Perhaps after I have slept I will know better what to do.

He slept with Jane, his wife, and in less than a month she and the children were on the way to New York with Joseph. This was Joseph's sixth crossing and *The City of Brooklyn* did it in record time. A splendid crossing and they reached Liverpool just in time for Joseph to go and adjudicate at our National Eisteddfod, which was being held at Bangor in North Wales that year. The National Eisteddfod Committee had been informed that Joseph was on his way across on *The City of Brooklyn* so the invitation was handed to him by messenger who was waiting at the foot of the gangway calling out 'Professor Joseph Parry, Professor Joseph Parry ...' Joseph and his family went direct to Bangor, where the Secretary of the National Eisteddfod Committee found them excellent accommodation for the whole week, crowded with visitors though the place was. Now aren't you glad that you decided as you did? said Jane. Indeed I am, said Joseph.

He had a wonderful reception at the Eisteddfod, where he was introduced to the huge audience as 'Professor Joseph Parry, Mus.Bac., Cambridge, now Head of the Music Department of the University College, Aberystwyth'.

There were at least ten thousand people present at that afternoon session on the second day of the National Eisteddfod at Bangor in North Wales that year and every one of them stood up to welcome Joseph Parry back to Wales. It was a great thrill for him and his family, but what I did not like was the Arweinydd's words in English in the middle of his introduction of Joseph in Welsh. 'Music Department', he said as though the University College of Wales at Aberystwyth was some sort of general store. Music 'Section' would have been better but Music anything would have been better than 'Department'. Never mind. Call it what you like it was delightfully situated in the College by the sea.

Perhaps you know Aberystwyth? Joseph and his wife and the children, particularly the children, were settling down there nicely and I would have stayed there longer but I went back down to Merthyr, and Joseph came with me, to attend Rosser Beynon's funeral. There are times when we have to go to one funeral after the other and there are some funerals one is not bound to attend. But when a man and a musician and a conductor like Rosser Beynon dies then one must make an effort to attend. It was the first time I had been in the new cemetery up there in the Cefn and there must have been a thousand of us following his body and singing all the way through Merthyr and up to the Cefn. Many of us were feeling more bitter than sad, for the man who had done so much for music had had to work down a wet mine up to a month before he died of bronchitis and pleurisy. Now there were a thousand of us combining to give him what in Wales is called 'a grand funeral', slow march and funeral hymns and the procession like a huge and long black snake in travail. Rosser Beynon's few books had been sold periodically during his lifetime when there was no money to buy food with. For forty-five years he suffered us and tried to inspire us and we kept him on the short end of the poverty-line most of the time. Now we were giving him a grand funeral. What good me say now that he should have

245

left us and the town and district of Merthyr when he had more than one chance to go elsewhere and better himself?

Now, of course, the whole town and district was uneasy if not conscience-stricken. So we hurried up a Memorial Eisteddfod at the Drill Hall to make enough money to put a stone at the head of his grave. Of course, I know that we were hardly ever in a position to do much for each other or for our great men – the miners of Merthyr have only just been allowed to return to work after having been locked out for twenty-two weeks. Oh, yes, the bosses paid us out for having gone on strike in '73. Now the miners and the ironworkers are getting themselves organized and perhaps the day will come when the bosses will be locked out of everywhere by those they are so fond of locking out now. But still we could have done more than we did – which was nothing – for Rosser Beynon. Here was Joseph Parry walking beside me at Rosser's funeral, Joseph wearing a top-hat and a frock-coat and carrying a rolled umbrella for fear it would rain. Professor Joseph Parry, Mus.Bac., Cambridge – and who was it that took him into the choir when a boy? Rosser Beynon. Who was it that let him attend choir-practice in his pit-clothes more than once? Rosser Beynon. Who was it that took that girl over when Ieuan Ddu left Merthyr for Pontypridd? Myfanwy Llewelyn, I mean, the one who now calls herself Lina Van Elyn and who, strangely enough, was on the way to America when Joseph Parry was on his way from America to take up his new duties at the University College at Aberystwyth. She has a manager and a maid and her professional name in the newspapers and on playbills and programmes, but what has Rosser Beynon got? His death of bronchitis and pleurisy by working in a wet mine.

Joseph Parry cried whilst standing at the graveside and so did others who were there, but what is the use of shedding tears after you have killed a great man? Never mind. Perhaps as we grow more educated men like Rosser Beynon will be honoured and appreciated more so than he was during his lifetime. I shared a cab with Joseph Parry from Cefn Cemetery back down into Merthyr and more than once he said: Poor old Rosser. Once he said: Dear old Rosser. Quite a number of graves in that new cemetery already. Yes, I said. Are you staying over Sunday or are you taking the train back to Aberystwyth in the morning? Oh, I must get back as soon as possible, he said. I am single-handed up there and when I am from there then my students do not know what to do. Are you composing much now? I said. Yes, yes, quite a lot, he said. But my work at the College takes up most of my time. I have more students than the Department can accommodate, including three from America. How do you like living up there in Aberystwyth? I said. Well, he said, as I told you when you were there, quiet it is, particularly in the winter. Then the people of the place – well, Cardies they are when all is said and done. What is wrong with a good Cardiganshire man? I said. Nothing, he said, but in Aberystwyth they are not all good Cardiganshire men. They are neither town nor country people. After the summer visitors have left they take a stock and fall into a state of coma and there they are till the following summer. I wish they had built the College in South Wales. It is down here most of the people live after all. Yes, I said.

The cab stopped on Pontmorlais Square and I got out and felt for my purse. No, no, I will pay, said Joseph, who was going on down as far as the *Merthyr Express* offices to talk to the Editor about things. The Editor was at the funeral but he had had a ride back down to Merthyr with Dr Dyke. I want to find out if I can get some of my things published here in Merthyr, was what Joseph said as the cab took him away from me. It was easy to see that Joseph's heart was in South Wales more than in Aberystwyth where his work was. Joseph liked being where the people were and Aberystwyth in the long winters was nearly as quiet as the grave. As you perhaps know there were more people in the two industrial counties of the south than in all the other counties of Wales – I am speaking, of course, of Glamorganshire and Monmouthshire, insisting that Monmouthshire is a Welsh county so that you will know.

Yes, it was down south with us Joseph wanted to be, but it was north in Aberystwyth he had to content himself. But not for long. He simply could not, for he was a most sociable and gregarious man. For such a man Aberystwyth in the late '70's was impossible. So he fled the place as often as he could and returned to it only when practically dragged back by the College Court of Governors, who were most patient with him. The Principal of the College was also most patient, but when Joseph went away for a week at a time and sometimes for longer, leaving only the sick and unenthusiastic students behind him to drift around like lost lambs, then something had to be said and done. Joseph was not too well paid – but it was not that that made him neglect his duties and his students as he did. He had to get away from the place and in order to get away from the place as often as possible he took most of his students with him, took them to present them at concerts as a Glee Party, as soloists, as anything as long as they were away from Aberystwyth. Yes, 'the Professor' was certainly a problem for the Principal and the Court of Governors.

For when he was at Aberystwyth it was little time he devoted to actual teaching. He composed and composed and only between compositions did he devote a little time to the teaching of his pupils. He wrote an opera, his first and best, 'Blodwen', to be sung in Welsh, and he also wrote the work for his Cambridge doctorate. He took the Aberdare Choir up to Cambridge to perform the work at St John's Church, Cambridge, and from there he took the choir to London to perform the work under his baton at the Alexandra Palace, where he also presented his opera, 'Blodwen'. It was just one mad rush and it almost killed Joseph. One performance had to be conducted by his best student, David Jenkins, who miraculously and more or less off his own bat got his Mus.Bac. at Cambridge at the same time as Joseph got his doctorate.

But Dr Joseph Parry – Professor no longer – went back to Aberystwyth with a new honour but with empty pockets, having lost £300 on the performances of his 'Jerusalem' and having had to fork out £400 to get his opera, 'Blodwen', produced and published. To try and get some of this back he presented both these works at Bristol, Cardiff and, of course, at Merthyr. Also at several other places in South Wales. The people of South Wales heard the first opera in Welsh ever presented in Wales and they hardly knew what to make of it. I was at the Merthyr performance at the Drill Hall, which was only half-full. The music was good and the singers, as singers, were satisfactory, but when they tried to act they were pitiable. Then the production was slipshod and to cap it all the scenery collapsed in the middle of the love duet. Still, it was a bold experiment and as we were leaving the Drill Hall we had to admit that if the work was given fair play, meaning a good production and competent acting and a good orchestra, then it would be a good evening's entertainment. It was little we knew about opera anyway. Oratorios were what we liked.

Oh, dear, sighed Dr Joseph Parry when at last he got back to Aberystwyth. There was the usual note from the Principal. He, the Principal, hoped that Dr Parry would find it possible to call at his office as soon as possible. H'm, said Joseph. Well, he had brought back one student, David Jenkins, with a Cambridge degree, and there was his own doctorate. What more did they want? Four children he had now and if he did not earn a little to supplement his salary as Head of the Music Department it was a hard time of it they would have. He simply could not allow the Principal to keep him tied to the work at the College. He would try to get them to give him David Jenkins as assistant, then he would have more freedom to go about and earn a bit as a singer and adjudicator, and compose things for performance and publication as well. What had happened to all the things he had written, that big box of compositions he had brought over from America? What had he got for all those songs that were being sung all over Wales? His hymn-tunes that were also being sung?

He had known what he had got in money-prizes in the days when he competed, but now that it was *infra dig* for him to compete it was next to nothing he was getting for what he was composing. He remembered having received three guineas for one song from a publishing firm in North Wales – and that was the most he had ever received as far as he could remember for the copyright and everything. I think you should have an agent, said Jane, when he returned to tell her of the almost disastrous loss sustained by the presentation of his 'Jerusalem'. The money I paid to have 'Blodwen' published will come back to us ten-fold in time, he assured her. I hope so, she said. I wish you could get a post in London. We were so happy there. I am not very happy here, said Joseph. I do not know what to do for money. I do not think opera in Welsh is going to bring much money. If only I shall have quiet I will write an oratorio. Oratorios always pay in Wales.

So we will leave him to face the Principal in the morning and to write his oratorio, remembering that the University College of Wales at Aberystwyth is carrying on on a day-to-day basis. Same as everything else in Wales, short of money as most good things and men in Wales were at this time. Any one of at least fifty who had made huge fortunes in Wales, South Wales in particular, could have handed a hundred thousand pounds over to the College and still have had at least twice that amount left for themselves. I am not talking just by the weight of my head either. The fact that William Crawshay, William II not William the first I mean, the fact that William II took eight million pounds sterling out of Merthyr and away from Merthyr when he left for

Caversham Park near Reading, that fact was published and he was glad not to be able to deny it. Right. Then what did Sir John Guest leave to his widow and his son, Sir Ivor Guest? These two names were still attracting money by the hundred thousand from us but I have said all I want to say about them. The hundreds of comparatively new fortune-makers are the chaps I am alluding to, for those other two, as I told you, left Merthyr and district and this life without leaving us as much as a hospital to get patched-up at. But the comparatively new crowd who swarmed all over us in South Wales were better educated and I for one expected them to do more for Education in Wales, where they made their fortunes, than the 'pioneer' iron and coal kings had the gumption to do. But did this new crowd do anything for the infant University College of Wales at Aberystwyth? No fear. A few, including Lord Aberdare, who had not made a huge fortune out of our blood and sweat and tears, did what they could, but the vast majority of this new crowd kept the money they had made out of us to make more money for themselves.

Then take the Marquis of Bute, who is only a young man not yet thirty. His father, who started the Bute Docks down Cardiff, had died leaving this young man when a boy in the good hands of trustees, who had to take care of millions and millions of pounds, not to mention property, until the boy attained his majority. Same as Sir John Guest left his boy, Sir Ivor, in the good hands of trustees, who looked after millions for the boy, millions of pounds sterling, I mean. Now these two boys, young men now – Sir Ivor Guest you might call middle-aged – were what you might call the top and bottom end of the golden ladder. Bute was at Cardiff in his castle by the sea – I will call him Bute not out of dis-respect but because it takes such a long time to keep telling you about all his titles and castles and things. He was at Cardiff, the receiving end of the golden ladder, and Sir Ivor Guest's ironworks and coal mines were at the top end, at

Dowlais, twenty-five miles from Cardiff, the receiving end, and Dowlais was also one thousand two hundred feet above sea-level. Of course, in between Bute at Cardiff and Guest at Dowlais there were hundreds of other money-making coal mines and say a score of money-making ironworks.

So the man said: 'The great development of the coal trade created the necessity of providing more rapid facilities for the shipment of coal.' Having plenty of money in hand from ground rents and royalties and other charges Bute, the Lord of Glamorgan as we sometimes called him, spent some of it in the provision of the necessary facilities for the more rapid shipment of coal – and iron, of course. That, they said, was the making of Cardiff as a port. That Bute had to die and now this Bute, not yet thirty years of age, is spending more millions in increasing and extending the facilities provided by his father. Yes, he is spending millions on the making of a new dock which will itself handle an additional trade of five million tons per annum. We simply had to have more rapid facilities for the shipment of our coal and iron, if we did not then the great development of the coal trade and kindred industries would be arrested. Then we had to have another railroad to bring it down from our valleys to the port of Cardiff. Mr Boyle, Bute's managing trustee, saw to that, and he was the first chairman of the Rhymney Railway Company, which, with the Taff Vale Railway Company, took all our coal and iron out of our valleys down to Cardiff. Talk about developments and facilities! We had them regardless of cost and we were told that it was the making of Cardiff and South Wales, including the industrial part of Monmouthshire. Regardless of cost, remember. I am not going to say anything here about the human factor, me and mine and you and yours living and working in the valleys, where, at Merthyr and Dowlais and elsewhere, we have not so long ago been locked-out for twenty-two weeks. Neither will I do more than just mention that we were on strike for thirteen weeks less than two years before we were locked out.

No, no, we will leave the starvation and degradation and brutalization and all that alone for now anyway.

All I will say is that it is a thousand pities, a million pities that our College of the Welsh University that we hoped to see before our call came was short of money to carry on all the time, the time when millions and millions were being spent on our industrial development, and millions and billions being made by those who took a chance in a big way. Where did all the money come from in the first place? and where did it go to in the second? We in the valleys of coal and iron knew where it got to in the end. London, of course, and that is where I am going soon to hear the first performance of Joseph's first oratorio. He is calling it 'Emmanuel', and when I met David Jenkins last week at Troedyrhiw he told me that Joseph's 'Emmanuel' is a great piece of work. He had gone over some of it with Joseph at Aberystwyth, where he is now assistant to Joseph, and David Jenkins is a musician who knows good work when he meets it. So I have made up my mind to go up to the St James's Hall, London, for the first performance by the London-Welsh Choral Society and a half-dozen of the best soloists available.

But before going there I must tell you of this day in Cardiff. I went down by train from Merthyr with the Editor of the *Merthyr Express* to see how the work was going on at the new Bute Dock. Three Irishmen who had gone down there from Merthyr to work on the making of the new Dock had been buried under a fall of sludge with a ganger – who was a Cardiff man bred and born – the day before and they had not found them yet. So down to Cardiff we went, but I was not allowed to go to where they were trying to get at the four men. The Editor of the *Merthyr Express* was allowed to go for he had met the Editor of the *South Wales Daily News*, which was a Cardiff newspaper, and it was he that managed to get the Editor of the *Merthyr Express* to where they were trying to get at the four bodies.

I walked by myself back up what they called the 'Bute Road', and I thought it was all 'Bute' down Cardiff. Bute Docks, Bute Road, Bute Estate, Bute this and Bute that. Then the fuss they were making over the loss of four men in one day. What about us in the valleys? In one pit in Ferndale in one and the same day a hundred and seventy-eight miners wedi popi, as we say in South Wales Welsh. In my time I could remember three explosions in three mines which between them took four hundred and thirty-eight men and boys. That is taking only the three-figure explosions. Another score of double-figure explosions would give you a total of a thousand up to '78, when a coal-mine at Abercarn broke the record by taking two hundred and sixty-eight lives in one and the same day. And here at Cardiff there was all this fuss over the loss of four lives. Still, four is four, as you say.

Now I could see how Cardiff had grown. It was now as big if not bigger than the town of Merthyr. That day nearly thirty years ago, the day Betty Parry and her two sons and two daughters left Cardiff for Philadelphia on the *Jane Anderson*, well, Cardiff was not much of a place then. But now, after having been fed for another thirty years by the valleys, it was getting to be the biggest town in Wales. All those offices down by the docks, more offices there than in Merthyr and district. Coal exporters and coal brokers – and I could not for the life of me think what 'coal brokers' were good for. Shipping offices all over the place too, and along the road named after Bute there were more coloured men than I had seen in my life before. I said to myself that I would not like to walk alone along the road named after Bute in the dark.

I was glad to get back to the streets where the shops were. I had promised to meet the Editor of the *Merthyr Express* at the Taff Vale Railway station at seven o'clock but what was I going to do until then? I had seen all I was allowed to see of the Docks, the offices down there and the Bute

Road. I had seen the castle in which Bute lived when in Cardiff and I had seen the old church of St John's and the two main streets. I had seen the canal and the River Taff and the fine houses along the bank of the river in which some of the shipowners and coal exporters and people like that lived, so I was getting to feel a bit tired. It is when you are tired and by yourself in a strange place that you get to feel like a glass of beer, isn't it? And threepennyworth of bread and cheese I was feeling like as well. There were plenty of public-houses and I was going to turn into the nearest one when a thin man arm-in-arm with a fine young woman passed me by on the pavement. I stood looking after them and saying to myself: I know him, don't I? But he had an overcoat on which had an astrakhan collar and he walked like a lord. Then he laughed out loud and I knew him and I shouted at the top of my voice: Will! Will, hoy!

He stopped like if he was shot and turned about so quick that his top-hat fell off and the young woman had to pick it up and brush the dirt off and flatten the bulge. I went towards him and when he saw it was me he ran and embraced me. Well, well, he said. A Merthyr face at last – come and have a drink. Here is your hat, said the young woman. Thank you, my dear, said Will, speaking English to her after speaking Welsh to me. No drink, please, she said. Now, now, my dear, said Will. I shall not over-indulge. This is an old friend of mine from my native town and we have much to say to each other. So run along and do your shopping, my darling, and in all probability I shall be at our rooms by the time you get back there. So run along, dear. Come on, he said, taking my arm. He walked me away from the young woman. We are passing public-houses, Will, I said. Will Full-Moon said: We are going to the hotel. I never drink in public-houses. Do you know that you are going to save me a trip up to Merthyr? Am I? I said. Yes, said he. I had a letter from Myfanwy this morning – she is singing in America. A letter asking me when I had been to Merthyr to see if her father's grave is neat and clean. In every letter she reminds me about Dick's grave – here we are. We will go to the little room behind the bar – good afternoon, my dear, he said to the barmaid as shepherding me around the bar. Good afternoon, sir, said the over-ripe barmaid. Anyone in the little room? whispered Will. No, Mr Morgani, said the barmaid. Signor Morgani, if you please, my dear, said Will. Two large tankards of ale and I will be obliged if you see that we are not disturbed. I would like some bread and cheese as well, I said. So would I, my dear, said Will. And some pickles. Come along.

Well, well, he said, taking off his top-hat and his overcoat and rubbing his hands after. Sit down – and before I forget. You know where Blind Dick is buried in Thomas Town Cemetery? Of course, wasn't I at the funeral? I said. To be sure you were, said Will. I promised that girl, Myfanwy, that that grave would always be cared for. But I don't want to go up to Merthyr unless I am bound to. I don't want to see the place or the people ever again. What in the name of God have we Merthyr people done to you then? I said. The barmaid came with the two tankards of beer and went back for the bread and cheese and pickles. Drink, said Will. After drinking he said: What have the people of Merthyr done to me? Look, look at me. Yes, you are if anything thinner than when I met you that time at Pontypridd, I said. I am as thin but no thinner for only this morning I weighed myself again, he said. That is what Merthyr and the people of Merthyr did to me. The barmaid came with bread and cheese and pickles on a tray. Thank you, my dear, said Will, putting his hand in his pocket. I will pay, I said, feeling for my purse. He let me pay and he asked the barmaid again to see that we were not disturbed. Eat, said Will to me in Welsh. And you too, I said. He waved his hand and said: No, no, no, I am singing this evening and the rôle is most exacting. My food has to be specially prepared for me by that lady you saw me with. Nice little girl. In the soprano section of the chorus. Thinks the world of me. Don't tell me that you are living tally with her, I said. He sighed and said: That is Merthyr all over. What if I am living tally with her? You kept me in Merthyr on water and tea and singing holy words only until now I cannot get the flesh back on my bones. Am I to have no pleasure in life? He drank the rest of his beer and tinkled the little hand-bell. Finish your beer, he said. I am taking my time, I said. Two tankards, my dear, he said to the barmaid.

And after that I am not drinking any more, I told him, and I let him pay this time. What name was that you told the barmaid? My professional name, Signor Morgani, he said. Is that wrong again? If it is you tell Carl Rosa to put Will Morgan or Will Full-Moon on the bills and programmes. Oh, yes, you told me that time in Pontypridd that you were going to sing opera, I said. But I did not know they had a theatre for opera here at Cardiff. They have a theatre and you will be there to hear me sing tonight, said Will. Indeed I will not, I said. I am meeting the Editor of the *Merthyr Express* at the Taff Vale station at seven o'clock to go home on the train with him. Let the Editor of the *Merthyr Express* go home by himself or bring him with you to the theatre, said Will. I can get two passes for the front seats downstairs or upstairs. I am the only principal singer who is allowed two passes to give away each week. Carl Rosa knows that I am the only principal singer worth his money and two free passes a week. You must come to-night for it is my best of the week. To-night I am singing the devil in 'Faust' and being thin like I am does not matter. Thinner the better for to sing the devil's part in 'Faust'. I would like to hear you sing opera, I said, but I promised the Editor of the *Merthyr Express* – Have I not said bring him? said Will. If he will not come then come yourself and go back to Merthyr on the rodneys' train.

Very well, if the Editor of the *Merthyr Express* will not come then I will come by myself, I said. I have not got the

257

passes with me, said Will. But I will have them ready when you come round to the back and up to my dressing-room about seven o'clock. I will show you where after we have had another tankard apiece. No more beer for me, I said. Then no more for me either, he said. Is it harder to sing opera than oratorio? I said. Harder, no, he said. Easier of the two. Some nights when the band do play up I only open my mouth and make faces. I will do it to-night for you to see. Singing the holy words in Merthyr with only the piano, organ or harmonium, it was no good me make faces at them. Had to sing full-blast all the time – have one more tankard with me? It is not often I meet a man from Merthyr now. Then this will be the last, remember, I said, and never mind feeling for money. I am paying. There is only one thing, he said, tinkling the little hand-bell. In lodgings all the time. Every Sunday on the train.– the same again, my dear. Yes, that is what I am afraid of. What are you afraid of? I said, feeling for a shilling in my purse. Afraid of dying in lodgings I am, he said. Thank you, my dear. I paid and he said: Drink. I am taking my time, I told him again. Are you feeling bad then? He shook his head and said: Not in myself but in my heart sometimes. Strange places and strange houses and strange beds all the time. If I did not have that little girl to keep me company it would be more than I could stand. And you old enough to be her father, I said. She is older than you think, he said. I know what your poor old mother would say if she was alive, I said. Look, said Will. Look now at me. I am as tidy a man as any Carl Rosa has got singing for him. Remember the girl was lonely too. Then marry her tidy, I said. Perhaps I will, he said. I cannot finish my beer, I said. It is many a year since I took more than two pints in one day. You have paid for it now, said Will. It is no good me turn my stomach, I said. It will not turn mine, said Will, emptying the beer from my tankard into his. Take this half-a-sovereign before I forget, he said. What for? I said. To pay a man to put Blind Dick's

258

grave tidy, he said. It is Myfanwy's money and she has got plenty so do not be afraid to take it. Yes, she has got plenty. She has not got to live in cheap lodgings. Perhaps you would be able to pay for better lodgings if you drank less, I said. Must I not keep trying to get my flesh back on my bones? he said. I must go and walk the roads before I fall to sleep in this little room, I said. Come now and go back to your lodgings like you promised that girl. Come on now.

I walked with him as far as the house where he lodged but I did not go in. On the way to the house he showed me the little door up two steps at the back of the theatre, and it was up those steps me and the Editor of the *Merthyr Express* went just before seven that evening. Oh, yes, Signor Morgani told me to expect you, said the man. Follow me, please. Across the stage with scenery and up a twisty stone stairway we went to find Will looking like a red rushlight in his dressing-room. There was only one chair in the small room and he was seated on that and the girl he was living tally with, who was dressed and made-up ready, was putting little bits of something shiny right on the balls of his eyes. After she had done this she hurried out of the room and Will stood up and said: Right. Now where did I put those passes?

He looked enough to frighten anybody in his red tights and false pointed beard on his chin. I would never know you – this is the Editor of the *Merthyr Express*, I said. Ah, here they are, said Will, the passes in his hand. I am delighted to have the honour of meeting the Editor of the *Merthyr Express*. I knew the previous Editor very well – sit down, please. Here are the passes. Two best seats in the house – dead-centre front-row upstairs. Better upstairs for opera, I think. I hope you enjoy my performance as Mephistopheles. I feel sure that we shall, said the Editor. This is for me an unexpected privilege. They went on talking and I looked about the little room and fingered several costumes hanging from hooks in the walls. Then I noticed eight quart

bottles with a pair of high-boots under the little table. I see
you are all right for after, Will, I said, pointing to the bottles
filled with beer. Will laughed out loud and said: I am all
right for during and after my performance. The devil must
look after himself, mustn't he? Do you know what? No, I
said. The two strictest chapels in Merthyr, Zoar and Pontmorlais, are quite close to each other, he said. With a cloak
over me I would like to go one Sunday, under my cloak
dressed and made-up as I am now, and walk into those
two chapels just as their congregations would be settling
down to the sermons, and throw off my cloak and sing like
hell – That is you all over, I said, walking out of the room.
Wait a minute, he said. Have a share of one of these bottles
before going. Who could be nasty to him?

He sang for us that night – no, no, it is no use me try to
tell you. And his acting was if anything better than his singing. After talking all Welsh to me during the day he was
now singing in English as well if not better than H. A.
Bruce, who is now Lord Aberdare, could speak English.
The audience – and the place was full – liked him, Mephistopheles, better than they liked Faust or the poor girl they
ruined between them. We did not have a chance to see Will
after the performance for we had to hurry across to the Taff
Vale station to catch the rodneys' train back to Merthyr. I
wanted to tell him about the performance of Joseph's
opera, 'Blodwen', in Welsh at the Drill Hall, Merthyr, but
I forgot after all. Someone told me – I forget who it was –
but someone told me when I was in London that Will Full-
Moon had married that girl and that he was on the steady
again. I hope that is true, don't you?

It was good to be back in the dirt of Merthyr and now I
was sorry I had promised Lewis Morgan to go to London
with him to hear the first performance of Joseph's oratorio,
'Emmanuel'. Too much running about I was doing and
me getting no younger. But Lewis Morgan wanted to hear
the work and, if he thought it worthy of presentation by his

choir at the forthcoming National Eisteddfod at Merthyr, to conduct it there. If it is any good, said Lewis Morgan, then we in Merthyr could give it a better performance than ever those London-Welsh people could. H'm, I said, but no more. Conductors and choirs and singers in Wales have been engaged in a kind of harmonic and melodic civil war ever since I can remember. We have a saying in Wales, 'Y cythrael yn y canu', which I would translate as 'the little devil in the singing', and that little devil operating in Wales has been responsible for more arguments, differences, rows and splits than all the other little devils specializing in the arts put together. This same little devil in the singing has on thousands of occasions made it most unpleasant for those who have to adjudicate at our singing festivals, national, regional and local. So I did not say a word to Lewis Morgan one way or the other.

Still, it was rather a pity that we had to travel to London for the first performance of 'Emmanuel'. Of course it was Jane, Joseph's wife, who was mainly responsible for that. She had got on so well with the London-Welsh during the two years she and Joseph and their two little boys had lived amongst them. Then the London-Welsh were ready to give the new work everything in the way of support. They had the choir and they would arrange for an orchestra, book St James's Hall and engage soloists. They had in the conductor of the London-Welsh Choral Society a very good man to rehearse the work and they hoped Joseph would be able to come up to London for the final rehearsal to conduct that and the performance itself. Every welcome and hospitality for himself and his wife and his children and, as their draper friend pointed out in his letter, the good friend with whom they had lived for two happy years as paying-guests, as he said twice in his letter, 'London is the place after all.'

So to London they went, and to London I also went with Lewis Morgan. You knew Lewis Morgan, of course. You will remember the sensation when he left the chapel to join the Spiritualistic Movement. Then it was that the members of the Merthyr United Choir showed real artistic loyalty. People meeting them said: Your conductor has left the chapel and joined the old Spiritualists then, and the question implied was: What are you as members of the Merthyr United Choir going to say to him? What the members of the Merthyr United Choir did was to remember that he was as good a conductor as ever, and whether he went to Seion Chapel or to the Spiritualist Temple was a matter of indifference to them. So they stuck to him to a man and to a woman and that was loyalty.

Say what you liked he was a good conductor. John, his brother, was a good singer, but he was killed in the Gethin Pit explosion. Lewis Morgan helped to carry his brother's body home from the pit. Yes, and Lewis Morgan was a good all-round musician and he was a good miner. He conducted chapel choirs as well as the Merthyr United Choir and he lived for a while next-door but one to us in the Twynyrodyn district of Merthyr. That was how we grew friendly and went to London together to hear the performance of Joseph's 'Emmanuel'. Yes, said Lewis Morgan, after we had heard the performance. A very good piece of work. But I did not think much of Joseph's conducting. Did you? Perhaps a bit rough here and there but on the whole I thought he handled it well, I said, picking my words carefully. Splendid audience for a new work, I added. Yes, the London-Welsh saw to that, said Lewis Morgan. It was during that middle section that he lost his grip on both choir and orchestra. I shall have to watch that middle section when we do it in Merthyr. Yes, I said.

But all the music critics of the London newspapers gave it high praise and also praised Joseph for the way he had conducted. I told Lewis Morgan about this when I returned from the reading-room of the Merthyr Library and all he said was: Yes, no doubt the London-Welsh saw to that too.

So you can see that it is not only in the singing but in our conducting too the little devil resident in Wales is always busy. 'Emmanuel' was repeated half-a-dozen times in North Wales with great success and there was a demand that Joseph should conduct it in South Wales. But there was some difference of opinion as to who should conduct it, the local conductor, who was the great Caradog, or the composer himself. So Joseph bothered no more with them. He was feeling tired and dispirited and in need of a change that would be a rest as well. Jane, he said, we will go to America to see our people there. What do you say? I say yes with all my heart, she said.

Then get ready to go as soon as I can arrange things, he said. It was not, he found, so easy to arrange for leave of absence even after he had got enough money, some in advance. But he was, after all, 'Dr Joseph Parry', and the recent London success of his oratorio, 'Emmanuel', had directed considerable attention to its place of origin, the Aberystwyth College of the University of Wales. So the Principal said: Yes, I suppose we shall be able to manage for a few months without you, Doctor, and Joseph after he had left the Principal heard the echo of the other meaning of what the Principal had said. He did not mind, neither did he care, if he never saw the place again. It was his mother who had been right and he should have listened to her and stayed in America. But Jane ... she was his wife and as such her opinion was worthy of consideration above all others. Never mind. Already he could see the new world opening its arms to receive him back, now as *Dr* Joseph Parry. The first and still the only Welshman to call himself Mus.D., Cambridge. With that he would make a tour of where the Welsh were all over America and then he would have money again. Working like a dog he had been for nearly seven years since he had left America and short of money they had been all the time. But now ... He squared his shoulders and threw his head back and looked out to sea.

Somewhere over there was America, he told himself with a smile, his back to Aberystwyth. But was America over there, in the direction he was looking? Who knows? Anyway, he stood listening to the sea saying: Come, come ...

CHAPTER II

Breakdown in Cincinnati

JOSEPH and his family are on their way to America, where, no doubt, they will find people and places and things changed quite a lot. But before we talk about that we must look at things from our own doorstep in the town of Tydfil the Martyr in Wales. For things are changing here all the time. They have opened the Oddfellows Hall at Dowlais and I caught a cold going there for the opening of it. It was built to accommodate twelve hundred but we were about fifteen hundred there that night it opened with a grand concert and I do not remember how many speeches. It was an event. Having a Hall to accommodate twelve hundred after being without any sort of hall for nearly a century is an event. Just think what you would feel like if you were living there yourself at the time when the Oddfellows Hall was first opened, living at Dowlais, I mean.

Then a Chamber of Trade had been started at Merthyr, so we were going into the '80's as a town and district that meant business. Mr Fothergill was not very well so he retired from Parliament and we had a hotly-contested by-election, and just before that Robert Crawshay died. Poor old Crawshay – though he was not so old as all that. The name of Crawshay meant much more to the mass of the people of our town and district than the name of Queen Victoria did, that is why I must say something about him. For after him it was only the echo of the name that was heard in our town and district. Yes, the echo, that was all. He was the fourth of the Crawshay dynasty which for over a hundred years had reigned over us. Now he was gone too.

Robert Crawshay was not what you might call a bad man. He lived amongst us, in his castle inside the walled park of sixty-two acres, most of the time. He gave us the famous Cyfarthfa Brass Band and he did something for the widows and fatherless children of those who were killed in the Gethin Pit explosion. Not a lot, it is true, but something all the same. He and his wife, Rose Mary, did identify themselves in the life of our town and they were always more pleasant than otherwise. He had lived to see the end of the Plymouth Ironworks and it was only him and Guest of Dowlais when Crawshay's call came. As far as the management of the great Cyfarthfa Ironworks was concerned his passing made but little difference now. For his works and the Guest works less than two miles away as the crow flies were no longer 'family' concerns. Agents, trustees, managers were preparing the way for 'Company' control in which the names which had meant so much would mean but little.

It is funny how these things happen and funnier still how they change the life of a town and district when they do happen. For there is something worthwhile in having even bad bosses living amongst us, where we can see and hear them now and then, and know that they are there in the castle or at Dowlais House so as we can say 'that bloody monkey up at the castle' or 'that flaming slave-driver up at Dowlais House'. These phrases are used only to try and tell you what the physical presence of our lords and masters amongst us meant to us, so please do not take them literally. When they were with us and we could refer to them in Welsh as 'Yr hen Crawshay', or 'Yr hen diawl', meaning that old Crawshay or that old devil, we felt we were having our bang out and felt all the better for it. The same applied to the Guests when they lived at Dowlais House. What we now feared as much as anything was long-distance control from London, the control of the unseen, the unheard, the mysterious thing known as 'the Company', sending its orders and imposing its will on us without giving us a chance to have our bang out. So many of us felt that we would miss Robert Crawshay for that if for nothing else.

When he died there was a little more water coming from the waterworks into the town and district, but not anything like enough, for more people were coming into the town and district from somewhere or other all the time. Then we were still without a hospital to get patched-up in. Now that was one thing which Robert Crawshay might have done for us. Well, say him and Guest between them. For between them and their ironworks and coal-pits they had killed more men and boys and emptied more sleeves and put more men and boys on crutches than any war had done up to then, any one war, I mean, and taking the Crawshay and Guest operations over the hundred years. Never mind, Robert Crawshay was gone and under the 'Company' that was getting ready to take us over we feared we might be worse off.

Still, whoever was or was not at Cyfarthfa Castle or Dowlais House life in the town and district went on. On the Saturday after Robert Crawshay died fifty couples got married, two-thirds of them in the Registrar's office. And talk about children! They were coming all the time into little homes overcrowded with children already. The word 'large' was not used when referring to a family in which there were only six or seven children. That was only what we called a 'tidy' family. When a young woman in the early thirties could point and say: These are my eight, then we would say: H'm, you are getting to be a large family. Getting to be, that is all. Ten children was conceded to be a 'large' family but nothing to brag about.

The ironworkers, puddlers, rollers and others, were getting to feel a bit uneasy, not only in our town and district but all over South Wales and South-West Wales and

Monmouthshire. For there was all this talk about steel and about closing down all the ironworks to reconstruct them to make steel. So steel was a word on the lips of many who were shaking their heads in our town and district. For we were still in a more or less elementary state of mind and it was little we knew of the experiments that were being made here and there. We only heard rumours that something was on the way that would change our lives and our way of thinking and living, and that it would be domino on many of us. That word 'domino' was with us at that time, the composite word which meant finished, scrapped, superfluous and so on, and we were workers who dreaded being reduced to that state more than we feared death itself.

Never mind, it may never happen, so why worry? But we kept on worrying all the same. Some, not all of us. We were getting ready for the following year's National Eisteddfod, which was to be held at Merthyr, so there were ever so many committees to be set up and I found myself on two of them. Already I have no doubt told you plenty about our National Eisteddfod of Wales but who knows how much work the people of a town and district have to do to make ready for it? A solid year's advance work! The Merthyr United Choir had to be trained ready to sing at all the evening concerts under Lewis Morgan, David Jenkins, Mus.Bac., and others. Dear, dear, at it most nights for a year. The Music Committee alone had to arrange for the Eisteddfod Choir – leave that to me, said Lewis Morgan, Conductor of the Merthyr United Choir. We were glad to. Fifteen professional singers we had to engage in advance. An orchestra with solo violinist. Two to accompany singers on the organ and piano, two harpists and a Penillion Singer. Then what about the famous musicians to act as adjudicators? I will not say anything about the Poetry and the Arts and Crafts or about the contracting for the building of the huge Pavilion – for we would not consider holding it in a marquee after what happened some years before, when there was a terrible storm during National Eisteddfod week and the huge marquee it was being held in went up like a monster balloon, leaving thousands of people exposed to the fury of the storm. No, no more big tents, we said. We will have a proper Pavilion.

Some think that when they have paid for their ticket to go to our National Eisteddfod that they have done wonders. On their way in to listen to whatever is going on they pass us with our stewards' or committee-men's badges as though we were nobodies who are having a week on the cheap without paying for tickets or anything. They do not think of the years' work we have done to see that ten thousand people each and every day for a week shall have the time of their lives. They do not trouble to think of all the difficulties we have to overcome behind the scenes during the week, when the little devil in the singing is trying to upset things. That little devil takes a lot of handling – and what about men like old Llew Morlais, who seem to think that our National Eisteddfod, the greatest literary and artistic and musical festival the world over, was started to give them more chance to show off? I am speaking of old Llew Morlais and not Eos Morlais, remember. Eos Morlais was most helpful but as for old Llew Morlais – never mind, he died not long after, God help him. We will have to come back to the Merthyr Eisteddfod if only to hear Mary Davies singing – you remember Mary? Of course you do. The daughter of William Davies, the son of Moses Davies. Myfanwy Llewelyn used to live in London at the home of William Davies when she was studying at the Royal Academy of Music, remember. Mary Davies was only a tiny little girl then but she is a young woman now and one of the best sopranos the world over. So we have engaged her for two of the evening concerts at the Merthyr National Eisteddfod. I wish her grandfather, old Moses Davies, was alive to hear her. But her father is coming from London with her and he is staying with me for a couple of nights before going back to London. There again. The Hospitality Committee. Talk about work!

People from away cannot sleep on the road, can they? Then where are they to sleep when they come to Merthyr to be present at the National Eisteddfod of Wales when it is held there? We are expecting ten thousand people to come to Merthyr National each and every day of the first week in August of next year. Say more than half will be from the town and district itself. Right. Say half of the other half will be coming and going in special trains and in brakes. Right. Say two thousand of the total daily attendance of ten thousand will want place to sleep. What can the town and district of Merthyr do for them? Hotels, you say. What hotels? About three in Merthyr and one in Dowlais and there you are. What are four hotels between two thousand people wanting place to sleep? That was the problem that we of the Hospitality Committee had to solve somehow. Oh, we are on the way to solving it. The membership of the chapels of Merthyr and district have been very good, though some of them wanted to pick and choose their guests, of course. Dr Joseph Parry and his wife and children will be looked after by the preacher and deacons of Bethesda Chapel – I forgot to tell you that Joseph is to be one of the chief adjudicators. With all these old committee meetings I have nearly forgot about him altogether.

He was not well on the ship going to America this time. He was happy now that he was on his way to see his parents, his brother and sisters and relations and friends, yet he was feeling low with it all. He did not organize a ship's concert this time but he listened to his two little boys singing and playing at the ship's concert which a committee of passengers organized. Haydn played the piano and Mendelssohn sang in a way that made Joseph proud and made him feel a little better. I said 'little' boys but the two boys are not so little now. Haydn when he stands straight is up to his father's shoulder and Mendelssohn is only a few inches shorter than his brother. Well, Haydn will be fourteen next birthday and is it fourteen months younger Mendelssohn is? 'Mendy' is what they all call him so perhaps we had better call him Mendy too. Yes, Joseph's two boys were following their father and the two little girls were also showing signs of musical talent. The only member of the family without music in her was Jane herself. She did not mind music but she was not in the least fond of it, so it was strange how Joseph fell in love with her and still loved her as much as ever.

She was feeling rather worried about the education of her two boys, their general education. For it was only a mixture of scraps of education they had had in America, London and Wales; the last seven years in Wales had been their best period. Their passion for music and their ambition to become what their father was were not altogether to the good. Already both of them were thinking that it was only a question of time before they would naturally grow to be great musicians like their father. They did not agree that it was necessary to work hard at other subjects outside music so as to get back well inside music. This was how Jane saw the problem of their future, but she made no determined effort to grapple with it. She was easy-going in her lady-like way and as long as she was not worried overmuch by money-matters she was content to let wrong tendencies right themselves, as, in the case of her boys, she felt they would. Yet there were times when she was afraid they would not. In this connexion Joseph was unhelpful in the extreme, for his mind could not be kept off music for more than two minutes at a time. Sometimes, with that sluggish underlying stubbornness of hers, she would keep him bound to a family or money problem and away from his music until he cried like a child and promised to do whatever she wanted him to do if only she would let him go. Now, Joseph, now is the time you should take those boys in hand, she said. They are getting too big in every way for me. Nonsense, my dear, he said. You can handle them as well as you handle me.

But she found that she could not. Two self-willed boys of about fourteen and thirteen years old respectively were a more difficult problem than her delightful music-mad husband. So she just gave it up and hoped for the best. She went about the ship with her two handsome boys and two pretty little girls whilst Joseph just sat and sat on the sunny side resting and hoping he would feel better by the time they reached New York. I think we might stay a night or two in New York, said Jane. Joseph shook his head. Why not? she said. I am sure the New York friends, particularly Mr and Mrs Eliazar Jones, would be delighted to have us stay. I want to see my mother and father, said Joseph. Of course, said Jane. But a couple of days in New York to – I want to see my mother and father first, said Joseph. Plenty of time for New York after.

You forget, Joseph, she said, that you have been going about quite a lot whilst I have been at home with the children for the seven years we have been over in Wales. Now all I ask is a few days in New York to see the shops and – Listen, Jane, said Joseph. Seven years you said. Yes, seven years and I have not set eyes on my mother and father – Have I seen *my* people during that time? said Jane. Am I saying that you have? said Joseph. We shall have to get money from somewhere before you can go to look at shops in New York – and I am not feeling any too well, my dear. What I think is that seeing my mother and father will make me feel better to go on that tour. We will be coming to New York then. But the children will not, said Jane. It is their granny and all our people at Danville the children want to see more than they want to see New York, said Joseph. You may be right, said Jane.

He was right – and wasn't Joseph himself glad to see his mother and father. Talk about crying. He cried and cried until he made everybody, including Jane and Betty, the last two to cry in each other's presence, cry as well. But please remember that he was a sick and a sentimental man and that he had not seen his parents or his brother and sisters for seven long years. It is easy to make fun of a man forty years old crying but it might do you and me good if only we cried a bit oftener than we do. Cry for the reason Joseph is now crying, I mean. Now I will soon get to feel better, he said. But he was not much better when he set out on the tour which had been hurriedly arranged for him. The two little boys were left with their granny, one little girl with Henry's wife and the other little girl with Elizabeth, Joseph's married sister. Henry had made good use of the seven years during which Joseph had been away in Wales, for Henry was now a Professor of Music in Philadelphia, if you please, and he was making a better living at music than Joseph was. Henry was coming home from Philadelphia to Danville every night to his wife and children, but he had stayed two nights at Philadelphia recently to arrange a lecture-recital there for his brother, 'Dr Joseph Parry, Mus.D., Cambridge.'

The tour started at New York, which had changed a lot since Joseph last saw the city. A city like New York changes almost out of all recognition in seven years, and so had most of the other cities Joseph visited during the tour. In one city he saw steam street-cars for the first time, and the trains were ever so much more comfortable now. He and Jane had a splendid reception everywhere and the hospitality left nothing to be desired. Financially the tour was not a great success although the audiences were on the whole pretty good. Joseph asked for and got a hundred dollars per lecture-recital and he must have done about thirty-six before he broke down at Cincinnati. Whatever it was he had brought over from Wales with him he had not been able to shake it off. His body had felt as heavy as lead and his spirit was low throughout the tour. So many old friends everywhere and they all wanted to entertain him. He was the white-headed boy of all Welsh-Americans and they all wanted to show him how proud they were of him. There were receptions and banquets and many speeches were made at each and every one.

They had to put him to bed at Cincinnati and he stayed in bed at the house of friends for two weeks before he was able to travel back to Danville. So the last two weeks' lecture-recitals were cancelled, including the one which Henry had taken such trouble to arrange and ensure the success of at Philadelphia. I am very sorry, Henry, said Joseph. Never mind, you will come again and then I will arrange an even better concert for you, said Henry. You are not going back over the water until you have had rest and are quite better, Joseph, said Betty. I do not want to go back over the water, said Joseph. Then why go, said his father. All is wanted is a letter saying that you are staying on this side. Yes, said Betty, and you and Henry between you can work together. If it is a college you want then they are talking about starting one at Pittsburg. Jane stood and listened to all this without saying a word. She had her say later, for she and Joseph were staying with Jane's brother, Gomer Thomas, the children staying on where they had stayed during the time their parents had been on tour.

They were in bed that night and Jane said: So it is all arranged. What? said Joseph. That we are staying on this side, said Jane. Your mother did not trouble to ask for my opinion. You were as free to express an opinion as she was, said Joseph. What do you think of us staying? I don't think it would be wise, said Jane. I think London is the place for you. The London-Welsh will do more for you than the Welsh of America or Wales. Easy to talk but I must have work to go to in London, mustn't I? said Joseph. That will come, she said. But you must be within reach of whatever comes up in London. So it is no use your staying here, thousands of miles away from the world's greatest musical centre. I am not so sure that London is anything of the kind, said Joseph. Whether or no you like London, don't you? she said. I don't dislike the place, said Joseph. You have friends at the

Royal Academy and London-Welsh friends all over London, she said. Now is the first chance I have had to tell you about the letter I received from the Lloyds this afternoon. The London-Welsh Choral Society are putting your 'Emmanuel' on at the Crystal Palace this time and they are hoping that you will get back in time to conduct. The Crystal Palace – light the lamp for me to see the letter, said Joseph. Why did they not write to tell me? You know that it is to me that Mrs Lloyd has always written, said Jane, lighting the lamp. Where is the letter?' said Joseph. Jane got out of bed and fetched him the letter. The Crystal Palace, he murmured after he had read the letter. To be sure I will be there to conduct. He read the letter again. Another thing, said Jane. What? he said. I think I am going to have another baby, she said. No, he said. Yes, she said. H'm, he said. That will be five. Never mind. No doubt those notices in the London newspapers praising the performance at St James's Hall have made them want to repeat it at the Crystal Palace. That will hold ten times more people than the St James's Hall, won't it? Yes, I should think so, said Jane.

Joseph was ever so much better when he woke up next morning and there was no more talk about him staying in America. He told his mother that morning that he would have to go back to Wales soon. Well, you know your own business best, she said. No doubt Jane have had her say. We are all entitled to our say, mam, said Joseph. She is going to have another baby. When? said Betty. I did not ask her, said Joseph. Before long it was goodbye again and Joseph much better leaving than when he came. On the ship he was as lively as a cricket. After all expenses he had cleared about two thousand dollars on the tour, but the first-class passage home for him and Jane and the children made a hole in that. As soon as he arrived at Liverpool he sent a telegraph message to the Secretary of the London-Welsh Choral Society to say that if and when they gave a repeat performance of his 'Emmanuel' he was now available and would like to conduct the performance.

The performance at the Crystal Palace was a great success, no doubt about that. The London-Welsh can certainly make a thing go when they put their backs into it. They sold enough tickets to pack that huge place and a few of the richest of them contributed between them enough to engage and pay a good orchestra. There was a solid week of rehearsing under Joseph himself and his assistant, David Jenkins, carried on at the College. It is now time, I think, to tell you about the way things were at this time between the Principal and Governors of the College and Joseph. It was bad enough being short of money all the time without also having a footloose Head of the Music Department who only came to the place when he had nowhere else to go. The Music Department had not proved a success under him and if, through shortage of money, the College had to curtail its facilities, then the Music Department would be the first of the departments to come under consideration for suspension. But first they would see what could be done with the Head of the Music Department, Dr Joseph Parry. They had tried two years previous to make him stick around the College when they, the Governors of the College, passed the following:

That the Principal should confer with Professor Parry on his position at the University College, and propose to him a new arrangement based on his discontinuance of teaching Music to any but the ordinary male students of Art at the College. It has been suggested with the general approval of the Council, that Dr Parry should retain his Professorship at a salary to be agreed upon for such teaching as above-mentioned. Dr Parry would be free to give such teaching, of a public or private nature, at Aberystwyth or elsewhere, as he may think proper on his own account, and outside the walls of the College – it being, however, clearly understood that during the Sessions of the College, Dr Parry should not give, nor professionally attend, concerts in Aberystwyth or in its immediate neighbourhood.

That 'immediate neighbourhood' could cover the whole of such a small country of Wales, in the middle of which the University College was situated. Joseph would not abide by that then, and now that they were about to bring more pressure to bear on him he resigned. Let there be no inquest for there were faults on both sides. Joseph was difficult and unconventional in the extreme but if any student had the root of the matter in him then Joseph could inspire him to win through. To the average or backward student Joseph was fatal. But he was when all is said and done the greatest personality in that College. He went about and did things which enhanced the prestige of the place and he stayed at home and composed things which were also a credit to the College. He simply could not divide his Professorial life into 'Sessions' and 'Vacations' and he recognized no authority greater than the mysterious thing which prompted him to do just what he did irrespective of whose time it was supposed to be, College time or his own time. And what had he as an artist to do with time and place anyway? If students wanted to learn they would take what little he could find time to give them and go on learning and leave him in peace to go on learning as well. He only had one short life and a lot to do and if he was going to allow College rules and regulations to bind him then he would rather be dead. So he resigned and the University College was the poorer for the loss of a personality if not a power. He was liked by all his students and loved by some and it was those who loved him that got most out of him and did well because they worked even as he had worked. Take a personality like that out of the rather anxious teaching staff of a young College so short of funds and how poor indeed the College is after.

Now, said Joseph to Jane, let us get away from this place as soon as possible. He did not like the little town of Aberystwyth, neither could he bring himself to like the people, and perhaps the fault was mainly his. They were a cautious and quiet people and did not like being rushed. Joseph was fiery and impulsive, always rushing himself and everyone else into one thing after another. When an idea came to him he did not say: Now let me see. So he did not like people who were always saying: Well, we'll see. So he was glad to get away to where the response was greater and more immediate. He went to Swansea.

Swansea was getting to be a big place and it was growing as a port as well. It was for the most part as fouled by industry and as musical as Joseph's native town of Merthyr was. It had coal valleys running into it and it had a greater variety of metallurgical enterprises. It had 'Iron kings', 'Copper kings', and 'Tinplate kings', so it had a greater variety of refuse from its more varied works. The approach to the town from the east was made under a pall of almost permanent smoke and when this did clear over week-ends and during works' holidays the scene revealed was an ideal setting for an open-air performance of Dante's 'Inferno'. But when one went through a number of mean and narrow streets one came upon an unforgettable sight, one of the world's most beautiful bays, Swansea Bay.

The town was thriving, musical, religious, and more Welsh than the town of Merthyr, for fewer English and Irish had gone so far west as Swansea. That was where Joseph and his family went and received a warm welcome. He hoped to establish a Welsh School of Music in the town and whilst he was working towards this end he was organist at one of the chapels. Here is another of those long stories but you shall have it as short as I can make it. The trouble is that Joseph will not stay long in any one place – oh, I must correct something here and now. I just said that fewer Irish and English went to Swansea than to Merthyr and district. To work, I mean. The employers of Swansea and district were as predominantly English as those of Merthyr and district. As one writer said: 'It was once more reserved for the Englishmen with capital to come along and exploit the wealth of Wales ...' The same writer continued, 'But in justice it must be admitted that many an Englishman entered the country with high hopes and after spending his all had to retire impoverished.' I did not meet any of those English 'losers' in Wales, but no doubt there were a few, very few compared to the English 'winners' of huge fortunes. The same writer did not hear that native Welshmen 'of slender resources' accomplished any very big things in connexion with colliery ownerships. But a few native Welshmen did eventually manage to get a few pickings. I thought it best to explain that the Englishmen referred to by the writer I have quoted from saw to our development right across our rich coalfield from east to west, and right from the foothills near our coastline back up into our valleys for about twenty-five miles. I wanted to make that quite clear.

For this coalfield of ours was something of a money-making mystery at the time I am speaking of, particularly to the English gentlemen who were in the majority in the House of Commons. Time and again the Englishmen who were developing our coalfield, who were also members of the House of Commons, had to try and explain the mystery of our rich coalfield in the House of Commons. One of them, a Cornishman resident at Singleton Abbey, which overlooked Swansea Bay, made a speech in the House of Commons in which he claimed that he was 'as intimately acquainted with the South Wales coalfield as with the floor of the House'. This Englishman, Sir Henry Hussey Vivian, afterwards Lord Swansea, Eton and Cambridge and the 'Metallurgical King' of South-West Wales, had, we are told by the same writer, 'a great and glorious career of usefulness'. The spectacle of Swansea as we approached it from the east with Joseph and his family about this time, on towards the winter of 1881, did not seem to us to be a very 'glorious' or 'useful' job of work as far as the Welsh of Swansea and district were concerned. It looked much better, of course, from Singleton Park, inside which the noble pile called Singleton Abbey was situated. This was the home of the Vivians, the family which had done most of what was done for and to Swansea.

I suppose it is because my own mother was born in the Swansea district that I am still interested in that part of our country. Then again Joseph Parry and his family are going now to settle down at Swansea, where the name of Sir Henry Hussey Vivian is a name to conjure with. 'Fair but firm, that's me,' he once said. Firm he certainly was, for in 1875 it was he was the firmest of the colliery owners who locked us Welsh miners out for twenty-two weeks. He moved a resolution at a meeting of coal-owners held at the Royal Hotel, Cardiff, moved that we Welsh miners should have our wages reduced by fifteen per cent. This was too much not only for us miners who were locked out but also for some of the coal-owners. Two of them moved and seconded an amendment that we miners should have a reduction of only ten per cent in our wages. But Mr (as he then was) Henry Hussey Vivian was firm and he carried the meeting and we miners were told that we would have to accept a reduction of fifteen per cent in our wages. So we miners of South Wales did not think very highly of Sir Henry Hussey Vivian, no doubt because we were still feeling bitter after having been locked out for twenty-two weeks six years before this time.

Some say strike and others say lockout and it is well to know the difference, isn't it? If we miners said to the coal-owners: We want a fifteen per cent increase in our wages, and the coal-owners say no, and we all stay away from the mines, then that is a strike. We have struck work. But if one day the coal-owners say, as they did say in '75, if they say: We are going to reduce your wages by fifteen per cent, and we say no, and the coal-owners say: Yes, from the beginning of next month your present wages will be reduced fifteen per cent, take it or leave it; then if we miners do not accept that huge reduction we are locked out. It is complicated, I know, but I want you to understand these things better than the House of Commons did at the time. I also want you to be better acquainted with the South Wales coalfield and iron-works and things than were the members of the House of Commons at the time, the time when Joseph and his family were going to settle down at Swansea. I say 'settle down' but I doubt very much whether Joseph has got it in him to settle down anywhere. That is his own look-out.

Before going to hear Mary Davies singing at the Merthyr National Eisteddfod better for me to say something about what we call the Swansea district, and I must say something about why Joseph picked on Swansea as his next place of residence and work. Now the district – I had better not include Llanelly or the Llanelly people will kill me. Llanelly people would be most indignant if I included them in any district. The thing to remember is that we are speaking of what we call the 'stone-coal district', which others would call the anthracite coal district. There are many places in this district starting with Pont, Pontardawe, Pontardulais, Pontyberem and so on. Gowerton and Gorseinon – all sorts of names meaning coal, iron, tin-plate, copper and other things. All running down to Swansea, but as Swansea is short of facilities for the shipment of coal and things then some of it has to go to other places to be shipped. Some even had to go nearly sixty miles to Cardiff and when that happened the Swansea people, who do not like the people of Cardiff much, said: We must have a new dock in Swansea and the sooner the better. Swansea was the natural centre of population of – well, upwards of two hundred thousand say, excluding, of course, the population of Llanelly and Neath.

With all this work going on it is unnecessary for me to say that there were hundreds of slag-tips and clinker-tips and ash-tips and tips of all sorts of industrial refuse all over the place. Bound to be, I know. Such disfiguration and discoloration of the landscape, not to mention pollution of rivers, streams and the air, is inseparable from such rapid development as ours. In the middle of all this was the up-and-coming town of Swansea with its own newspaper and all. It had four if not five times more Welsh chapels than Cardiff had but not one more Welsh chapel than Merthyr had. Yet it was much more Welsh than Merthyr was for Swansea had not felt the weight of alien influences to the same extent as Merthyr had. Its two main streets were narrow and crowded on Saturdays and holidays. Housing generally was as bad as at Merthyr, so Joseph had great difficulty in finding a tidy house there.

That is, in brief, the Swansea Joseph took his family to from Aberystwyth in 1881. Some of you may have known Dr Thomas Rees, one of our greatest preachers. But before I tell you about him and Joseph I must, in fairness to the people of Aberystwyth, tell you about the farewell performance there of Joseph's opera 'Blodwen'. Hundreds were turned away after the Hall was packed. Now that he was leaving the people of Aberystwyth wanted to show how much they appreciated both the man and his work. The opera could have been performed there three nights and each of the three performances would have had splendid audiences. It was Joseph's students that organized this farewell performance and it was most gratifying to Joseph. When you are leaving a place and after you have left the earth people do seem to think more of you than they seem to when they know that they will be seeing you next morning and the morning after same as usual.

Still, that performance of his 'Blodwen' at Aberystwyth did much to encourage Joseph on the eve of his departure to Swansea. I was going to tell you about Dr Thomas Rees, our great preacher, who at that time was preaching at Ebenezer Chapel, Swansea. But I will have to leave him and Joseph for now to go back to Merthyr to meet the train and William

Davies and his daughter, Mary. Better have a cab ready, for with their luggage it will be too far for them to walk up as far as our house. I knew William at once but I could hardly believe my eyes when I saw the young woman who was with him. This is never Mary, I said. Who else would she be? said William. Well, well, I said. Talk about ladylike. She and her father dressed the London way and when they spoke English it was the highest English. I have noticed that most Welsh people after they have lived in London for some years do talk the English very high. But after four years there Moses Davies, this lovely young woman's grandfather, came back to Merthyr speaking no sort of English. He had stuck to his Welsh during the four years he was working as a plasterer in London.

Looking at this young woman with a sun-umbrella and everything, who would believe that her grandfather was a plasterer? Who would believe that her own father, looking every inch a gentleman in the cab on the way to our house, was also a plasterer for many years before he became known as a sculptor? That is how it is. Now this young woman in the cab with us is R.A.M. and earning more money by singing than her father earns as a sculptor. Yes, and as a singer she was worth every penny she got. In Welsh and in English she sang for us and every word of the songs in both languages she gave us. Then in the oratorio with Ben Davies – but I must not start or I will never finish, for it is soft I am about good singing.

On the Thursday morning it was that I saw Will Full-Moon with that same young woman, who looked much older now. It was outside the Pavilion on what we committee-men called 'the Prom'. It was the grass of the Big Field all around the huge Pavilion in which the National Eisteddfod was being held that we called 'the Prom'. For standing about or walking around and talking – and every day weather permitting the same – were the same few people who each year attend our National Eisteddfod not for what goes on but just to see who is there and to have a gossip. When it threatened rain or when their legs got tired of walking or standing they went into the pavilion to try and find a seat in which to sit for a bit. These 'Eisteddfodwyr' as we call them in Welsh were elderly and they remembered ever so much about past National Eisteddfods. They stood and watched singers and conductors and adjudicators and others going into the Pavilion and noted all changes for better or worse from previous years. They were the loyalist diehard brigade of Eisteddfod fans who were never absent nor ever there at the same time. Most of them were distinguished-looking men and a few of them were undistinguished and small, and it was the small busy little men that hurried from group to group with 'the latest' from inside the Pavilion.

Then Welsh singers who had not been engaged to sing at our National Eisteddfod concerts walked with a don't-care air around outside the huge Pavilion, and with the slightest encouragement they would air their grievances to group after group. Did you ever see such bad arrangements as this year? And the muck they are giving us at the evening concerts? The entries for the competitions do not interest me for that's not Art. Why singers and adjudicators from London? It is not myself I am thinking of for I have been rushed to death and I am glad of a rest, but surely singers here ... And they walked around and around the Pavilion and they saw and were seen by all who came in and went out.

It was out on this 'Prom' that I saw Will Full-Moon walking arm-in-arm with that same young woman, who now appeared to be almost middle-aged. Will, I remembered, had said that she was older than I took her to be that time down Cardiff. I tried to think how old Will himself would be. Must be getting on for sixty, I thought first, then when I remembered him singing that time with Blind Dick under Ieuan Ddu at Market Square Chapel then I knew

283

that he was well over sixty. But he did not look it now, and fatter he was too. The woman with him was better-dressed and more handsome than when I saw her that time down Cardiff. But what were they doing here at the National Eisteddfod? I waited for them to come round to where I was standing and wait I had to. For they stopped at group after group of the gossips and Will kept on raising his top-hat and talking and laughing. I waited nearly a quarter of an hour for them.

Hullo, Will, I said. I see you have got some of your meat back on your bones. Yes – but please talk English for my wife to understand, he said. Certainly, I said. I am glad to meet you, Mrs Morgan – or should I say Mrs Morgani? No, Morgan is good enough here in my dear husband's native town, she said. Yes, I am getting back to something like I used to be, said Will. You are on the Committee, I see. I am on two committees, I said. We were at Bristol, where I sang last night, he said, and as I was not to sing again until Saturday night, I thought I would bring my wife to Merthyr for the National Eisteddfod concert tonight. It will be a good concert, I said. Mary Davies will be singing tonight again. My wife is a principal now, he said. Well done, I said. Everything is going well since I gave up the drink and we got married, said Will. I have been to Thomas Town cemetery to see Blind Dick's grave and very tidy it is indeed. I paid the man the half-sovereign you gave me to turf it up and wash the stone down, I said. Please take this half-sovereign for it will want doing again next year, said Will. Perhaps this is the last time me and my wife will be coming to Merthyr. I have very near had enough of the place already. Do not stay another minute if you do not want to, I said. Merthyr has managed without you for a long time and no doubt it will manage after you are gone. My husband does not mean to offend, I am sure, said Will's wife. If I offend by saying that I have had a bellyful of Merthyr then I offend, that is all, said Will. And if I offend by saying that Merthyr has had more than a bellyful of you and your sort, then I offend, that is all, I said. Please, sir, said his wife. My husband does not mean what he has just said. Sometimes he cries like a child for this, his native town. Yes, more fool me, said Will. Am I saying it is your fault? he said to me. Nor I won't have you saying it is the town of Merthyr's fault either, I said. Here all the time I am and here I will be if I live to be as old as old Ben Watkins the Graig Farm lived till he died. Damn, there was a man if you like, said Will. If there was a handful of his sort left here I would never leave the place. We cannot all be the same but most of us are respectable all the time, remember, I said. I am glad you have married tidy and now I will wish you joy and go about my duties – Wait, said Will. Wait till you have heard my wife speaking the bit of Welsh I have taught her. Every night before going to sleep she do say it. Say it for him, my darling. She smiled and said in Welsh, the way a child would say it: 'Yr wyf fi yn dy garu di', she said. Well done, I said. Those seven words in Welsh are only three in English. 'I love you' was what she said in Welsh and Will smiling and looking soft at this half-English half-something European woman who had said 'I love you' in Welsh to please him. Where are you stopping the night? I said. No place to sleep there is in Merthyr or in Dowlais either. I knew that so I booked a room at the Royal Hotel down Cardiff, said Will. Will this evening's concert be over in time for us to catch the last train back down to Cardiff? Yes, I said. Listen. You must come the two of you to our house to have food. I would like you, now that you are married tidy, to meet Mary Davies, who you will hear singing tonight. She and her father, William Davies, are staying the week with us. Are they stuck-up? said Will. Not a bit, respectable, that's all, I said. H'm, said Will. They will be glad to see you and you will be glad to talk to them about Myfanwy Llewelyn, I said. It was at their house she lived the years she was studying in London at the Royal Academy.

Oh, that William Davies, is it? said Will. To be sure, I said. Then Myfanwy has asked me in more than one letter to call and see him and his daughter, said Will. Of course I will be glad to meet them. Then I will have something to write to Myfanwy about. My husband is very fond of the lady Myfanwy, said Will's wife. He is going to show me the awful place where she used to live. China in Merthyr is no more awful than some of the places in wherever you come from, Mrs Morgan, I said. He won't hear a word said against Merthyr, said Will. You still live in Twynyrodyn, don't you? Yes, I said, and in the same house. Dinner will be ready there for you at one o'clock. Then there is just time for me to take my wife down as far as the Iron Bridge, said Will. See you at one o'clock. Many thanks for having us to your house to dinner, said his wife. You shall have tea there as well, my gel, I told her, and off they went.

She was a nice woman and Will Full-Moon was lucky to have her for his second wife. She and Mary Davies got on very well during the short time they were together in our house, and it was only now that I got to know that she could talk and sing in Italian. So could Mary Davies, come you. They were there to dinner and they stayed talking till tea-time, then Mary Davies went to rest a bit before going to sing at the concert. I went down to the station for one of the new cabs, the ones that the tops go right back to make them look like open carriages. Four sat in it, Mary and Will's wife and Will and William Davies, and I sat up in front with the driver. Mary looked lovely in her concert dress with a lace-edged shawl over her head and shoulders. Will's wife had helped her to dress and whilst she was doing that Will ran down town to look everywhere for some flowers to give Mary to wear. He came hurrying back with a most expensive bunch of flowers and his wife fixed them, but not all, to look lovely on Mary. We drove right into the Big Field and right around to the back of the Pavilion to the room where the singers and the conductors sat until it was time to start the concerts. Will jumped out of the carriage to give his hand first to Mary and next to his wife and I must say that he behaved in every way like a gentleman. He had not talked rough once in our house. A perfect gentleman, that is what Mary Davies said he was, and who can say that he is not now that he has married the woman tidy and is keeping away from the drink as well. No doubt it is a contented mind have helped him more than the drink to get fatter than he was.

Who will ever forget Mary Davies singing that night? She more than Ben Davies, the tenor, was the talk of the town and district and of Wales for months after. But we have talked enough about singing, goodness knows, so we will say no more about Mary's singing now. Joseph Parry was there and heard her and said that she was – now I am starting again. Joseph soon had something else besides singing to think of, for a week or so anyway. The baby came, a little boy, and for nearly a week both Jane and the child did anything but well. The second week they both grew stronger but Jane was confined to bed for a month with this one. Yes, she had a very bad time with Willie, which was his first name. What name shall we give him? she had asked Joseph the day she got up for the first time. For long it was doubtful if he would want a name in this world but now it seemed that he would stay so she asked Joseph: What name shall we give him? I have got it ready for him, said Joseph. After the greatest of all British musicians and teachers we will call him William Sterndale Bennett Parry. Four names is a lot for a child to carry, said Jane, who was still very pale. Perhaps so, said Joseph. We will knock one out and call him William Sterndale Parry. Yes, that would be nice, said Jane.

So the boy was named after the Principal of the Royal Academy of Music in Joseph's time. Joseph thought there was no one living like Sir William and Jane thought that four names were a lot for the boy to carry. When I first saw Willie I thought one name was plenty for him to carry, for if ever there was a delicate child then it was Willie. He was his mother's darling and his two sisters, whose names I can't for the life of me remember, thought the world of little Willie. But what were the names of Joseph's two daughters, who used to call me uncle though I was no relation to them or their parents? No doubt I shall remember their names when I don't want to. I am feeling worried about not being able to remember things and people and their names when I want to. I know I am getting on but surely I am not too old to remember. I can remember far back like if it was yesterday but when I try to remember things that happened and people I met only yesterday then I cannot. This again is no doubt some sort of mystery. Acting on two committees during the year of preparation for the National Eisteddfod and during the week it was on at Merthyr I had to meet hundreds of people. I would meet a man, or perhaps two men, and they would say: Hullo, how are you this long time? I would shake hands and say Oh, I am grand, thank you – and you are looking grand too. All the time I would be asking myself: Who are these two? I had to pretend that I knew who they were until I could get away from them. In bed that night I would ask myself: Who were those two men? No, I could not remember. Then when I did not want to remember them they and their names would come to my mind and push out two other people whom I wanted to keep in mind. Awful, it is getting. Soon I will not be able to remember my own children and grandchildren. It is no use me try to force my memory now. I have tried and the more I try the less I remember about those I badly want to remember, like the names of Joseph's two daughters now. No doubt they will come to me too late like all those others.

Did I finish telling you about Dr Thomas Rees, the Minister of Ebenezer Chapel, Swansea, and Joseph's very good friend? It was he was mainly responsible for Joseph's coming to Swansea in the first place. He thought Joseph was a great musician and as such entitled to more fair play than

Dr Rees thought he had had in Wales up to now, 1881. This talk about 'fair play' for a man of genius in Wales is as much beside the point as elsewhere in this old world. In Wales we all know chaps who are always saying: I have never had fair play. When it comes to musicians did Beethoven have what we in Wales call 'fair play'? Whether or no it is no good us talk that way. Joseph had a wife and five children and he claimed that he was in the direct line from the great Mendelssohn. His parting words to one student who was going to try his luck in the musical world were: You are bound to succeed and I will tell you why. Mendelssohn taught Sterndale Bennett, he taught me and I taught you so there you are. Enough said.

Now Joseph was composing and running what he called 'The Musical College of Wales' at Swansea. On Sundays he was playing the harmonium at Ebenezer Chapel and on week-nights he had his choir. Most of the best voices of Swansea and district were in Silas Evans's choir so Joseph had to build his choir from Silas's leavings. Joseph had no patron but he had many friends and well-wishers. The men who were growing richer and richer in Swansea and district could easily have built him an Academy of Music and made him Principal at a salary which would have left his creative mind free from the many worries which forced him to live and compose from day to day. The 'local' conductors were jealous and unfriendly and unhelpful and the men of wealth were indifferent to the fact that there was a Welshman of undoubted genius struggling to establish himself and his 'Musical College of Wales' in the town.

Joseph left Aberystwyth a disappointed man; he left Swansea a bitter man. I met him from time to time during those seven years he was at Swansea, seven years of the prime of his creative life, and each time I met him and asked him how he was getting on at Swansea he would sigh first and then brace himself to say: Oh, middling. My College is going very well and my other work is coming

289

middling, thank you. But behind his eyes behind his glasses there was, I thought, the creative mind labouring under a sense of frustration. This again is something about which I cannot be positive, for who knows what happens to a mind like Joseph's in a place like Swansea during seven long years from 1881 to 1888? I went to Swansea to see his College there but I did not see Joseph at the College. His son, Haydn, was in charge, and Mendy, his brother, was helping him that day. Where is your father? I asked. At home, said Haydn. Oh, I said. Is he poor in health or something? No, said Haydn. He is middling in health but he has to get a work ready for the National Eisteddfod at Liverpool. Oh, yes, I read something in the *Merthyr Express* about that, I said. If it is a student you are thinking of sending here then I can tell you all about that, said Haydn. No doubt, I said. But on other business I am in Swansea. Tell your father I called. Yes, and thank you for calling, said Haydn.

At the railway station when I was taking the train back to Merthyr who should I meet in the compartment but Dr Thomas Rees. Well, well, I said. Going away to preach you are, is it? Yes, he said. Not to Zoar in Merthyr again? I said. No, to Pontypridd I am going, he said. Then the brothers and sisters at Pontypridd will enjoy you on Sunday same as we did at Zoar that Sunday in Merthyr, I said. After they have heard me preach three times on Sunday they will have had enough of me, he said. No fear, I said. He was a preacher we Welsh could never have enough of, 'Un o hoelion wyth', as we called such pulpit giants. One of the 'eight-inch nails' of the Welsh Pulpit, that was how we spoke of such grand preachers as Dr Thomas Rees of Ebenezer Chapel, Swansea. In my young days I would walk a long day through to hear him preach and walk back home after through the night. For there was drama in the Welsh Pulpit when the likes of him were in it. He and his sort, standing in their pulpits, could open the mouth of hell until you could see it for yourself, and then they would, in the twinkling of an eye, snatch you from the brink of hell and it would be the gates of heaven you would see opening before you next. Oh, yes. If you do not believe me ask anyone who heard them preach. And here I was having the pleasure of the company of Dr Thomas Rees more than half the way from Swansea to Merthyr on the train.

How is Joseph Parry getting on amongst you in Swansea? I said. Oh, fairly well, I think, he said. I think he is happier with us than he was at Aberystwyth. I called at the College but he was not there, I said. Working at home, his boy said. Oh, yes, said Dr Rees. No doubt he is hurrying up to finish that work for the National Eisteddfod in Liverpool. He have always had to hurry over his work, worse luck, I said. That eldest boy of his seems to be a good boy. Haydn is a good boy, said Dr Rees. In some ways better with the students than his father. Then Mendy is not bad either. Joseph would like if he could to send the two of them to London to the Royal Academy. No doubt, I said. But like will be their share I am afraid. The Welsh of America it was that sent Joseph to the Royal Academy but it won't be the Welsh of Swansea that will send his two sons, no matter how much they are worth sending. Haydn is certainly worth sending, said Dr Rees. Then tell the people of Swansea to send him, I said. Every Sunday for years I have told the people of Swansea many things, said Dr Rees. I know, I said. Perhaps, said Dr Rees, perhaps it is better for Haydn to stay and help his father. If his father had to be every day at the College what chance would he have to do a big work like he is now doing for the National Eisteddfod at Liverpool? H'm, I said. Do you think that you in Merthyr, where he was born, could do more for Joseph than we are doing for him in Swansea? said Dr Rees. No, I said. There you are then, said Dr Rees. At the Merthyr National Eisteddfod – I do not need to tell you for you were on the Committee – I know, I know, but I was only one, I said. And I am only one in Swansea, said Dr Rees. Joseph, remember, is not an easy man to help or to handle. Genius he is, no doubt, and men of genius will go up or down their own way. Dr Rees chuckled and said: You are talking about my preaching. Joseph sits behind me at the harmonium twice every Sunday but I doubt very much whether he has heard one of my sermons. His head is too full of music for anything of mine to go into it. It is only now that he is working on this work for the National Eisteddfod that he has asked me a few things about the Bible and Nebuchadnezzar. His mother saw that he had plenty of the Bible when a boy at Bethesda Chapel at Merthyr, I said. True, and he has not forgotten, said Dr Rees. But by now he has got it all mixed up in his head with the stories he wants to make operas out of. He has not long finished an opera out of a story written by Major Jones and it is soon to be performed at the Royal Theatre in Swansea. Another opera he has got half-finished and he will go at that as soon as he has finished Nebuchadnezzar. A trwchwant for work he always was, I said. Then songs, hymns, and goodness knows what all are coming from him in a stream all the time, said Dr Rees. He do bring manuscripts or scores or whatever you call them to chapel with him and some Sunday he will be sure to forget and play something of his own on the harmonium instead of the hymn I have given out. That would be Joseph all over, I said. I want the chapel to get a pipe-organ for him to play, said Dr Rees. But my deacons are afraid. Afraid of what? I said. Not afraid of the cost, said Dr Rees. Afraid that if we buy him a pipe-organ it is more music than religion we shall have on Sundays at Ebenezer. Nonsense, I told them. Religion can stand the best pipe-organ and the best player in the world. If it cannot then our religion is not the right religion. I think we shall get him a pipe-organ.

When did you say his new opera is to be performed at Swansea? I asked. Let me see, said Dr Rees. Is it the week before or the week after Christmas. I will find out for sure, I said. And you will have to make sure of getting in too, said

Dr Rees. If you are coming say now and I will get a ticket for you. You will not get a train back to Merthyr after so you are welcome to stay the night with us. Right, you get a ticket for me for the same night as you will be going, I said. Then if it is good I will try to get it performed at the Drill Hall in Merthyr. What, after what happened at the Merthyr National Eisteddfod? said Dr Rees, smiling and going on to quote from the Bible. 'A prophet is not without honour –' I know, I know, and perhaps you are right, I said. But do not forget the little devil in the singing. No, neither will I forget the big devil in the world at large, said Dr Rees.

We had to change at one place and cross from one platform to the other and that was all the tidy talk we had, for the train from there to Pontypridd, where Dr Rees got out, was cram-jammed with women with baskets and babies and everything. I went down from Merthyr to Swansea to hear Joseph's new opera, but it was performed in the English language. I thought it was to have been in Welsh same as 'Blodwen'. The story was about the American Civil War. 'Virginia' was the title of the opera and Virginia and Edgar were the lovers and there was some sort of a villain in it called Captain Bragg. I would rather not say anything more about this second opera of Joseph's. The people who had packed the Theatre Royal seemed to like it, for the story and the music were no worse than in some of the operas they had paid to see. But both story and music ... but I have said I will say no more. It was done and it could not be undone, so why bother? Well? said Joseph to me as I was leaving the theatre with Dr Rees. Leave it there, Joseph, I said. I think I will, he said. Thank you for not saying lies.

The next time I went to Swansea was for the annual College concert, which in three years had come to be regarded as the town's most popular musical feature. I went there because Mary Davies, who had been singing at Merthyr the night previous, when she had stayed with us, was the guest-artist at the annual concert of Joseph's College.

Now that was something like. Mary Davies sang as gloriously as ever and Haydn Parry played the piano like a master. The students, as choir, glee party, quartets and trios and soloists, were very good indeed. Joseph conducted and accompanied and made a happy little speech. Yes, that was something like a musical evening.

CHAPTER 12

Steel !

THE first accident case and the very first patient as well was a steelworker, if you please. I am speaking, of course, of our new General Hospital, which cost £6,000 to build. And now the first to be admitted was a steelworker. The doctors could not save his leg but they did manage to save his life, the doctors and the nurses between them. Had that first patient died it would have wanted all the police in Merthyr to drag the next patient into the place, such was the ignorant fear of the place and the prejudice against it in our town and district. I will tell you some of the things they were saying about the new Hospital after I have told you first about Cyfarthfa Works. You will no doubt notice that I did not say Cyfarthfa *Ironworks* that time. For it was not an ironworks any more. No big old song will I make about this but I want you to know what it meant to us at the time. We men of iron – and there were families that up to then had five generations of ironworkers in line from 1765 to when it happened in 1885. Families who for a hundred and twenty years had made iron in Cyfarthfa Ironworks, the first generation making charcoal-hammered iron into cannon before it was known that there was plenty of coal for making iron under our hills and valleys. But I said I would not make a big song about it, neither will I. Transition from iron to steel, some who had had schooling were saying, and the puddlers gathered on our street-corners said: What is transition? They were made to know, come you. Victims of progress we puddlers and ironworkers were. No good us stand on street-corners and talk all time.

But what if you had been an ironworker in Cyfarthfa Ironworks for fifty years up to 1885? You would talk too. Oh, yes. Steel be damned you would no doubt say, same as us. On the darkest night we used to find our way about Cyfarthfa and Dowlais and Plymouth and Penydarren Ironworks but now ... now we did not know what to say, now that Penydarren and Plymouth Ironworks were derelict and the other two great ironworks, Cyfarthfa and Dowlais, were reconstructed and were making steel. There were old men in 1885 who remembered what their grandfathers had told them about making iron with charcoal and about the farmers who sold their farms cheap to the first English Iron King. He gathered them all together and gave them plenty food and beer and promised them all jobs in his ironworks if only they would sell their farms both free and leased to him. Most of the farmers took the hundred golden sovereigns and became ironworkers, only a few, like the grandfather of old Ben Watkins of Danygraig Farm, told the English Iron King to go to hell in 1765.

What good me talk about 1765 in 1885? Iron is finished and steel is now the thing. Men were getting cleverer and cleverer every day after all the schooling they had been having from when the National School started in Merthyr in 1845. Forty years of schooling had produced the man of steel by 1885. Men and boys in the steelworks, for that is what we must call them now, most of the men and boys working in the steelworks could read and some of them could write as well. Many of them going about the steelworks with pencils in their waistcoat-pockets to write with – not making marks, mind you, but writing words and long words at that. More men writing in more offices for steel than for iron. More men walking about doing nothing with hands, only looking and thinking as they watched the steel and the furnaces as though it were babies they were looking after. Then after looking they would hurry back to offices.

We were told in 1885 that the change-over from iron to steel would not make much difference to those of us who were coalminers. If anything, they said, the steel will be better for you miners than ever iron has been. We shall want at least four if not five tons of coal to make a ton of steel in the steelworks. H'm, we said, and no more. Something goes and another thing comes. Our ironworkers for a hundred and twenty years had had to manage as best they could without a hospital. Now there was one for steelworkers to go into if they were injured and had a mind to. Perhaps you know our General Hospital. We had a great day when it was declared open for the reception of patients. People came from all parts and Sir William Thomas Lewis said – but if I repeat what he said I shall have to tell you some of what the other speakers said at the Opening Ceremony. It was nicely situated overlooking the ruins of Penydarren Ironworks and after it had been open a year me and Lewis Morgan were co-opted on the Hospital Committee. Being workmen ourselves it was thought that we could help to overcome the prejudice against the Hospital and make the people less afraid of going there when there was something serious the matter with them. Then Lewis conducted the Male Voice Choir and he could tell the members what a grand place the Hospital was. I was connected with several bodies in the town and district and I was asked to put in a good word for the Hospital whenever I could.

It was a long time before the people of the town and district lost their fear of the Hospital. Silly they talked. Grown men injured in our mines and steelworks being carried home through the town crying: Don't for God's sake let them take me to the Hospital. They feared that if they were taken to the Hospital then the doctors and the nurses between them could do just as they liked with them, and without any member of the injured one's family there to prevent them. Don't be silly, I kept on telling them. Same doctors there as come to your houses. Not murderers they are but doctors. But after a town and district has been a hundred and twenty years without a Hospital it takes some time to get used to it. Same with our new Workhouse. Old people with no one to look to or to look to them afraid in their heart to go there too. I would rather die on the road than in the Workhouse, they said, so you can tell what a hard fight our Institutions had to establish themselves after all this time. Our old puddlers were the most afraid of the Workhouse, though those still able to walk were allowed out once a week to beg a bit of tobacco or a penny to buy a pennyworth of tobacco. Many of those old chaps abused this great privilege by getting drunk same as they used to when they were working in the ironworks. We blamed those who gave them beer more than we blamed the old chaps themselves.

One other thing and I will get on with my story. Gambling. Yes, gambling. Above and between the derelict Penydarren Ironworks and below one of the biggest clinker-tips of the Dowlais works, there was a fair-sized stretch of rough grass. A man named Scott rented this bit of rough grassland and made a sort of sports' ground of it and there was whippet-racing there for a start. We called whippets 'milgies', and they used to run and catch hares if there were any available, if not then rabbits were used instead. There was a lot of betting and between races many played pitch-and-toss. There were also foot-races for men and many a champion sprinter appeared on Scott's Grounds, as they called it. There were many fist-fights up there too. Men would quarrel and then fight. Our chapels protested in vain. We had to put up with the Sports in the Big Field at holiday times, but the Sports in the Big Field were under the supervision of the police and there was always a band, the

Cyfarthfa Brass Band or the Band of the Merthyr Volunteers, playing throughout the day in the middle of the Big Field. But as for Scott's Grounds – oh, it was awful what went on up there. I used to like the Sports in the Big Field, on a fine day it was very nice up there. You could get refreshments in two big marquees and there was racing from about ten in the morning to about eight at night, and the Band playing between races. Foot-racing and pony racing and about this time there was high-bicycle racing as well. No old fighting though. Only up on Scott's Grounds the gambling and fighting, worse luck.

Now to get on with my story. I went on an excursion train to Swansea to see the Prince and Princess of Wales when they came there to open the new Dock, and someone told me that they were going to call it Alexandra Dock after the Princess. There were a lot of us down from Merthyr that day and we were all as proud as could be of Joseph, who was after all a Merthyr boy. For the occasion he had composed the grand march, 'Hail! Prince of Wales', for three brass bands and a choir of two thousand voices. This was conducted by Joseph himself, so you can tell how jealous the 'local' conductors were. You know how it is when royalty comes to a place. All the local notabilities want to be seen or heard or both seen and heard. Lord Swansea, who was only Sir Henry Hussey Vivian when we last met him, was there, of course. Though English he was regarded as the Lord of Swansea and therefore 'local'. But the conductors of Swansea and district, particularly Silas Evans, would not have it that Joseph was a 'local' man. So why should he have the honour of conducting the three brass bands and the choir of two thousand voices? Oh, they knew that he was a Doctor of Music and all that, he took good care that they should never forget that, they said, but when all was said and done he was not a Swansea man.

True, he was not, he was a Merthyr man and he was glad to see another Merthyr man late that afternoon. Now I noticed that his black hair was beginning to turn grey but he looked better in health than when I last saw him. Oh, you are here, he said. There are a lot of us here from Merthyr, I said. Excursion train there was from Merthyr. They are gone down to the Bay to wash their feet if no more in the sea. I will be going after them soon. No, you must come with me to the house for a cup of tea, he said. What good me come to Swansea if I do not go to see the sea? I said. You shall see it from the back of our house, he said. We are in another and better house now. Come on. How are things in Merthyr? Middling, sure, I said. How are things with you? Bit better than they were, he said. What did you think of my march for the Prince of Wales? What did he think of it? I said. What odds about him? said Joseph. He knows no more about music than the dock he has just opened. He told Lord Swansea to tell me that he was most pleased with it, then Lord Swansea sent some man to me with his compliments and the Prince's message. Still, you had it in the end, I said. Yes, I had it for what it is worth, he said. You are going up this hill too fast for me, I said. How old are you, Joseph? Forty-five next birthday, he said. And your hair turning already, I said. Were you up at Liverpool for the National Eisteddfod? he said. No, how did it go? I said. The National or my 'Nebuchadnezzar' do you mean? he said.

I stopped to catch my breath half-way up the hill and before walking on perhaps it would be better if I explained. You may be wondering why the National Eisteddfod of Wales was being held at Liverpool. Well, we Welsh claim Liverpool, which we call Lerpwl, as a Welsh town, and to try and keep it Welsh we send the National Eisteddfod of Wales there about once in twenty years. It is doubtful if we can keep the place Welsh but we shall keep on trying. We are also sending the National Eisteddfod of Wales to London, but not with the hope of making that place Welsh. We send it there for the sake of the London-Welsh to try and keep them Welsh and away from the English of London.

We in Wales do not want to lose the London-Welsh altogether, for by now there are thousands of Welsh people living and working in London, where hundreds of them are getting on very well indeed. Big businesses of their own many of them have got.

But it was about the National Eisteddfod at Liverpool that Joseph asked me now and I was trying to think what was best to say. He had been commissioned by Liverpool to write a new and a big work for one of their evening concerts and he had written the cantata, which I always called an oratorio – anyway, the name of it was 'Nebuchadnezzar', or Scenes in Babylon, and it was dedicated to the Prince of Wales, by His Royal Highness's permission, of course. I was not at Liverpool to hear it performed there but I had heard all about it from Merthyr people who were there and did hear it. I took no notice of what Lewis Morgan said about 'Nebuchadnezzar' but many other Merthyr people who were as well-disposed towards Joseph as I myself am told me more or less the same as Lewis Morgan had told me. They said that Joseph's 'Nebuchadnezzar' was not half as good as his 'Emmanuel'. So there you are. Joseph is writing and presenting so many things that I am getting mixed up trying to follow him. What with oratorios, cantatas and operas – and now he was going to be a writer and an editor, if you please. He was writing a book on 'The Theory of Music' and he was going to edit a book in several volumes as soon as he could find time.

He did not ask the second time what he had asked before I stopped half-way up the hill to catch my breath. He went on to tell me that he thought 'Nebuchadnezzar' was the best work he had done. H'm, well done, I said, knowing that his last work was always the best in his own opinion, if you can call it an opinion. Knowing Joseph as I did I knew how fond he was of his work and how uncritical he was of his own work. It was no use trying to tell him to think twice, for he had as much as he could do to catch all the things that came to his mind one after the other. If he stopped to think for long they would be gone or if taken in it would soon be crowded out again. So he had to put them down on paper to see how they would shape. In most of his work the first shape was also the last, so lovely it was to him, and when he did force himself to re-shape something then its last shape was worse than the first. He very near poisoned me with his talk about music, talk almost entirely about his own work.

This is where we are living now, said Joseph. Much better house than the other. Come around the back way for to see the view from there. There you are. Isn't that a lovely view of the Bay? Indeed it is, I said. Now let us go round the front again, he said. My wife would not like it if I took you in the back way. It was when I went inside the house that I realized why it was that so much of Joseph's work was half-baked, slap-dash or whatever you choose to call it. Why it lacked depth and finish, why it was in the main unoriginal and enclosed between the leek and daffodil of Wales. So much of it went into the stream of Welsh music that dried up before it reached the great sea of world music. His music was full of promise but it was still only promising and him forty-five next birthday. Yes, I thought when I went with him into the house, this is where he loses some of his strength and inspiration. My dear, I have brought an old friend from Merthyr to have tea with us, he said, speaking English. You are most welcome, said Jane, putting little Willie down on the couch between his two adoring sisters. There was a piano being played and someone was singing in the room we had passed on the right as on our way in through the passage. Jane and the two little girls and little Willie were dressed in what I took to be their best clothes and I assumed that they had been somewhere along the route that royalty had taken down to the dock area earlier in the day.

Go and help your mother to put tea, my dear, said

Joseph to the eldest of his two little girls. She got up and he took her place on the couch beside little Willie. So you have seen the Prince and Princess and heard the bands and all, he said to the little boy. I am afraid that it has given him another of those dreadful headaches, said Jane. Pity, pity, said Joseph, lifting the little boy on to his lap. I wish our Haydn would stop playing that piano, said Willie, and he said it for me too. Haydn must play when he can, lovely boy, said Joseph. All day that piano, said Willie plaintively. I sat wondering how old he was. Must be three. You must excuse the look of the place to-day, said Jane. Such a great day and we have all been into town, our maid as well. I do not expect to see her until late this evening. I do not want to see her ever again, said Willie. Now, now, darling, said his mother. Mummy must have help you know. The youngest of the two little girls was playing with her dolls and the piano kept on playing in the next room. When it stopped the voices of Haydn and Mendy were heard differing on some point of composition, Mendy illustrating vocally and Haydn doing likewise on the piano.

In Welsh we have a saying about the running of a home, 'Nid oes llawer o drefn yn y ty hwn,' which in English could be said in this way: 'There is not much method in this house.' Joseph's home was not dirty or very untidy but everything seemed to be wit-wat somehow. Somehow crazy, as some of Joseph's American friends would say. This day I am speaking of I could not actually put my finger on any big fault in the household arrangements but I hope I never again have such a scrappy and noisy tea. Tell Haydn and Mendy to come along, dear, said Jane to her eldest daughter. I do so wish I had known you were coming, she said to me. Will you please sit here. They said they will come in a minute, said the eldest girl. Which may mean an hour – Joseph, you go and tell them to come to their tea. Mendy came out of the other room with a sheet of music in his hand and Haydn followed him out. All right, all right,

we'll ask dad, said Mendy. I don't need to ask dad or anyone for I know, said Haydn. Yes, you know a lot, don't
you? said Mendy. If I didn't know more about music than
you do I would give it up, said Haydn. Now, now, said
Joseph. Please, said Jane. We have a guest, a friend of your
father's from Merthyr. How are you, boys? I said, smiling.
How are you? said Haydn. You called at the College one
day when dad was not there. How is little Willie? said
Mendy, taking the child by the wrist and feeling his pulse
whilst making a face like a doctor. You leave him alone,
said his mother. Sit down at once. Dad, said Mendy, what
that boy wants is more fresh air and less coddling. Running
along the sands of the Bay instead of lying on the couch –
Will you sit down and get on with your tea? said Joseph.
There's this piece of music, said Mendy, waving the music
sheet. Our Haydn says – I said sit down and get on with
your tea, said Joseph. You must not take any notice of these
boys, he said to me.

Mendy sat down and reached across the table for bread-
and-butter and commenced eating. Merthyr, he said with
his mouth full, looking across the table at me. If I was dad I
would never go near the place again. Please mind your own
business, said his mother. Where are you going, Joseph? I
won't be a minute, said Joseph. Go you on with your tea,
he said to me. He went into the next room and Jane sighed.
So you are turning against Merthyr too, are you, my boy? I
said just for something to say. Please don't mind him, said
Jane as the sound of the piano was heard from the next
room. Now dad will be there for the rest of the night and I
will not be able to finish writing that song, said Haydn. Go
and tell your father to return here immediately, said Jane.
Haydn went to tell his father and Mendy said: It was you
people of Merthyr that turned against my dad. No great
man was ever treated more shabbily than my father was
treated at Merthyr. Haydn returned, followed by his father
who said: Sorry, but something came to my head and I had

to make a few notes. He sat down and Haydn also sat down. Then that means you will be working tonight, said Haydn. Don't I work every night? said Joseph. All right, I can go down to the College to work, said Haydn. So will I, said Mendy. And start arguing again? said Haydn. It was you that started the argument, said Mendy. And it is I that will finish it, remember, said Joseph, trying to look stern. Tea with our friend from Merthyr we are having now. Will you be coming down to Cardiff to see my new opera performed there? New opera? I said. Yes, the best I have written, said Joseph. Then why take it to Cardiff when there is a theatre here? I said. Cardiff is the best place at which to present a new opera, said Haydn. What do they know about opera here at Swansea? said Mendy. No more than they do at Merthyr. You have got it in for Merthyr, my boy, I said. These boys of mine took that affair in Merthyr too much to heart, said Joseph. I was saying about this opera – and I may send it to Merthyr after Cardiff. Not without a guarantee, dad, said Mendy. I do wish you would keep quiet, said his mother. Another cup of tea? she said to me. No more, thank you, I said. Come on, you have not had enough tea, said Joseph. Pour it for him, Jane. Haven't we got more cake than that? No, said Jane, I am afraid that is all we have. If I had only known you were coming – Never mind, he shall have some cheese, said Joseph. Fetch the cheese one of you gels. Sit where you are, said Jane, going to get the cheese. What did you say the name of this new opera is, Joseph? I said. 'Arianwen,' he said, then went on to tell me about it. 'Arianwen,' I said. Funny name for a gel. You have never had such a grand turn-out in Merthyr as we had here in Swansea to-day, said Mendy. Leave Merthyr alone, good boy, I told him. A choir of two thousand and three brass bands – that is something to conduct, he said. H'm, I said, looking not at him but at his brother. I was calling them boys but they were getting to be young men. After tea Joseph got the vocal score of his new opera, not the published score but the rough draft of the fair copies now being used in rehearsal. I am not paying to publish any more, he said. The publishing and the putting on of 'Blodwen' for the first time cost me £400. Come and hear a bit of this. It is getting time for my train, I said. Plenty of time, come on, he said. He took me into the room where the piano was and Haydn and Mendy followed us in. Joseph played and they sang all voices between them and it sounded pretty and rather good. Then you will come to Cardiff to hear it? said Joseph. I am afraid I am running about too much, I said. Where in Cardiff will it be? At the Theatre Royal, said Mendy. Right, I will see, I said. Haydn now had the piano and he was playing a bit and then making marks on the music sheet as though he were alone in the room.

Sure you know your way from here to the railway station? said Joseph. I will find it, I said. When are you coming to Merthyr again? Never, said Mendy. I was talking to your father, I said. I'm going down as far as the College and that is on the way to the railway station, he said. Don't stay there too late, Mendy, said his father. And mind to turn off the lights and lock the doors when you have finished there. Goodbye for now, he said to me. Mind to call whenever you are in Swansea. Thank you, I said. Mendy walked all the way to the railway station with me and talked all the way. A managing-agent was what his father wanted, he said. He was doing too much for nothing and for too little. Wales was not worthy of such a great man as his father. In a few years he and Haydn would see that their father got all he was entitled to. No more thank-you-Doctor jobs when he and Haydn took charge of the business-end – though our Haydn is a good bit like my father, he said. So perhaps I shall have to handle it myself. Then you won't let your father come near Merthyr, his native town, I said. Not without a guarantee that will ensure that he gets all he is entitled to, said Mendy. This native town talk and Hen wlad fy nhadau yn annwyl i mi is what my father has to be raised above if he is to take his rightful place in the world. You are talking very big, my boy, I said. And you and all like you in Wales are talking very small, he said. You will find you are smaller in the end, I said. Now you are letting your father make one big mistake. Making his living here in Swansea and taking his new opera to Cardiff for those people there to hear it first. If I had my way, said Mendy, it is beyond Cardiff to London we would take my father's new opera. Wait till our Haydn finishes his opera. Humph, and what about your opera too? I said sarcastically. I don't want to quarrel with an old man, he said. I am talking about our Haydn's opera. He will in time be as great as my father and I will look after both of them. Look after yourself, good boy, I said. It is our house and our little Willie so delicate is the trouble, he said. Mother is gone she only thinks of Willie and the girls. But they don't matter. It is my father and Haydn that matter. Every fair-play they should have to write the great music. My father was telling me about some girl from Merthyr who went to Italy. Did you know her too? Yes, I said. That is where I would like to take my father and Haydn for a few years, said Mendy. Away from hen wlad fy nhadau and the chapels. Harmoniums – He laughed out loud and said: Harmoniums and hymns and how are you to-day twice every Sunday. What do you think of the sermon and did he not pray lovely? Don't worry about that for your father never listens to sermons, I said. Why should he? said Mendy. He is far in advance and above that kind of thing. That is all right for people like you – Listen, good boy, I said. I am waiting for the train and I don't want you to wait with me. Go wherever you are going. I am going to write a song in an empty college before our Haydn comes to leave the piano at home for dad to work on, he said. You could not write a song in an empty college, could you? Go, go with your old cheek, I said. Perhaps I have been too cheeky, he said. But thinking of my father I am. Did you notice how his hair is turning? Yes, I said. That is worry and overwork, Mendy said. I do worry him too. Before long the well will be dry. He should be taken away somewhere where he could get new and fresh inspiration. He should have the money to go somewhere. Short of money we are in our house all the time. My mother has not been the same since Willie came. Cannot you in Merthyr do something to help my father to get away? How do you know that your father wants to get away? I said. My father does not know what he wants and that is the pity of it, said Mendy. Only you know what he wants, I suppose, I said. Yes, said Mendy. Sometimes he do get afraid and he flies away from the fear into his work. He cannot sit quiet away from his work. That is what I mean. He is afraid of us all together around the table, that is why he got up from the table and you there to see him to-day. He is always doing it. You are talking too deep for me, good boy, I said. I am talking too deep for myself, he said. Your Welsh is keeping good, I said. It is too good for my own good, he said. Now you are talking more silly than deep, I said. I am going to write my song, he said. Do what you can for my father before it is too late. None of us are very strong. Haydn do cough a lot in the nights. H'm, I said. Goodbye for now, he said. Goodbye – and thank you for sending me all the way to by here, I said. Your train is on that other platform, he said, and off he went.

I did not know what to make of him or his talk. Joseph no doubt was not finding it easy to work with Mendy and Haydn doing the same sort of work. Asking him this and that when he wanted to be left alone to think and work. Three musicians in the one house is two too many, as bad as three M.P.s trying to talk same time or three women trying to do their washing in one and the same tub at the same time. It is not Joseph that wants to be taken away but those two boys – and I must stop calling them boys. If only

Joseph could send them away somewhere perhaps then Joseph would have a better chance. But if he sent them away to study who would look after the students in the College when Joseph was away conducting or adjudicating? Or when he stayed home to work on an opera or oratorio? No doubt he had a few days home to write 'Hail! Prince of Wales' ready for this day's visit of the Prince and Princess. On the train taking me back to Merthyr I was thinking more of what that Mendy had said about his father than about the Prince of Wales. Joseph was more to me than the Prince of Wales, more of a Prince to me as well. A lot that Mendy had said was nonsense no doubt but there was some sense mixed up in it. What he said about their always being short of money was hurting me most. I would talk to Dr Thomas Rees about it next time I met him.

I had promised Joseph so I went down to Cardiff to hear his new opera at the Theatre Royal. Cardiff had two theatres but we in Merthyr did not have one, not a stone-built theatre anyway. All we had in Merthyr was the little wooden theatre at the top end of the old Tramroad. That could be taken down and put on a couple of carts and taken away to be put up somewhere else. But you could not do that with Cardiff's stone-built theatres. Of course we in Merthyr had the Temperance Hall and the Drill Hall, but they were not proper theatres like those down Cardiff. Easy now to see that Cardiff was bigger than Merthyr at last. Yes, much bigger than Merthyr now that Cardiff's new docks and our coal and steel – yes, steel – from the valleys were attracting big ships from all the countries of the world. At last I was beginning to see how it had happened, how places had grown to be bigger than the town of Tydfil the Martyr, onetime coal and iron capital of the world. As I told you Merthyr had then been bigger than Cardiff, Swansea and Newport if you had put all three together. I had not been to Newport for years but here I was in Cardiff after being in Swansea not so long before and I had to admit to myself that both Cardiff and Swansea were each of them bigger than our town, the mother town as you might say. No doubt when I did manage to go to Newport I would find that that was bigger than Merthyr too. Yes, that was what these bits of places by the sea had now grown to, and just because they were there to send our coal and iron and now steel further.

I had plenty of time in which to feel my position as a Merthyr man in Cardiff getting so proud and I had to go down to the docks this time again. I was walking down Bute Road when I saw men black with coal same as our miners in Merthyr. What coal-pit are they working at? I asked myself. More of them passed me and at last I asked a man who was standing on a corner. What pits are about here? I said. Pits? he said. Yes, coal-pits – or coal-mines if you like, I said. No coal-mines in Cardiff, he said. All the coal-mines are up in the valleys. I pointed after the men so black. Then where do those men get so black? I said. Oh, those coal-trimmers, he said. Those chaps earn good money, and they do earn it, no doubt about that. No doubt, I said, not knowing what a coal-trimmer was any more than I knew what a coal-broker was. This man on the corner went on talking and I listened until I had gathered that coal-trimmers worked down in the bellies of ships, into which our coal from the valleys was tipped, and it was they who put the coal tidy to keep the ships balanced properly to cross the seas in storm or sunshine. One is never too old to learn. The man on the corner seemed a tidy man and I was feeling like a sit down and a glass of beer so I asked him if he would have one with me. We went into a public-house in which there were women. Me and the man went the other side of the partition to where there were only men and we had a pint apiece and he told me a lot about the docks and the way they had grown. You are a Cardiff man, I said. Yes, but I was born across the water in Somerset, he said. I am going down the docks to see for myself in a minute, I said. Then I'll come with you, he said. I have business to do down there.

Dear, dear, it had grown since that time I was there with the Editor of the *Merthyr Express*. There you are again. We in Merthyr only had the *Merthyr Express* once a week and now in Cardiff they had two daily papers selling on the streets and down the docks. The man left me to go about his business and I walked slow till I could see where some of the ships were. I did not go close to them but turned back to where all the new buildings were. Most of them offices belonging to companies who had steelworks and coal-mines up in our valleys. Men and boys with papers in their hands and pens or pencils behind their ears all the time hurrying across the roads from one office to the other. Brass plates fixed to the walls outside the doors, brass plates with names on. Some of the names I knew but most of them I did not know. Cabs all the time bringing men from Cardiff down to the docks and wagons with two horses taking loads they had got from ships up into Cardiff. I was very near run over twice, so I asked a cabby who was turning his horse around if he was going back up to Cardiff. Better pay a shilling for a ride than get run over or too tired, I thought. It was only ninepence he charged me for the ride after all. He stopped his horse near Tabernacle Baptist Chapel and I got out and paid him what he asked. Tabernacle was a Welsh chapel, one of about a half-dozen Welsh chapels in Cardiff by this time. You know why that was, don't you? More and more Welsh people coming down from the valleys to live and work at Cardiff now that it was getting on like it was. More money to be got in Cardiff by handling coal and steel than by getting and making it up in our valleys in the first place. There were new big shops all over the place, one of the shops I saw would make a dozen of our Merthyr shops. There were also new streets of fine houses and more carriages and pairs on the streets than you would see in Merthyr in a month if not a year.

The two main streets were chock-a-block with horses and traps, horses and brakes, horses and wagons, hansom and the other sort of cabs and the carriages and pairs I have told you about. There were also some men riding horses and the narrow pavements were streaming with people all the time. Poor old Merthyr I was thinking as I walked towards where I had been told they were starting to build a College, another College of the University of Wales. I must have gone the wrong way for I did not find the place, but I found the hotel into which Will Full-Moon took me that time. Lucky it was the same barmaid and she remembered Will under his false name of Signor Morgani but she could not remember me. I reminded her that she had served me with bread and cheese and pickles that day and told her I would be glad of the same now with a pint of beer of course. Certainly, she said. But I had to have it in the crowded bar for the little room behind the bar was engaged, she said. You are busy, I said. Cardiff is getting to be a busy place.

All English talk in the crowded bar and me in the corner sitting quiet and listening and eating my bread and cheese and pickles and making the one pint last. If only you sit quiet in the corner of a crowded bar of an hotel in a big town you will hear a lot, and much that you do not want to hear if you are a tidy man. I heard the voices of women in the little room behind the bar, and their laughter I heard coming from there too. I did not like that. I do not hold with women drinking in public-houses. I am not one of those men who say that their women-folk should walk yards behind the man when they are out together, but I do not hold with women drinking in hotels and public-houses. It is the way I have been brought up, no doubt, but there it is. It was wrong of me to be in a public-house – for an hotel is only a public-house when all is said and done. Yes, perhaps it was wrong of me, but I had never signed the pledge. Neither have I ever been the worse for drink. That is what I say, of course, not what poor old Rosser Beynon or Moses

Davies would have said when they were both conducting Temperance Choirs. They would have said a man was worse for drink as soon as he entered a public-house and came under the smell of it. What Moses Davies and Rosser Beynon said about women drinking in public-houses was perhaps more to the point – but never mind that now.

I remembered my way to the theatre for it was the same theatre as Will Full-Moon was at that time, and as I wanted to wish Joseph success with his new opera I went around the back to the little door up two stone steps which Will Full-Moon also showed me that time. I am a friend of Dr Parry's, I said to the man. Is it this way he will come to conduct the opera? He has come, said the man. You'll find him upstairs in one of the dressing rooms – and if you are a friend of his tell him to come down and shift all these blasted amateurs back to their dressing-rooms. Look, just look at them. Like a lot of blasted kids. Our chaps can't get on for them. Go and tell them that the darned theatre isn't open yet. It is not for me to tell them, I said. I looked at the young men and young women dressed and made-up ready, peeping from behind the big curtain and from round the sides of it as excited as could be. Others were in groups talking and laughing and two men with their coats off went about the stage placing things and looking disgusted. No doubt those two were belonging to the regular staff of the theatre. I crossed the stage and went up that same twisty stone stairway that Will Full-Moon took me that time. I found Joseph sitting by himself in a tiny dressing-room with his cape-coat over evening dress and a top-hat on his head. Here I am, I said as jolly as could be. This is going to be a great night for you, Joseph. We shook hands. Yes, a great night I am sure, I said. He shook his head sadly. No? I said. My dear father is dead over in America, he said. No, I said. He nodded his head. When did you hear? I said. This morning before leaving Swansea, he said, then he sighed like if his heart was bursting and murmured the first two lines of the hymn which he had made the tune for and which was being sung all over Wales and by Welsh people the world over:

> 'Beth sydd i mi yn y byd
> Ond gorthrymder mawr o hyd ...?'

In the English that could mean:

> What is there for me in this old world
> But sorrow all the time ...?

Yes, indeed. How is your mother over there? I said. She is middling, said Joseph. She is leaving Danville in Pennsylvania to live with my sister in Portland, Maine. Your father was a good man, I said. Yes, Daniel Parry is still remembered in Merthyr by the old people of Bethesda Chapel. I should have listened to him, I tell you, cried Joseph, tears running from his eyes now. In America he wanted me to stay and spread my music. But I would not listen. Come back to Wales to be shut in I would – o fy nad, fy nad annwyl.

There he was crying for his earthly father who had left the earth and all I could say was: Try not to cry. Remember you have got to conduct your opera. I am not going to conduct, he said. No? I said. No, he said. Then who is? I said. Haydn, he said, and again he cried: O fy nad, fy nad annwyl, which in English means: O my father, my dear father. In translating some of the things Joseph and others say in Welsh one can easy go wrong for one good Welsh word may mean three times as much as the word for it in English, and one Welsh word can have three different meanings or, if you like, implications. That, of course, is because our Welsh language is so much richer than the English. Haydn! I said. Is he not a bit young for the job? To-night, and now, this very minute, said Joseph, Haydn is older than I am. It is like a baby I am feeling. All the time I am remembering my father in the home in Chapel Row and in the Cyfarthfa Ironworks. I am remembering him in America, everywhere I am remembering him. If I tried to conduct to-night it would be him I would be seeing on the stage. Perhaps so indeed, I said, then thinking to turn his mind away from his grief I said: The man down there on the stage said something about keeping those young men and women up here out of the way till it is time to start. What man? he said indifferently, and I could see it was no good me bother. You are going to listen if not conduct, I said. It will help to ease your mind perhaps. I may listen a bit from side of the stage, he said. I will not see you after for I shall have to run to catch the rodneys' train back to Merthyr, I said. Where is Jane with you? In Swansea, he said. Willie was too ill for her to leave him and come. Then I will go to sit in the theatre, I said. Plenty of time, he said. Try not to grieve, like grass we all are, remember, I said. Yes, indeed, he said. And try to come to see us in Merthyr before long, I said. I don't like leaving you to sit by yourself here. Where are Haydn and Mendy with you? No doubt talking to the musicians in that place under the stage, he said. Then you go and talk to them too, I said. Come now when I tell you.

He wiped his eyes dry with his handkerchief and followed me out of the room and down the twisty stone stairway. He went down lower to some place from where the sound of fiddles and other musical instruments were coming in whispers and I went out and around to the front of the theatre. The theatre was nearly full and plenty of talk in Welsh there was going on. It sounded as though the Welsh of Cardiff were there in strength, as they should be, for a new opera by Dr Joseph Parry was an important musical event when all was said and done. I looked around to see if I could see anyone I knew, but there was no one I knew downstairs and I was too far back to see any of those seated upstairs. Then it was that I saw William Davies and his daughter, Mary Davies, coming in through the door and going right on to the front to seats which had no doubt been reserved for them. I nearly shouted William's name but I stopped myself in time. I would see them after the first act. Had they come special all the way from London to Cardiff to hear Joseph's new opera? Or was it that Mary had come to sing or had been singing the night before somewhere in South Wales? She was looking like a queen and William, her father, though looking a lot older looked every inch a sculptor and a gentleman. There were a good many in evening dress present. I was dressed in my Sunday best which has always been good enough for me. The hair of the woman sitting directly in front of me was a bit of a nuisance, for she had piled it up till it was like a wall before my eyes. So to see who was there and who was coming in I had to lean sideways and look over her shoulders one after the other. Now the woman sitting next to her had her hair tidy behind and not on top of her head. I wished I was in front where William Davies and Mary, his daughter, were sitting with no one in front of them. Or up above in the seat Will Full-Moon had given me a free pass for that time. The place was chock-full now and there were many standing at the back behind me.

How many of them, I wondered, knew that Joseph was not going to conduct? All the members of the orchestra, most of them men of the theatre's regular orchestra, had all come to their places from under the stage and they were scraping and whistling and blowing to get into tune. This is the minute or two when an audience tunes itself up too. They begin to talk louder as soon as the fiddlers begin scraping and sawing and plucking their strings, and the man with the cornet softens his mouth before glueing it to the mouthpiece of his instrument to blow little twiddly-bits to get himself and his instrument into trim. The man with the trombone was doing the same and getting his back-and-fore arm loosened-up as well. It is the minute or two when the members of the orchestra combine to heighten the excitement and accelerate our expectation, particularly when the occasion is one when an opera is to be performed for the first time on any stage.

Perhaps in London a new opera by a Dr Joseph Parry would create little or no excitement, but Cardiff, though far from being as Welsh as Swansea, was still Welsh enough to make a new opera by Dr Joseph Parry an occasion and an event of first-class importance in the Welsh section of the musical world – though this opera will be sung in English mind you. The thing to remember is that by this time Joseph was 'The Doctor' to all Wales. Beside him was no other. He was 'The Doctor', and for a dozen years he had been seen and heard and spoken of more so than any other dozen men of the Principality. Handsome and distinguished-looking he had appeared at concerts, Eisteddfods and the more sacred musical festivals we Welsh call 'Gymanfa Ganu'. All the Welsh were singing his hymn-tunes, choirs and soloists were performing his oratorio, 'Emmanuel', and several of his cantatas. Amateur operatic companies were performing his 'Blodwen' in English and Welsh and choirs and singers were singing his choruses and songs. Little children, for whom he did some of his best work, were singing his choruses and songs. 'Gan Dr Parry', meaning 'By Dr Parry', was to be seen on song-sheets in the hands of hundreds if not thousands all over Wales. So he was 'The Doctor'. Yet, though he neither smoked nor drank strong waters he was more often than not without money in his pocket. Well-known but not well-paid, a personality who was a great draw but who drew very little in the way of pay for himself. There were times when he tried to be business-like and firm and those were the times he got least. But a new work by 'The Doctor' was what I was talking about, wasn't it? Here was the Theatre Royal, Cardiff, crowded right out to the doors. How much would he get out of this and the following six performances, which includes the Saturday matinee? How much did the place hold in real money? I suppose it held on an average about £5 per hundred persons – I say that because it was a shilling I paid. Right up against the roof there were people who had paid only sixpence and right in front of me there were people who had paid two shillings. There were many who had not paid anything. Let us say that the first-night takings were £50 and we shall not be far wrong. Go and pay for the theatre, orchestra, advertising and things out of that and see what you have left. You will not get fat on what will be left and it is no use you thinking of the other performances and royalties to follow, for in the case of Joseph they did not 'follow'.

Here comes Haydn looking handsome in evening-dress and there is first dead silence and next an excited buzz of conversation in an undertone. Haydn with his father's baton in his hand turns about to face it and there is dead-silence again. Ladies and gentlemen, he said. He swallowed hard and then continued. A word of explanation is due to you. As a family we have suffered a bereavement which, though it was in America, comes very near to us, particularly my father. My Grandfather, Daniel Parry, has died in America. My father is therefore not feeling himself this evening so he has asked me to conduct in his stead. I cannot hope to equal him but I shall, with your indulgence, do my best. Thank you. He turned his back on us and the little applause and silenced the beginning of murmured conversation with a tap-tap on the music stand in front of him. Well done, boy, I was saying inside myself. Your mother's English talk you talked very well. The overture began and I settled down to listen.

Some of you may have heard 'Arianwen', and perhaps you will agree with me that it is fairly good. The trouble with me this night was that I remembered the performance of 'Faust' at this very same theatre that time Will Full-Moon gave me and the Editor of the *Merthyr Express* free passes. Not fair it was to compare the two but I could not help myself. The bits of acting, if acting you could call it, between the singing of 'Arianwen', made me feel glad of the head of hair like a wall on top of the woman's head in front of me. They say that we Welsh are natural actors and actresses; if we are then it must be off the stage. Oh, the bits of acting were terrible. The singing was very good and I am sure that Joseph himself could not have conducted any better than his son, Haydn, did that night. There was not much story in this picture of Wales in the eighteenth century. There were lovers and a villain and a funny man – and wasn't there a woman who was supposed to be a witch? The chorus of splendid voices sang well but as though they were singing competitively at one of our National Eisteddfods. If they could act then they did not try to the night I was there. Still, the spirit of the thing was truly Welsh, what else could it be with a libretto by Dewi Mon and the music by 'The Doctor'? It was much better than the last opera Joseph wrote music for, that 'Virginia' which made me feel sorry I went all the way from Merthyr to Swansea to hear it.

After the first act I sidled out and walked down to the front for a word with William Davies and his daughter, Mary. As luck would have it they were coming up from the front to go out to where the tickets are sold to get more air. Well, well, said William. Look who is here all the way from Merthyr, Mary. What about you all the way from London? I said. Mary's been singing at Pontypridd and at Porth, he said. What do you think of the Doctor's new work, Mary? I said. Doctor Mary now, if you please, said William. What now? I said. Mary is a doctor, a doctor of music, said William. Mary smiled – she hardly ever laughed – and said: Dad is advertising the fact everywhere he goes. It is nothing really – Nothing to be a doctor of music same as Joseph Parry! I said. I think it is a great thing, said her father. So do I, I said. Well done, lovely gel. Pity your grandfather is not here to call you Doctor Mary

Davies – now being as you are a doctor of music tell me what you think of this opera? Quite a nice little thing so far, she said. That is what I think too, I said. Nice but little, too little for the man who swept the boards of our National Eisteddfods with his compositions twenty years ago. I think Haydn conducts extremely well, said Mary. He has got it in him, that boy, said William. He's no longer a boy, father, said Mary. He certainly is very good. He should come up to London. Why must all the Welsh who are very good go up to London? I said. Now, don't start that again, said William with a chuckle. No joking matter, I said. I agree, said Mary, and I still maintain that London is the only place for an artist. Your grandfather did not think so, I said. My father does, she said. I would very much like to do something to help Haydn Parry, father. We will have a talk with him, said her father. A bell rang and we went back for the second act. See you again after the next act, said William.

I went back to my place behind the woman with the wall of hair and after the second act I went to have another talk to William Davies and his daughter, the lovely new doctor of music. She had her own opinions and I had mine and we went at it hammer and tongs about her theory that London was the only place for an artist. I have been fighting that nonsense all my life, I told her. Then you have been sinning against the truth, she said. No truth but a lie, I said. I love Wales as much as anyone who lives here, she said. But I am convinced that artistic growth and development is not yet possible here. Now you are talking more like a doctor than a Welsh gel, I said. Mary shrugged her shoulders and smiled and tried to change the subject, but I would not let her. Why should London have all the money and all our talent into the bargain? I asked her. For Wales you will ask more questions than twelve wise men could answer, said William. Some of us must stand up for Wales and try to keep some of our talent and genius here to nourish the soul of Wales, I said. If this drift first to Cardiff and then to London goes on then soon Wales will be no more than a carcase for the crows to pick at. I have seen it all happening here whilst you have been in London, William. Most of our farm-workers made into miners and iron-workers first and most of Wales turning into a wilderness. Then all the bright ones leaving the dirt of the coalfield for Cardiff or London, leaving our farms, hills and valleys to get on amongst the English. Why did we not try to get on in Wales before the English came to turn our country upside-down to get rich quick –?

Again the bell rang and Mary turned to go back inside the theatre. I will not see you again for I will have to run to catch the train back to Merthyr – in *Wales*, I said quite nasty. Mary stopped and caught my arm. We are not part-ing in that spirit, are we? she said. I am for Wales, I said. So am I, she said, in lovely Welsh. Do you not believe me? Well, yes and no, I said. If they were all like you in London then – but never mind. Are we coming to your house when Mary comes to sing in Merthyr next? said William. You had better not go anywhere else, I said. Mary put her hand to her lips and then touched my face with the same hand and if it were Iceland or India she was living in I would have forgiven her.

When it was all over I hurried out whilst the audience was still applauding, but I stood in the doorway when Haydn went round to go up on the stage with the singers and chorus, and the next thing I saw was him coming on hand-in-hand with his father. Then I started clapping my hands, and when some started shouting 'speech' I shouted with them. Joseph took two steps forward and then there was louder applause. Then he spoke in a way that held me. It was a speech from the heart and it made me lose the rodneys' train back to Merthyr. The rodneys' train from the Taff Vale Station is the last train back to Merthyr and it is, as some of you no doubt know, called the rodneys' train because it is only those who stay out late and who do not have to get up early in the morning to go to work use that last train. We called those who used it 'rodneys', why that name I do not know for sure. But the women of Merthyr used it as a term of reproach if not contempt when speaking of those who neglected their work to run about until midnight, which was the time the rodneys' train got to Merthyr.

Here I was in Cardiff not knowing what to do, whether to go and look for a bed or start walking. Then the railway-man said: There is a train on the Rhymney line leaving the Rhymney station in five minutes if that is any good to you. I ran across to the Rhymney railway station and caught the last train to Rhymney and walked the five or six miles from Rhymney to Merthyr. My grand-daughter who was keeping house for me gave me a talking to and put me to bed. Her husband, Edwin, a nice young man, had been to meet the rodneys' train at Merthyr railway station and when he went back to tell my grand-daughter that I had not come on it she wanted him to go the police-station for the police at Merthyr to get in touch with the police at Cardiff to see what had happened to me. You will have to stop this run-ning about at your age, she said when she brought me hot milk up to bed.

I had to keep my bed for a week after that, so I will remember the first performance of 'Arianwen' whatever else I forget. Talk about stiff. I heard not long after that Haydn Parry, who conducted so well instead of his father that night, had got married down in Swansea to the daughter of a builder named Thomas – or was it Evans? And not long after that again I heard that he was gone to London, to teach music in some school or college there. So London had him after all. I wonder did Mary Davies and William, her father, speak to him about coming to London that night in Cardiff after the first performance of 'Arian-wen'? Whether or no he is gone to London. Good luck to him. I do not think Mendy will get married or go to London. He is nothing like the musician Haydn is, but he is a good old boy all the same. Tall he is and rides a high bicycle and not only along the roads but in sports as well. He has won several prizes riding in sports much to his father's disgust. After the boy – man now – won a prize at Pontypridd Sports I met Joseph in Merthyr, where he was conducting a Gymanfa Ganu, and he said: Mendy's brains are gone to his legs and into that old bicycle. Leave the boy alone, I said.

CHAPTER 13

Joseph Moves Again

THEY come and they go, these Members of Parliament, I said after listening to young D. A. Thomas. Handsome young man he was but not a very good speaker after all the schooling he had had. Finished his education with four years at Cambridge University – or was it Oxford they said? My old head will never save my feet any more than it did the night I lost the rodneys' train. In bed for a week and stiff for a month after that. But it was M.P.s I was talking about. When I was a little boy it was Sir John Guest and him so proud of being M.P. for the town and district. Yes, I heard him when I was not much bigger than a milk-can thanking the people of Merthyr and district for returning him again. He was not much of a speaker but he took a lot of beating at an election. William Crawshay tried to beat him by putting Meyrick the lawyer up against him but it would have been better William Crawshay keep his money in his pocket. For when it came to spreading money about at election time, as it could be spread about without much fear in those days, then Guest could go on spreading it for as long as Crawshay could. But Sir John Guest died, remember.

Then we had a good speaker and a good man, H. A. Bruce, who has been Lord Aberdare this many a year now. Now it was a pleasure to listen to him making a speech or delivering a lecture. He was a good member. Then why was he beaten out of Merthyr and district? Well, we were made a double-barrelled constituency and Henry Richard and Mr Fothergill got in and Mr Bruce was out. Now Henry Richard was a fine man but I did not have much looks on Fothergill. Still, others must have thought him a good man for he was again returned with Henry Richard in 1874. He retired from Parliament, having had enough of it, in 1880, when there were plenty to fill his place, anxious to fill it, I mean. Mr James got in and he was a middling speaker – but judge me by my work in the House of Commons, he said. He and Henry Richard were returned in 1885, and in 1888 Henry Richard died and Mr James retired. Now our members are D. A. Thomas and Pritchard Morgan and goodness only knows who we shall have next.

Remembering all this and all these M.P.s for our town and district helped to make me content out of Parliament. I had heard them all saying one after the other what they were going to do for Merthyr and district and I knew what had been actually done. What did we get from them all? Well, I have told you that it took us a hundred and twenty years to get as much as a hospital to get ourselves patched-up in. Whilst we were without water in a watery land we were wiped out by the thousand by the old cholera – I have told you all that. Then how long did it take us to get the first College of the University of Wales – and all these men I am telling you about going to Parliament to speak for us one after the other? What does the Bible say about not putting our trust in princes? I am getting to forget what I have read in the Bible but I think there is something about that in it all the same. Whether or not it seemed not much good us put our trust in Members of Parliament. Another thing, when they do come and go like they did in our town and district, it made us ironworkers and miners think that our M.P.s with all their fine talk and letters after their names were not much better off than us in the long run.

But coming to the two we have got now. I do not know this Pritchard Morgan. They say he has a gold-mine in North Wales and this was the first I heard about gold in North Wales. Anyway, he is not a very good speaker. If he had to preach in Wales for a living it is in the Merthyr Workhouse he would be before long, and there are better men than him in the Merthyr Workhouse, remember. There are old puddlers who have worked fifty years in our ironworks before steel was born in someone's brain, and some of those old puddlers are in the Merthyr Workhouse. That is all I will say about Pritchard Morgan but I will say a little more about our other M.P., for he is Welsh and almost as much a Merthyr boy as Joseph Parry. Yes, D. A. Thomas's father was a grocer to whose shop Joseph Parry was many a time sent by Betty, his mother, for bread and flour and groceries. Samuel Thomas was a good grocer and one of the few Welshmen who could see farther than his nose at that time. He started a small colliery on the mountain-side and soon he stopped being a grocer to be a colliery proprietor and nothing else.

So he got on better and better and now here is his son our M.P. and a colliery proprietor as well. Handsome and rich and brains he has got and he has promised to get what he can for Merthyr and district out of Parliament. We will see. There are plenty of things wanted in Merthyr and district, some decent houses for a start. More water from the waterworks too. I will not talk about the long hours worked in the mines and in the steelworks and the low wages, for the men themselves are now talking about that. I don't need to be told when the men of Merthyr and district are getting to the end of their patience. I am hoping something will be done to avoid another stoppage of work for I have seen enough of half-starvation.

Joseph Parry once told me that he believed that Swansea was the musical centre of Wales and that he would never leave the place unless he was bound to. Yet he is now leaving it for Cardiff and we are all hoping it will be a good move for him. I told you that they were building another College of the University of Wales at Cardiff, remember. Well, Joseph was offered the post of lecturer in music there at a salary which was not very tempting. But Haydn, his right-hand man at Swansea, had got married and had gone to London, so Joseph was finding it hard to carry on with only Mendy to help him at the Swansea College of Music, which was what you might call his own creation. But without Haydn there to help he felt it would prove to be a failure before so long. Mendy was not much help. Yet he could not make up his mind. Nearly eight years he had been at Swansea and his lack of success had made him more than a little bitter. He had failed to do what he had hoped to do and he would not admit that his failure was largely his own fault. He went one night to see Dr Thomas Rees. What would you do if you were me? he said. I am not you, said Dr Rees. You have got a fine pipe-organ to play here on Sundays and it will take you a long time to get as good a footing in Cardiff as you have got here in Swansea. Jane thinks the change will do Willie good, said Joseph. H'm, said Dr Rees. I only want to do what is best for us all, said Joseph. In Cardiff it is only lecture in the College and teach a bit outside I will have to. The business with the College students they will do. Here in my own College I have to do everything as you know. Hard it is here to compose big things. It is not that and you know it is not that, said Dr Rees. You have composed plenty of all sorts here in Swansea. Still, between you and me, perhaps it is better you go now to Cardiff. I would like you to stay but your heart is in two places if not three. That being so you will not get much farther here in Swansea. All the time I am starting and never do I seem to finish, said Joseph. First in America, then London, America again and my Musical Institute at Danville. To the College at Aberystwyth and to the College here. All of them taking my years away and now to start all over again in another place. I will come and see you again before saying yes or no. Certainly, certainly, said Dr Rees.

From talking the matter over in Welsh with Dr Rees, Joseph went to talk the matter over in English with Jane, the 'American lady', as some of the Welsh of Swansea referred to her. I am as much for Wales and the Welsh language as the next but we Merthyr people were not so aggressively Welsh as the Welsh of Swansea were at this time, 1888. To most of them Jane was the 'American lady' Joseph had married in America, the 'lady' who could neither speak nor understand Welsh. It was a great pity, they said, a great pity that such a great Welshman as Joseph had to turn to the English as soon as he went into his own home. Neither one thing nor the other for him, poor man, they said. What little Welsh Jane had left America with she had now completely forgotten, but her English had considerably improved. She was reading serial stories by the leading American writers in the best English magazines and when she went out with Joseph or down to the sands with the two little girls and Willie she only bowed and smiled when greeted by Joseph's Welsh friends. If and when she did stop to converse with any of them she annoyed them by compelling them to converse in English, and the comparison between their heavy handling of it and her more genteel and correct handling of the 'foreign' language made matters worse by inducing a feeling of inferiority in those to whom only the Welsh language came natural and easy.

So Joseph was all the time on the horns of a dilemma and a few of us knew how hard it was for him all the time, for it is hard for a man like Joseph to have to be all English in the home and all Welsh outside the home. Some of the Swansea

Welsh said he would end up by being neither one thing nor the other. Jane knew, of course, that Cardiff was more English than Swansea and she honestly felt that she and Joseph would be happier at Cardiff than they were at Swansea. Cardiff was also from fifty to sixty miles nearer London, where Jane hoped they would get to eventually. All this is very complicated, like two wheels going round and round different ways. A minority of a small people fighting for the life of their ancient language can be very nasty, mind you, and those who are not with them are against them. Joseph was not whole-heartedly with them and they knew it and he knew it, so the eight years in Swansea was a sort of armed truce during which Joseph was sniped at quite a lot from behind the all-Welsh front.

But do not try to put all the blame on the Welsh of Swansea. If it is English you are try to put yourself in their position. What if the Welsh of London were making the English of London talk Welsh and sing Welsh hymns and live like Welsh people? You would have enough to say I am sure. I am not making jokes. There is something in a language if you believe there is. Oh, yes. Now do you see the horns of Joseph's dilemma? He is getting on for fifty years of age and his hair is nearly all grey and he is still on the move. No abiding place yet, no security, no time or peace in which to compose in a big way. He had about a cartload of bits and pieces he had composed but not published and they were taking up a lot of room in the house. He showed me some notes he had made for his autobiography when he would find time to write it. With the notes in his hand he would speak of the twenty years of his life in America, less three years in London, of course. Of all he had seen in America before and during and after the Civil War, of the people he had met all over America. Then he would say: Wait a minute. He would go and stand at the piano and try something which had just then come forward from the back of his head. I took no notice for I was used to him and so I knew there would be no more talk of America that evening. When in the mood he talked well, particularly about America. He was getting to be more and more broadminded all the time and that was another thing which the all-Welsh chapel people did not like. They failed to appreciate the fact that America had opened Joseph's mind wider than Wales had opened theirs. No allowances would they make for that fact. Mind you, I am no spiritualist or evolutionist or anything of the sort. I am a Welsh congregationalist, but I take a glass of beer now and then and I do not go to chapel twice every Sunday like I used to. Some Sundays I do not go once, more to my shame, perhaps. Once when I was spending the week-end down Swansea with Joseph I went to sit on the sands of Swansea Bay all the morning. Jane Parry and little Willie were with me, Joseph, of course, was at Ebenezer Chapel playing the new pipe-organ for the singing of the hymns. We were on the way to Joseph's house for dinner when we met the people coming out of chapel, Dr Rees, the preacher, amongst them. Oh, he said, Joseph told me you were here in Swansea. Why did you not come to chapel this morning? I went to see the sea and it was lovely, I said. Of course it was lovely, he said. The sea was in its right place this morning. And I was not, I suppose? I said. Try the cap on, he said, and turned to talk to one of his deacons. H'm, I said, and went on with Jane and little Willie.

Some of our Welsh preachers about that time were famous for their reminders and they made no bones about reminding us of our duty to our chapels. I remember the Rev. Silyn Evans of Aberdare telling me one Sunday – but I was talking about Joseph and his dilemma.

He and his family left Swansea and went to Cardiff, but they went to live at Penarth, just outside Cardiff, in a house in Plymouth Road, if you know where that is. Joseph came into Cardiff on the train from Penarth to lecture at the new Cardiff College of the University of Wales, which was situated not far from the Taff Vale and Rhymney railway stations at the Cardiff end of Newport Road. It was not what you could call a proper Department of Music, for the College was short of funds. There was plenty of money being made at Cardiff on towards the end of 1888 but very little of it found its way to the infant College. At this time the 'merchant princes' of Cardiff were getting to be the talk of the world but they did not see their way clear to help the College much. So there was no proper Department of Music, so Joseph only lectured on music there to a handful of students on five days of the week. His salary was not big enough to enable him to keep himself and his family tidy, for Jane had to have a maid. Then Mendy was out of work and he had to have a shilling in his pocket. So Joseph took a room of a house just across the road from the College and took private pupils there after he had finished his lectures at the College. He also took pupils at his home at Penarth, where Mendy took them the evenings when his father did not get back in time from Cardiff. For there were evenings when Joseph had to stay late at Cardiff to rehearse the Cardiff Orchestral Society, of which he was the new conductor.

So short of money he was all the time, short of money and being worried about money matters in Cardiff, the town which was getting on so well. The first three years at Cardiff were three years of hard labour, for Joseph worked Sundays as well as week-days for a long time. He had found another Ebenezer Chapel at which to play – not a fine pipe organ as at Ebenezer Chapel, Swansea but – a harmonium. When he first went to play the harmonium at Ebenezer Chapel, Cardiff, the harmonium was on the ground floor and the choir Joseph was expected to conduct whilst playing the harmonium was upstairs. What good is this? he said after the first Sunday. What good me and the harmonium down here and the choir up there? That is how it has always been, said the deacons. Like this it will be the choir that will be conducting me, said Joseph. I must have this harmonium

329

moved upstairs where the choir is. The deacons considered this and again said that that was how it had always been. It had better be upstairs by next Sunday, said Joseph. Come on, Mendy. Only he and Mendy attended the Welsh Ebenezer Chapel at Cardiff, Jane and little Willie went occasionally to an English Chapel at Penarth, and the two girls – and I have remembered the name of one of them at last. Dilys, her name was, but I am not sure whether she was the eldest or the youngest. Perhaps I will know that for sure when I remember the name of the other one. The deacons considered what Joseph had said about moving the harmonium upstairs from downstairs, where it had been from the very beginning. It was a precedent and the deacons of Ebenezer Chapel, Cardiff, did not hold with precedents. A special meeting was held to discuss the matter and there was a long discussion. What carried the day and won the point for Joseph was the youngest deacon's insistence on the fact that Joseph was, after all, a doctor of music, the only one in Wales to be made doctor of music at Cambridge University. Which is in England, remember, said the eldest of the deacons. Let him be what he like he must not think he can come here and after one Sunday change things about. Here in front of the big seat we have always had the harmonium and it is here in front of the big seat I do like the harmonium.

In case you have not been inside one of our Welsh chapels – and it is your loss if you have not – perhaps I had better tell you where the 'big seat' is and what it is. It is where the deacons, the elders of the chapel, sit, and only they and the preacher are allowed to sit there. It is immediately below the pulpit and it is raised about a foot or eighteen inches above the floor of the chapel, the level of the congregation. The 'big seat' will accommodate about a dozen deacons and the preacher when he comes down to join them after he has finished his work in the pulpit. In many of our chapels the harmonium was directly in front of the 'big seat' and between the deacons in the big seat and the members of the congregation. So when the deacons, who sat with their backs to the congregation, got up to sing the hymns, they faced the congregation and they had the feeling that the man at the harmonium was accompanying first their singing and the singing of congregation and choir second. So if the harmonium was moved upstairs then they, the deacons, would feel lost during the singing of hymns. So they were most reluctant to agree with the change in the position of the harmonium. But Joseph was firm and somewhat flippant into the bargain. Why not put the harmonium outside the chapel and have done with it? he said. Or let me go back to Swansea to play for a choir singing here at Cardiff. It is the way it has always been, said the eldest deacon again. The harmonium was moved upstairs and some of the oldest deacons never forgave Joseph for that.

Half a minute though before you say one word against our Welsh deacons. They had their faults, but have you ever seen a dozen of them like twelve apostles in the 'Big Seat' of one of our Welsh chapels? There was dignity, a sobering, awe-inspiring dignity if you like. You may be a Catholic and you may have bowed low in the presence of the Pope and his cardinals. Then believe me when I tell you that no conclave of cardinals was ever more dignified than our Welsh deacons in their 'Big Seats' at the time I am speaking of. I have known hundreds of our Welsh deacons through the years and I am the better for having known them. They were the strong pillars of Welsh Nonconformity and who am I to talk about them? The waves of the world beat against them and tried to change them, but it was the world that changed. Not always for the good, remember.

But I must get on with my story. Three years hard labour the first three years in Cardiff were for Joseph, where we must leave him for now. I think I said that there was trouble brewing in the coalfield of South Wales and Monmouthshire, and I will not if I can help it say 'Monmouthshire' any more. From now on it is included in South Wales and shares its labours, joys and sorrows, sorrows in particular. We have been talking about people and places without thinking of what has been going on all the time in the mining valleys. I told you long ago about the record explosion up to then which in Abercarn took two-hundred-and-sixty-eight miners, including men and boys, in the twinkling of an eye. Since then we have had eighteen more explosions in fourteen different valleys, four of our Welsh mining valleys having had two explosions each during that time. Now every one of our Welsh mining valleys has had an explosion, the main valleys anyway. Down Cardiff, where Joseph now is and where most of our coal goes for shipment to all parts of the world, there are no explosions. We in the mining valleys have explosions below and slag-tips above. No slag-tips down Cardiff either. Only clean coal, coal without slag or any foreign matter whatsoever, goes to Cardiff. Coal-brokers live at Cardiff. Sales agents live at Cardiff and the Marquis of Bute lives in Cardiff sometimes for as long as two months at a time. We miners live all the time in the valleys, where, in cemeteries on the hillsides, we bury our dead after explosions. Mass burial as at Abercarn, two-hundred-and-sixty-eight buried the same afternoon. Hard-earned money in the valleys, lots of easy money down Cardiff these days, but not for the ex-miner and ex-ironworker who is now Mus.D., Cambridge.

In making these contrasts I am not being nasty to Cardiff. Cardiff as Cardiff cannot help itself any more than we have been able to help ourselves in our Welsh mining valleys. Something is wrong, that is all. In our valleys between the hills we are not known by the world, it is only by our fruits, coal and iron and now steel, that we are known. If there is coal then there must be colliers somewhere. If there was iron then there must have been ironworkers somewhere. If there is steel then there must be steelworkers somewhere. But where are all these people? That was the question at the beginning of the '90's, the Gay '90's as some wag called them. No doubt things were getting gay in some places – Pontypridd, which calls itself the greatest mining centre, has just got a new theatre and have named it the Royal Clarence Theatre after somebody. We in Merthyr have not got a theatre yet but we have still got the Drill Hall and the Temperance Hall, where there was a Minstrel Show only last week. But then our life in the Welsh mining valleys is one long Minstrel Show. But ours is a most unfunny show for us who play our parts in it.

It is the Llanerch explosion which is making me talk this way, for I had to go there to see if I could identify the body of a brother of mine. There were a hundred-and-seventy-six bodies but I could not tell which was my brother's. It was cold in February up on the pit-head for the Llanerch Colliery is on the hillside high above Pontypool. To go back to Merthyr I had to go down Newport and back up, for the train going the other way had just gone and I would have to wait a half a day for the next. There was a train leaving the other platform for Newport so I went with that. In the compartment men and women were talking about the explosion and me sitting quiet wondering which of those a hundred-and-seventy-six bodies my brother had left for me to identify. After he lost his wife in Merthyr he left the place and went from one valley to the other and he has left the last valley now. He was younger than me.

Another two hours to wait at Newport, so I went walking the town to keep myself warm. I saw the Square on which the Chartists gathered that time and I saw the shops but I did not go down the docks for fear of losing my train if I did. Newport again bigger than Merthyr now. It sounded more English than Cardiff to my ears. I had a pint of beer and some bread and cheese in one public-house and then went back to the railway station in plenty of time for the train. Newport was on the main line same as Cardiff and Swansea. No doubt that had helped them to grow bigger than

Merthyr, which is off the main line. A town on the main line has a chance to grow, especially when it is near the sea as well and has a good backing of coal-mines and ironworks and now steelworks. Simply cannot help growing, can they? In Merthyr we had no sea or main line and we were not far away from where the coal ends. What, I wondered, what will be the end of us at Merthyr? We were more or less all right now in 1890 but where would we be in – anyway, I would not be there to worry. As it was I could feel a cold coming on. No wonder after being up on that pit-head high above Pontypool. The train from London came in with the same fuss as all trains from London come into Wales and I asked the porter if it was my train. Where for? he said. Merthyr, I said. Well, he said, it could be. You may get up to Merthyr quicker from Cardiff than you will from here. Will this ticket do for me to go round Cardiff way? I said. Let's see, he said, taking the ticket from me to look at it. He handed it back to me and told me to get on the train. If they say anything tell them you made a mistake and got on the wrong train, he said. So I went looking for a place to sit and after I had passed a compartment of a first-class carriage I had to stop. I know that woman, I said. No, cannot be for she had white hair, I said. But I know the face, don't I? I went back to have a good look at her now and it was her. There were five in the compartment marked 'first-class' and she was sitting in the far corner. Three men looking tired in a first-class way and another woman and her. I had my hand on the handle of the door and a third-class ticket in my pocket when the whistle went, so I opened the door and jumped in to sit right next to her. A man shut the door after me and off the train went. Two lies I would have to tell now if they asked me but I did not care. I looked at her sideways until I was sure and then said quietly: I am from Merthyr too. I beg your pardon, she said. I know you, I said. Years and years since I seen you and heard you sing that time in the Temperance Hall in Merthyr. Long before that we sang together in Rosser Beynon's choir – and now that you are smiling it is sure I am that you are Myfanwy Llewelyn. Your face is nearly the same, it is only your hair has gone old – not going to Merthyr by any chance?

I was excited like a boy and not remembering my brother whose body I had failed to identify. For sitting next to and close by a lovely woman whose white hair made not much difference made me feel years younger all at once. She was the loveliness and the sweet personification of all the years between the singing of Rosser Beynon's choir and the bleak pit-head and the lines of bodies awaiting identification on the hillside high above Pontypool. It must have been the reaction for I could not stop talking to her smile. I must have been afraid to let her talk for fear she would say: You are mistaken. That day I had been mistaken more than once already. This is my brother, I had said at first look and looking a second time I had said: No, my brother was taller. Again I had said: This is my brother and after another look I had said: No, this man is taller than my brother. I was mistaken in my approach to the bodies left by their owners for identification and I did not want to be mistaken in this lovely woman whose soul was in her eyes and smile. At last I gave her a chance to tell me if it was her or not. The other woman and the three men were now looking at me and her and we did not seem to be on a train until the man came to ask for our tickets. I did not tell him that I was on the wrong train same as the man on Newport platform told me to. For I was on the right train and she was Myfanwy Llewelyn. She insisted on paying the difference between my third-class ticket and my first-class ride I had from Newport to Cardiff and the cold I had felt coming had gone. It is lovely to meet a lovely woman to whom the years had done so little as they had to Myfanwy. You remember Joseph Parry? I said. Oh, yes, very well, she said. He is in Cardiff, I said. He is a doctor of music and lecturing at the new college – perhaps you know? I said.

I was still talking when the train stopped at Cardiff and only then did I remember that she had not told me whether she was going to Merthyr or not. Where are you going, then? I said. I stay here at Cardiff, at the Park Hotel, tonight, she said. Tomorrow I go to Merthyr to see about my father's grave. You will find it tidy, I said. For I give the man the half-sovereign Will Full-Moon sends and I see that the man earns it. We were on the platform and a porter had her two bags. If I remember rightly, she said, there is a late train for Merthyr. Will you come and dine with me at the hotel, and perhaps we could get Joseph Parry – That would be grand, I said. Quick then for me to catch Joseph before he leaves for Penarth.

I went with her in the hotel bus as far as the Park Hotel and from there I went as fast as my legs could carry me to the house in Newport Road where Joseph took pupils after he had finished lecturing in the College. Lucky I was to catch him for he was giving homework to the last of that day's private pupils. You will not believe me when I tell you so I will not try to tell you, I said. Come to the Park Hotel to see for yourself. Oh, what a day to be sure! What is it? said Joseph. Who it is, not what, I said. Come, for I will not tell you. Then I will not come, said Joseph. How would you like to dine at the Park Hotel this evening? I said. Impossible, said Joseph. Pupils waiting me home at Penarth, worse luck. Mendy is there, isn't he? I said. Yes, but I must not leave them too much to Mendy or no pupils will I have, he said. If he thought more of his music and less of that old bicycle – Listen, I said. Better tell you, I suppose. How many years since you last saw Myfanwy Llewelyn? Myfanwy Llewelyn? he said. In the Park Hotel, I said. I travelled first-class with her from Newport. Then come, said Joseph. I will meet somebody going to the train for Penarth and tell them to tell my wife and Mendy ... What shall I tell them? Say you have met an old friend, I said. Or say that you have got a rehearsal with the orchestra or a meeting at

336

the College. Say lies, you mean? said Joseph. No, I will tell the truth. She is an old friend. Come quick.

We met two men going to catch the train for Penarth and one of them was Captain Jones, a retired sea-captain and a good friend of Joseph's. He said he would be sure to tell Jane and Mendy. Then we went to the Park Hotel. Myfanwy had had a wash and brush-up and had put on a lovely dress and she was waiting for us in the lounge. Here is Joseph, I said. She frumped her face and said: Go home, boy, then she laughed out loud and took Joseph's hand and held it in both her hands whilst she looked at him and he looked at her. Just looked. Dr Joseph Parry, she said at last. Si, Signora – or is it Signorina? said Joseph. Ask me no questions and I will tell you no lies, she said. The talk was in English, of course, for her Welsh had gone and gone for ever. She could no longer pronounce our Welsh place-names correctly. Joseph could not take his eyes off her for a minute, neither could I. We sat talking in the lounge over a pot of tea until dinner was ready, but I let her and Joseph do most of the talking and I looked and listened. Who could help looking? You have seen milky-mist over the faces of our Welsh foot-hills early on summer mornings, mornings when the song of the birds sounds not louder but clearer than ever before. There was something of that about Myfanwy now. How old was she? I looked and tried to think. Yes, she was older than Joseph and he was ... yes, fifty next birthday. Then she would be fifty-two if not fifty-three, but she looked years younger than Joseph under her white hair, which did not look old either. Her white hair, I mean. Funny how her white hair looked young. There was no wedding-ring amongst the rings on her fingers and no wrinkle on her face. No fullness of sorrow in her eyes or behind them, no sort of dependence about her anywhere. Not excited like me and Joseph, not talking fast one minute and at a loss for words the next. Words under control she had ready to come to her mouth when her mouth was ready for them and not before.

Around us in the lounge there were people sitting and others coming and going. I wanted to go somewhere badly but I was ashamed to ask or go until at last I had to. Without a word I got up and went out and they did not notice me for they were so busy talking. A man out on the landing showed me where to go and when I went back Joseph and Myfanwy were still talking. In some place she called Florence she said she lived all the time now and Joseph said he would like to go to Italy. Why don't you? she said. H'm, he said. Why, indeed. Have you ever seen Verdi himself? Yes, many times, she said. H'm, said Joseph. Do I know him? I said, not thinking. Myfanwy smiled and shook her head. It would be grand, I said, if in Merthyr you would sing and Joseph play for you at the Drill Hall for the Hospital. Is there a Hospital in the place? she said. Yes, didn't you know? I said. I do not sing any more, she said. I was co-opted on the Hospital committee on the workmen's side, I said. Me and Lewis Morgan. First the Hospital was short of patients but now that the people are getting over their fear of the place it is short of money all time. We could arrange a concert for the Hospital at the Drill Hall in no time for you to sing and Joseph to play for you. Send the town-crier around is all we would want to do to fill the Drill Hall for you. It would be a big feather in my cap on the workmen's side of the committee if only you would sing and Joseph play. From fifty to a hundred pounds for the Hospital too. Myfanwy shook her head but she did not say no.

I would play in Merthyr for you but not for Merthyr or the Merthyr Hospital, said Joseph. You know why, he said, turning to me. They would not let him conduct his 'Emmanuel' at the Merthyr National Eisteddfod ten years ago, I explained to Myfanwy. He should not have wanted to, said Myfanwy. He should have forgotten all about it for it is ten years since then, I said. No good him or you nurse grievances against Merthyr. It is only my dear father's grave that makes me remember the place, she said. We are not all in our graves in Merthyr, remember, I said, turning nasty to her. Now that I am here in Wales your suggestion – but not for years have I sang in a public place, she said. Yet I might – not for Merthyr or for the Hospital you speak of. For you, Joseph, I would do it. Together we would slap them in the face, just you and I, no local choir or conductor or president or chairman or whatever they call it. Even in that spirit I will take you and arrange the concert if you will only say the word, I said. Well, I shall have to stay in the place to see about the removal of my father's body from where it is to the new cemetery, she said. What do you think, Joseph? I have said that I will accompany you, he said. And I have said that I will sing for you, she said. But you must do more than accompany me. You will play for me some of your own work. I will see what I have got, said Joseph. And I will see that the Drill Hall will be full right back, I said. There may be time to get handbills out as well as the town-crier. If so I will tell them to put you on the handbills as two famous Merthyr artistes. You will advertise me as Lina Van Elyn and that is all, she said. If you add anything to that then I shall not sing. As you like, I said. Then the head-waiter of the hotel came to stand a yard or two away from us and waited for Myfanwy to notice him. She was the kind of woman who seemed to make others wait until she noticed them.

The man wanted to tell her that the dinner was ready when she was. Shall we go to dinner? she said to us, and we got up and followed her out. Do you want to go somewhere? I whispered to Joseph. Yes, where is it? he whispered back. She took no notice when he turned left to where I pointed with my thumb. We waited on the landing for him to come back and then went into the dining-room together. The place was full but we followed the head-waiter to a table over in the corner out of the way and he waited on us himself. Two sorts of wine there was and that was the first and only time I saw Joseph Parry taking drink stronger than water, tea or small-beer like his mother used to make. I had to watch out all time not to make mistakes in front of the head-waiter who was waiting on us hand and foot. He watched our glasses and as soon as the wine in them went a bit low back he was to pour more on top of it. Joseph and Myfanwy were talking all the time as though it was only they were in the room. He asked ever so many questions about Italy and she told him about those writing operas in Italy. She also told him about the times she was singing opera in America. Talking made them forget to drink much wine so it was me the head-waiter pounced on with the bottle in his hand all time.

On my way to the Taff Vale station to catch the rodneys' train for Merthyr I could feel that wine all through me. Joseph was catching the last train back to Penarth and his walk was not in the least unsteady. I was not drunk either, mind you. Oh, no. It was just that the wine had had time to work its way down into my legs. Another thing. It had put bad thoughts into my old head. Two pints of it I must have drank during the hours we seemed to be at the table in the corner of that dining-room. And they talking and me just looking at Myfanwy and thinking until at last I began thinking bad thoughts until I was nearly ashamed of myself. White hair shining like silver over a smooth and lovely face, like gold to my eyes, misty not with the mist of the morning. Me, many years a widower and with grand-daughters married. If that is what wine does to old men then better me stick to beer. Or was it she more than the wine? How did Joseph feel sitting closer to her than me and all the time eye to eye with her? Jane, Joseph's wife, was lovely and transatlantic as you might say, and most ladylike into the bargain, but Myfanwy at this time suggested – if that is the word – the strange and disturbing lovelinesses of continental cities. Then that white hair which would fall when loosened down like a veil of living silver over her face and bare shoulders – oh, I was ashamed of myself. Me it was, old scamp that I am, me it was and not the wine or her lovely white hair. Then whatever perfume she used was all the time suggesting things – no, I must not blame that either. A good wife I had followed to her grave in the new cemetery soon after it was first opened and I should have remembered her now but I did not, more shame to me. I would never tell this to anyone else but – no, I will not tell it to you, either. Better get on with my story.

Before I tell you about the concert which was such a feather in my cap perhaps I had better tell you what it was that had brought Myfanwy into Wales and up to Merthyr in the first place and after all these years. She stayed three nights in Merthyr, at the Castle Hotel, where she had two rooms this time. One to sleep in and one to sit down in, and she had all her meals up in the sitting-room. It was Will Full-Moon had written to tell her about the wall of the Thomas Town cemetery bulging out and some of it falling on the railway line. It was the old tramroad but it had been widened into a railroad for the Plymouth collieries engine to bring wagons loaded with house-coal for us miners up to the top-end of Merthyr town. No doubt in widening the old tramroad to make it a railroad they had weakened the retaining wall of Thomas Town Cemetery by taking the dirt and rubble away from the foot of it. So the wall began to bulge outwards and fall down on to the railroad. The bodies in the graves nearest the wall might fall down on to the railroad any minute, and Blind Dick's body was in one of the graves nearest the wall. So Myfanwy had come all the way from Florence in Italy to Merthyr in Wales to arrange for her father's body to be moved from where it was in danger of falling down on to the railroad to the new cemetery up at Cefn, where there would be no danger of it falling out on to any railroad. True she could have written to Will Full-Moon and he could have written to me and I would have seen to the shifting of Blind Dick's body to a safe place up in the Cefn Cemetery. But Myfanwy wanted to

341

see for sure that it was shifted and put to rest again in one of the nicest spots in our new cemetery.

Once an old cemetery is finished with it is more often than not neglected, as our old cemetery up in Thomas Town had been for years since our new cemetery had been opened. But the old Thomas Town Cemetery was only one of hundreds of old cemeteries of all sizes in our town and district. Try and think a minute. Before we opened the new Cefn Cemetery we had put about a hundred and fifty thousand bodies to rest right inside our town. The Cefn Cemetery was opened to receive bodies the year that Penydarren Ironworks was closed down for good late in 1859. For nearly a hundred years before then we had been putting our loved ones' bodies to rest right inside the town. Four generations at rest right inside the town before we opened Cefn Cemetery right outside the town. As the town and district was developed more and more by our English masters it was no use any of us say: Hoy, half-a-minute, my mother and father are buried there. No, for they had come to invest their capital, including the £15 Richard Crawshay, the first of the Crawshays of Cyfarthfa Works and Castle, got by selling his pony and walking the rest of the way to wherever he was going at the time.

I am bound to explain this for the reason that it explains many other things. When we were making the railway in 1840 we had to have a bridge to carry the railroad over the cartroad at the bottom end of the town. The cemetery of a little chapel which we call 'Capel Isha', Lower Chapel in English it is, was right in the way. But the stone supports of the bridge had to have a good footing there so what could you do? The bridge was built and it is there for you to see. But very little of the cemetery of Capel Isha is left for you to see. That is the way it was. Development and subsidence and walls bulging outwards and all of us walking over a hundred and fifty thousand of the bodies of our loved ones all the time. Driving railway engines over them as well. It also gave rise to a sanitary problem and it had a bearing on the water problem up to the time we had our waterworks made right outside the town. So we never know when we are putting our loved ones to rest what problems they will in time confront following generations with. It is only one phase of this problem that has brought Myfanwy Llewelyn to Merthyr now from where she is living retired just on the hill above Florence in Italy. I am not making fun, remember. There is nothing funny about the hundred and fifty thousand who have been laid to rest right inside the town of Tydfil the Martyr, my own parents among them. I am only saying, that is all. My father and mother are both in the same grave in one of our chapel graveyards, in front of Ynysgau Chapel, if you know where that is. That is on the left bank of the river Taff when you stand looking towards Cardiff, and more than once when the River Taff was in flood that graveyard was under water for days. I could go on to tell you about scores of neglected graveyards but never mind. Our loved ones are not there, never were there. Only what they threw away is there. So what odds about what they threw away? Myfanwy Llewelyn thought it important enough to come all the way from Italy to ensure more safe deposit for what her father, Blind Dick, threw away, so it is no use me trying to speak for everyone in this connexion.

I will not say anything about the concert, which was by no means an unqualified success. We made £89 11s. for the Hospital after paying for the hire of the Drill Hall and the piano and gaslight and tickets and handbills and 7s. 6d. to our town-crier. He only had one arm but he had the voice of ten men to make up for the loss of his arm. He and his bell were in great demand for he could cry any event in Welsh and English. He belonged to the Salvation Army. Anyway, we made nearly £90 for the Hospital, which is neither here nor there, for the Hospital was in debt when it opened and had been in debt ever since. No doubt it will be in debt when it closes, so why worry? No, I will not say anything about that concert. You can tell by what we made for the Hospital after paying all expenses that the Drill Hall was full right back to the door at the bottom of the steps. Two hundred at sixpence standing at the back and it was they were most dissatisfied. It is a long old Hall as you know and when you are standing right at the back you are all right if it is one of our big choirs is singing on the stage right down the other end. Not bad either when someone like Will Full-Moon is singing for all he is worth. Then you get most of it at the back.

But this night it was little those standing at the back got for their sixpences. Those in the shilling seats did not get much but those in front in the two-shilling seats got all there was. One of our two M.P.'s, Mr D. A. Thomas, was on in front with his wife, with the Matron of our Hospital sitting next to them. The two front rows were all big people of the town and district, managers, doctors, lawyers and things. Any amount of chapel-people and preachers behind them, the Rector was on in front, to the right of Mr D. A. Thomas, M.P. I would say that it was one of the best audiences the Drill Hall had had since it was first opened. Yet Myfanwy, aided and abetted by Joseph, treated that great audience as though it was dirt, 'llwch y llawr', as we call dirt in one of the finest of our Welsh hymns. It would be better me talk about that hymn than about this concert. Perhaps when there is a chance I will say something about that Welsh hymn if no other. In that grand hymn we Welsh thank God for remembering the dust of the earth, meaning ourselves, which was what Myfanwy and Joseph did not do the night of this concert.

You know that when we Welsh go to a concert we want our money's-worth in singing. We like 'y Llywydd', the President, to put us all in a good mood for a start, to 'jolly' us with a nice little speech containing a couple or three new stories. He will tell us that we are in for a treat and express the hope that we will enjoy ourselves. He will tell us how many prizes the choir we are soon to hear has won, give us short biographies of the conductor and soloists and perhaps what he remembers of their parents as well. When we have a choir as the firm foundation of a concert then we can build on that, can't we? A choir makes an audience at a concert feel like one large family, for each member of our big choirs will have a couple or three or more relatives in the audience. Then there is the forming up of the choir on the stage and relatives in the audience saying 'there he is' or 'there she is' as each member of the choir appears.

I wanted to arrange for a choir, which would have willingly sung for nothing for the Hospital. No, said Myfanwy. Then only a male-voice choir just to break the audience in for you and Joseph? I said. No, she said. You will be sorry, I said. So there was no bustle or excitement, just cold curiosity, that is all. The stage empty except for the piano and piano-stool – and you know what the stage of the Drill Hall looked like when it was empty. The audience made conversation for as long as possible and then began to feel uncomfortable. It was like waiting for a seance at a spiritualist gathering. Then Joseph led Myfanwy on to the stage to leave her standing there like a stone statue when he went and seated himself at the piano. There was a little applause which did not get as much as a smile from Myfanwy. Hostile she was to that audience and only one English song she gave it. All the rest French and Italian in groups. Joseph followed her lead and played only Beethoven and Chopin, but the Chopin pieces did not get to the back of the Hall. The general opinion was that he was trying to show off. What about all those lively and loud pieces he had himself written for the piano? and what about all our Welsh airs? It was I that got most of the blame and the Hospital got the money. Never again, I said.

CHAPTER 14

'Ond Gorthrymder Mawr o Hyd'

YES, only sorrow all the time. I told you that Joseph was not getting on very well with the deacons of Ebenezer Chapel, Cardiff, didn't I? Neither was Mendy, Joseph's son, who played the harmonium at Ebenezer to give his father a rest and a chance to compose some Sundays. Before the end it was an understood thing that father and son should play on alternate Sundays – and that boy of his is no doctor of music, said the older deacons. It was Tom Stephens, when I met him at Pontypridd, who told me that Joseph was not getting on any too well down Cardiff, in Cardiff as a whole and Ebenezer Chapel at Cardiff in particular. Tom Stephens was one of Joseph's best friends, though he had not known him half as long as I had, and I think I should say here and now, without any disrespect to Tom, mind you, that he was always prejudiced in Joseph's favour. Of course, he had learnt a lot from Joseph and there you are.

Some of you may have known Tom Stephens of Pontypridd, as good a conductor at his best as a choir could wish to have. He did not have a commanding presence for he was on the short side and stout, but he had a commanding way with him, every bit as commanding in his way as 'Dan bach' of Merthyr, little Dan, as we called Dan Davies. Tom Stephens was always saying that Joseph's right place was in Pontypridd or in the middle town of one of our mining valleys, where Tom was certain he would get the fair play which he was not getting in Cardiff, that is according to Tom Stephens who was telling me all this that day at Pontypridd. It was a holiday time and there was a Gymanfa

Ganu in the big chapel near the old bridge and there were Sports down by the side of the river at the place they called Taff Vale Park. So Pontypridd was crowded that day and there were a number of people drunk and fighting about the place. If you did not know Pontypridd you would have thought it was a terrible place that day. But remember that there were nearly fifteen hundred of us singing hymns throughout that day in the big chapel near the old bridge. How many did you see drunk and fighting that day? A dozen – twenty at most. Then down the Sports on Taff Vale Park how many would there be? Eight hundred at most. So there you are. Nearly twice eight hundred of us at the Gymanfa Ganu in the big chapel near the bridge. So you must not judge a town in South Wales by what you see on its streets, you must go into our chapels and see how many are there too.

He is not getting fair play, said Tom Stephens again. They are condemning him from the pulpit down there now. I heard something about that, I said. Well, is that fair play? said Tom. I did not say anything for there are two sides to everything after all. In Welsh we call a theatre a 'chwareudy', and at the time I am telling you about it was regarded as a most sinful place by Welsh nonconformity. The Puritanical storm which had been brewing from the moment Joseph presented his first opera on the stage of a theatre broke at Cardiff of all places. From the pulpit a preacher said: 'I am not judging Dr Parry or his operas. But in the name of God I make my protest against the whole business.'

When the storm broke Joseph was writing an oratorio, 'Saul of Tarsus', which had been commissioned for the National Eisteddfod. This was given before the largest audience ever assembled at a National Eisteddfod, and I went with the people from Merthyr to Rhyl in North Wales to hear the work performed. I had seen a copy before I went into the Pavilion to listen to it. 'Saul of Tarsus. Dramatic

Oratorio, or Scenes from the Life of St Paul.' It was dramatic and it was very good, in my opinion a better work than Joseph's 'Emmanuel'. I went to where Joseph was staying at Rhyl to congratulate him and found him looking downhearted. Don't look so down-hearted, I said. Your 'Saul of Tarsus' is a grand piece of work. It is not that, he said. Come for a little walk. It is late – but never mind, I said. Out we went together to walk along the now almost deserted sea-front. Lovely it was in the warm moonlight but only for me. Joseph was crying. What is the matter now again? I said. Our Willie, he said. Afraid I am that he will be dead by the time I get back to Penarth. He was never very strong, I said. But perhaps he will be better by the time you get home. I should not have come here, he said. It has been hard to work and him slowly dying in the house. But I must try to work. Then you have read in the papers? I nodded and we turned about.

Yes, I had read the controversy which had been going on in Welsh and English in the newspapers daily and weekly. Some went so far as to say that Joseph was leading the young people out of our chapels and into the theatres. One gave a list of young women performing in Joseph's 'Blodwen' and 'Arianwen'. A preacher's daughter, a curate's daughter and the daughters of deacons of chapels of more than one denomination of Welsh Nonconformity. Perhaps I will tell you more about this after I have talked to Joseph about something else. Here it was getting late and only him and me walking by the sea at Rhyl in North Wales. I named him after a great musician, said Joseph, and I was hoping he would grow up to be a great musician. H'm, I said. Perhaps the boy will get better and be a great musician after all. But never mind little Willie for a minute. Let us sit by here on this seat for a minute. If they lock us out of our lodgings we will knock and knock until they let us in. I am tired but I must talk to you, Joseph. I have very near finished running about to Eisteddfods. Not often we will

348

meet from now on. Change from one train to another I must to go to see you at Penarth and same you must do to come up to Merthyr to see me. No time have I got for much more of that, so better talk now and finish with it. Is it to me or the sea you are listening, Joseph? Thinking of Willie I am and I cannot help it, he said. It is only natural, I said, but try with me to think about yourself for a minute. No better place than this to fight your battle, Joseph. It was in this part we Welsh fought our last battles, and not far from where we are sitting now the last Welsh parliament was held, wasn't it? Was it? said Joseph. A man where I am lodging told me something about it, I said. He either said the last Welsh parliament or the first English parliament in Wales is not far from here. Never mind that now. We Welsh fought our last battles around these parts – are you getting cold? No, crying I can see you are again. Natural I know but the morning and the first train to take you back will not come quicker if you cry all night. I want you to listen to me, Joseph. I am trying to, he said. Then try hard, good boy, I said. Boy you are and boy you always will be to me, remember. Bachgen bach o Ferthyr, erioed, erioed. Is the sea coming this way or going from us? I can never be sure, said Joseph. We will say it is going from us and you are going with it, I said, going on a ship with Handel and Mendelssohn. You come back with an oratorio, 'Emmanuel', we will say. You are happy. Again you go out with the sea, but this time with Rossini and Verdi and perhaps Wagner as well. You come back with an opera, 'Blodwen', we will say. Now you are more happy –

I wish I could go to Italy, to where Myfanwy is living, to learn for a couple of years, said Joseph. Then I would write the grand music for operas. Let me finish what I am trying to tell you for your own good, I said. Never mind Myfanwy now. I was saying about you coming back with your first opera as happy as could be. Next time you go out it is with Handel and Mendelssohn again, and back you come with another oratorio. From the next voyage you return with another opera until now you have three oratorios and three operas, and still you cannot make up your mind to stick to one or the other. Am I right or wrong? Perhaps you are right, he said. You are gone fifty and it is time for you to make up your mind one way or the other, I said. You have got to go one way or the other now. You are between the chapel and the theatre and it is not for me to tell you to go back to the chapel or on to the theatre. You know I am not of those who are protesting against you and the theatre, but one thing I know for sure. The foundation of the best work you have done is the chapel and the Bible. With you, as I have told you more than once, your last thing is always your best thing, and for once I agree with you. Your 'Saul of Tarsus' is your last and your best work, but what next? Another opera, no doubt. It is only Willie I can think of, said Joseph.

I know, I know, I said. But you must try to think of your work too, I said. Here, to-night, before going back to Jane and the children, before going back to Cardiff and Penarth, here to-night you must fight your battle and win it or lose it. No more time for experimenting have you got, one way or the other you must go. If it is to the theatre with your operas then go full-pelt and stay there. If back to the chapel then stay there and do not ever again move from there. I will try to think, he said. You had better, I said, and the sooner the better you make up your mind one way or the other. Oh, I am stiff by sitting down, I said when getting up. The sea is lovely under the moon, said Joseph. Here I would like to sit and wait for the train in the morning. I will not sleep if I do go to bed in my lodging. You will rest if you will not sleep, I said. Come now, good boy.

Joseph was like a child in many ways and he was all for the young people in their revolt against the rule of our chapel deacons. But the fact that Joseph was what is called 'broadminded' and on the side of the young people does not mean that our chapel deacons were altogether wrong in the attitude they took up at this time. I do not want to say much about this old controversy but our deacons were very suspicious of the world and the way it was going at this time. Chwareudai, as we in Welsh spoke of the Playhouses, were springing up everywhere in South Wales, where two-thirds of the people of Wales were living and working. Big places too, most of them bigger than some of our biggest chapels – one sprang up in Merthyr but I will tell you about that when I have finished telling you about the thing in general. Here we are in what is called the 'Gay '90's' and theatres springing up everywhere, most of them 'Royal' theatres. Theatre Royal, Cardiff, Theatre Royal, Swansea, Theatre Royal, Merthyr, Royal Clarence Theatre, Pontypridd, and so on all over South Wales. Most young men and young women able to read and some Welsh young men and women reading novels in English on the sly. Going to theatres on the sly until they grew bolder and went in defiance of parents and chapel deacons. It is Wales I am telling you about and not England, remember.

In London they no doubt laughed when they heard of the fuss our chapel deacons were making about the young people of Wales going to the theatres. But with us it was no laughing matter. Then when it went farther and some of the young people of our chapels appeared, dressed-up and painted, on the stages of the theatres of South Wales, then the deacons and preachers thought it was time to protest. As I have told you preachers protested against 'the whole business' from our pulpits, mentioning Joseph's name and referring to his operas. Joseph took up the challenge of the chapels and after performances of his operas appeared on the stage and made speeches in which he said that he had long been of the opinion that the future of music in Wales was along the line he was labouring to lay down in his operas. After a week's performance of one of his operas at one of our theatres he said that that week would live for ever

351

in his memory, that it was the beginning of a new era in the history of music in Wales, and even though he might not live to see that era crowned with glory he was certain that crowned it would be – you know how men talk when demanded to by a most enthusiastic audience after a week's performances of one of their own operas.

I am telling you all this in order that you who were not in South Wales at the time may realize that it is of no storm in a tea-cup I am telling you about. There were factions, the chapel faction and the Parry faction, and in between those two factions there were thousands of sympathizers and supporters of both these factions. Perhaps you will not believe me when I tell you that all this played havoc with family life in Wales. I tell you that you shall not sing in any old theatre, fathers shouted. I tell you again that I will, said sons and daughters. Oh, dear, dear, said the mothers. It is a pity that Dr Parry cannot find something better to do, said the fathers. Yes, indeed, said our chapel deacons. A great pity, said many of our preachers. The opposition boycotted the performances but the 'loyalists' went and took with them as many friends and relations as they could persuade to take the risk. Theatre porprietors and managers willingly let their theatres for these weeks, which they rightly thought were a help in building up regular audiences for the weekly professional productions of drama, comedy and farce and opera and musical comedy.

It was an exciting time and a most trying time for many. The chapels and their preachers and deacons, the deacons in particular, fought unceasingly and prayed unceasingly for the souls of their young people, fought against the world for the souls of their young people. It would be easy for some people to make fun out of that fight but I am telling you that it was no sham-fight. Souls were at stake, no doubt about that. Those old deacons were not so far wrong after all, perhaps. It is for you to say, knowing them as you did and knowing the world as you do. I have told you that I sometimes take a pint of beer and that I have been more than once to the theatre, and I have also told you that I go to chapel more Sundays than I do miss going, so perhaps it is little room I have to talk one way or the other. Yet you will remember that I have said that our chapel deacons were the pillars of Welsh Nonconformity and, though I think young people are entitled to their share of pleasure, I am not going back on what I said then about our chapel deacons to please you or anyone else. Never mind about that now though.

I read in the *Merthyr Express* about the death of William Sterndale Parry, Joseph's youngest son, but I was not able to go Penarth to attend the funeral. I was in bed not able to move with my old back at the time, but Edwin, my granddaughter's husband, wrote for me to Cardiff to ask the man in the shop down there to send a wreath worth 7s. 6d. with a card from me on it. It was all I could do in the state I was at the time. My old back do give in every now and then. With some it is the back that do go first and when it goes where are you? Fast in bed like I was. But as I was thinking I had my stomach and my chest to eat and breathe with and my hearing was good enough to hear the carts passing and the children playing on the road outside. Then I had my glasses and my Bible and the *Merthyr Express* and my granddaughter as good as gold to me. Then her husband, Edwin, where would you find a better young man than he is? Edwin was working on the railway – no, what am I talking about? In the ticket-office of the railway he was working. Nice clean job. On the small side he is but if he was as big as the man I saw in the circus once he could not do more for me. As soon as he comes home from his work to his dinner he comes first upstairs to ask how I am and to tell me what has been going on down town that morning. Same again when he comes home at six o'clock when he has finished for the day. Sometimes I wish they had children. But there, that is not their fault, and if they did have children then less time they would have for me. Oh, I had a long bout in bed with my back that time. Dr Ward gave me some pills but they were no good. Then he said try oil and Edwin rubbed the oil in night and morning. No good. It must take its course, I said. No more pills or rubbing. It took its course and took a long time too.

But I did not hurry it. In my bed I had plenty to remember and the world was fresher when I got up and after a bit went out and about again. I have had many bouts in bed and after getting better and going out it is wonderful how fresh the world is for a bit after. I told you about our new Theatre Royal. Big place it was though too near the Morlais Brook for my taste. Inside it is like a palace, better inside of the two than the Theatre Royal down Cardiff. Only twice I had been inside the place but many Merthyr people were going there every week like the clock. Twice or three times a week when there were different plays every night. I saw the playbills about the place saying that the Moody-Manners Opera Company was coming but I did not know that Will Full-Moon and his wife would come with it. I thought perhaps he was dead for he was as old as me if not older. No, no, not older. Same age perhaps. No, he would not be as old as me either. I tried to think from the time I heard him singing with Blind Dick and those two young women ... what were their names? And how old was I then? Oh, yes, I was older than Will Full-Moon then so I was bound to be older than he is now.

He came with his wife up to our house, as fat as he could be he was and wearing a wig, if you please. His wife was still handsome and not looking much older but looking much more the boss of the two than when I had seen them together last. Well, Will, I said, you are gone too fat for that devil's part now. Too fat and too old, he said. Chorus-master I am now, but my wife is one of our principals. I have brought you a free pass for the night she is singing. You have never heard her singing by herself, have you? No, I said. You will

354

stay for a cup of tea and a bit to eat? said my grand-daughter. To be sure they will, I said. Wasn't it Carl Rosa company you were with when last we met? I said. Yes, but they would not give my wife the rôles she was better in than any of the sopranos, so we left them and joined Moody-Manners, said Will. Now my wife is getting fair play. Wait until you hear her sing.

From Cardiff they had come to Merthyr and whilst we were having food they told me of the fire down there. Talk about a fire, said Will. And quite close to the theatre, said his wife. The *Western Mail* building – you know, not far from that hotel I took you to that time, said Will. I cannot remember for sure where that hotel was, I said. It was after the Moody-Manners Opera Company had left Merthyr taking Will Full-Moon and his wife with it, that I heard about Joseph's loss in that fire down Cardiff. Tom Stephens was up in Merthyr to – but I must not let Will Full-Moon and his wife go like that for perhaps the last time. About him I have said enough but very little about his wife, this second wife, I mean. Never mind her singing now, it is not for that I will remember her. But for the look in her eyes when she looked at the man so different from the man she had married after having lived with him as his wife before she was his wife. Now he was old and easy to make fun of with his wig and all. His grand voice nearly all gone to rags and his eyes running like mine do in the mornings. He was now taking drink too, yet with it all I knew that the woman about twenty years younger than he was was going to stick to him and look after him all his days, if God spared her and her voice that is. Women like that, and no doubt there are thousands of them the world over, are worth remembering. My bed when I am tied to it will be the easier for the memory of her and I must try to remember her when I am saying my prayers. And Will Full-Moon too.

Tom Stephens of Pontypridd was up in Merthyr to see his wife's brother, I think he said. Anyway, it was someone who had been operated on at our Hospital. I was standing on Pontmorlais Square when he passed me. Hoy, Tom, I said. Hullo, he said. Which way are you going? No way, I said. Bit of a spell I am having here on the Square. Then walk down as far as the railway station with me, he said. If you will walk slow, I said. Then he told me about having been up at our Hospital. Pity for Joseph, he said after. Willie, you mean? I said. No, the *Western Mail*, he said. You know about it going on fire down Cardiff. Yes, Will Full-Moon told me, I said. He saw the fire. Burnt all Joseph's plates, said Tom. Plates? I said. Yes, you know, the stereotype plates of all Joseph's published works. Loss of nearly a thousand pounds to Joseph – and he can't get a penny of it back either. Joseph was up in London at the time of the fire. He conducted 'Nebuchadnezzar' at the St James's Hall and Haydn conducted that new thing of his, 'Gwen' I think it is called. I have just had a peep at the vocal score of another work by that boy. Romantic opera it is. Good too. That boy of Joseph's will go far if he lives long enough, which is doubtful. Last time I saw him in London he looked very ill. He can write music – wait till you hear this new opera of his. 'Cigarette' is the name of it. Wait until our deacons hear the name of it, I said. The deacons will be the death of Joseph, said Tom. Nonsense, I said. I liked that boy, Haydn. Have you got that vocal score for me to see? No, but I am getting one and when I do I will let you see it, said Tom.

Haydn was dead before I saw it. But long before he died I heard enough about 'Cigarette', his romantic opera. The very name itself was like a red rag is to a bull to our non-smoking and non-drinking deacons. Then to cap it all it was put on first at the Theatre Royal, Cardiff, and go to see and hear it I had to, though I was none too good at the time. If you are found dead on the rodneys' train coming back then it will be all your own fault, said my granddaughter. But don't you think that you are going by yourself for you are not. Edwin shall go with you to see that you do not have another walk from Rhymney. It will not cost him anything for train-fare for he will have a privilege ticket. I would not go at all, I said, only I remember the boy conducting so well down Cardiff the night after Joseph had heard about his father dying in America. Well, it is not cold, that is one thing, said my grand-daughter.

So Edwin went with me to Cardiff and we sat out of the way well back in the shilling seats. The programme Edwin bought said that it was 'A Light Romantic Opera' with a Plot by some Barry Montour and Libretto and Lyrics by some Warham St Leger. There were many names like that on playbills and programmes about this time. Anyway, the programme also said: 'The Music Composed by J. Haydn Parry,' and that was what had brought me to Cardiff. It was not worth the journey to Cardiff and back to Merthyr, but I am glad I made the journey, for I want to remember Haydn Parry too. With this opera he had broken for ever with his past as a boy of the chapel. In London he had mixed with theatricals and musicians writing for the theatre and had lived a more or less bohemian life. He regarded himself as the leader of a musical movement away from Welsh Nonconformity, away from the psalm-tune and the Bible. So during the week of rehearsal and the week of performances he walked the streets of Cardiff defiantly and when he met some of the disapproving section of Cardiff's half-dozen Welsh chapels he stared them out. He had a professional company to do their best for the opera but it wanted more than acting and singing. 'Cigarette' – but let it go. It is Haydn I want to remember.

When he died I asked Edwin to write to Joseph for me and to tell him from me how sorry I was for him – no, don't say that, Edwin, I said. Wait till I think. The man had lost his eldest and youngest sons and nearly a thousand pounds' worth of work in stereotype plates and I was going to tell him that I was sorry. If I had left Edwin to write and send that how ashamed I would be feeling now. Tell him, I said to Edwin, tell him that I have heard about Haydn again and that my heart is with him. That is all. My heart was with him in his sorrows coming one after the other. I was glad when I heard that he had gone with Jane and their daughter, Dilys, to see his mother in America. If anyone could comfort and strengthen him then his mother, Betty Parry, would. Then Henry, his brother, and Elizabeth and Jane, his two sisters, and their children all born in America, would no doubt help Betty Parry to comfort and strengthen Joseph. So would Jane's people in America, no doubt. It was fourteen long years since he had seen his mother; his father he would never again see in this world. From 1880 to 1894 is a long time without a sight of one's mother. It was five years since he had played organ or harmonium in a chapel, having resigned his position as organist at Ebenezer Chapel, Cardiff, when the deacons turned nasty on him for taking the young people to perform his operas on the stages of theatres. So on the *Etruria* Joseph was feeling sore with disappointment and his heart was bowed down with the weight of many sorrows. But the voyage and the prospect of America and the anticipation of meeting loved ones and friends there did him a lot of good and he was quite cheerful by the time the ship got to New York. He found that his people were now scattered all over America so there was no family reunion at Danville. Here again old Death had made sad paths for Joseph to walk along. His two old friends and one-time teachers, John Abel Jones and John Price, were no more. Life in America was much more spacious but little if any longer than in Wales. So Joseph went from place to place in America. First to his mother in Portland, Maine, where we will leave him for a bit till we see how things are in Merthyr.

I do not remember telling you that our new Theatre, the Theatre Royal, cost £8,000 to build. Yes, it cost £2,000 more to build than our Hospital, which was built for £6,000. Our Hospital is still in debt but not our Theatre Royal. Oh, no, the Theatre Royal paid for itself before so long. It made a big difference to the Drill Hall and the Temperance Hall. The Drill Hall, where there used to be something or other on every week, was now weeks and sometimes as long as two months without anything in the way of entertainment. It had the Volunteers there to drill every week in the winter and a big dance perhaps once a month. That was another thing. Dancing. That was something our chapels did not hold with again, and it was about this time that the first 'all-night' dance was held at the Drill Hall. From eight o'clock to-night until six o'clock to-morrow morning with the 'extras' and everything. This was too much for the deacons of our chapels, who protested, but in vain. It was the 'Gay '90's' and our chapels had to put up with it. This very year, 1894, as good as three new churches, two Church of England and one Catholic, were put up and opened in the town and district, yet there was more dancing and theatre-going than ever before. Sports every holiday too on the Big Field and two boxing booths nearly all the year round. Sometimes a big boxing tournament at the Drill Hall and swings and roundabouts down near the Iron Bridge on the patch of made ground between the River Taff and the now almost moribund Glamorganshire Canal. Whippet and foot-racing up on Scott's Grounds and bare-fist fighting and pitch-and-toss and card-playing every week-end all over the place. There was talk about a secondary school but as yet, in 1894, it was only talk and no more. Things were lively.

The chapels were as strong as ever in membership and the attendance at morning and evening services was still as good as ever. I do not say anything about the churches of the Church of England in Wales for the reason that they influenced little or nothing in Wales, certainly not in industrial Wales. The same applies to the Catholic Churches in Wales. They were not of the life of industrial Wales, our Welsh Nonconformist chapels were, and, to a lesser degree, so were the Nonconformist chapels in industrial Wales at which the services were in the thin English tongue. So there was plenty of life, religious and secular and all the way down to what is called 'low-life', in Merthyr and throughout industrial Wales at this time, 1894. Every town and village had its football team and its quoit club and these teams travelled singing in brakes drawn by three and sometimes four horses to play away. Rivalry was keen and supporters fought after matches played home and away. There was no 'high-life' in industrial Wales, so no Court Circular was printed to appear in the *Merthyr Express* or *Pontypridd Observer* or the *Rhondda Gazette* or any other of the weekly newspapers published in our Welsh mining valleys. There was as much singing as ever, hymn-singing in chapels and competitive singing at Eisteddfods. Also at concerts. The Cyfarthfa Brass Band, under George Livsey now, was playing better than ever, and an effort was being made to form a permanent orchestra for Merthyr and district. It was almost impossible to form a permanent orchestra for the reason that we in Wales were too choral and congregational to be orchestrally-minded.

I am telling you all this about Merthyr and district because it is more or less typical of all towns and districts of industrial Wales at this time, 1894. But because I have said all this do not jump to the conclusion that no work was being done. There was plenty of hard work and there were explosions as usual. This year, 1894, has broken the record for a single explosion with two hundred and seventy-six including men and boys, of course, killed at Cilfynydd. You know where that is. About ten miles down from Merthyr and about two miles this side of Pontypridd. You will no doubt remember that our previous record for a single explosion was two hundred and sixty-eight, including men and boys, killed at Abercarn. Perhaps you know where that is too. It is next to Cwmcarn.

It was about the Theatre Royal I was talking though, but

before I tell you as best I can what was on there sometimes, let me first explain why the deacons of our chapels were most bitter against the theatres. They were also drinking-places where men could get drunk in a quiet way if they wanted to. The Theatre Royal at Merthyr had three bars, the pit bar, the circle bar and the gallery bar. Plays were then in five acts so there were four longish intervals between the acts. You went to the theatre soon after seven and you came out just before eleven. Plays with only four longish acts or three very long acts were bad for the three bars and most unpopular with the regular patrons of the theatre who liked their drop of drink. I will say no more about that for the deacons of our chapels said enough at the time, goodness knows.

It was the beginning of a new era in the history of the English theatre in Wales and that being so I want you to know it as we came to know it week by week. Remember that I am speaking not of Cardiff and Swansea and Newport on the main line. Those places sometimes had number one companies. I am speaking of the Welsh mining valleys which up until now had only had small portable theatres which could be taken down and taken away on a couple or three carts to be put up elsewhere. But now a theatre which cost £8,000 to build, exclusive of the cost of seating, decorating and curtains and things! The poor families who used to entertain us in the little portable theatres were now banished to inaccessible mining villages and we had a new company of players each and every week in our up-to-date theatre. It was not often I went there but Edwin and my grand-daughter went there most weeks and twice some weeks. So I heard all about the place from them.

Most of the plays performed at our new theatre were about London, from where most of the companies came direct, so the playbills said. I remember a few of the London titles, 'The Streets of London'; 'The Lights of London'; 'Lost in London'; 'Alone in London' and 'While London

Sleeps'. There were many more with the word 'London' in the title but if it was not there it did not much matter for London was the 'place' of four out of every five plays performed at our theatre. So we got to know a lot about London both East and West. We had our share of Shakespeare and old English comedy and, as you would expect in such a musical town as Merthyr, we had our share of opera too. About half a dozen different opera companies altogether came to our theatre but I can only remember three, four with the Welsh National Opera Company. Carl Rosa, Moody-Manners and the J. W. Turner Opera companies I remember, and ever so many comic opera companies.

But it is only of the Welsh National Opera Company I am going to say a word. I do not know who financed and lost money on this tour which lasted in all for fourteen weeks. The chorus was made up of stage-struck young men and women who had left their homes and chapels to sing and act in Joseph's two operas, 'Blodwen' and 'Arianwen'. This was the disastrous tour that was the talk and shame of Welsh Nonconformity. It was semi-professional as far as the principals went, for Hannah Jones, the contralto, was a singer and actress who could have gone to London and made a name for herself. Edwin told me that she was the daughter of the Town Clerk of Swansea. Whether or no she was by far the best of the principals. As far as singing went the chorus was magnificent so we will say nothing of the acting. They were also good-looking young men and women who kept themselves tidy whilst on tour but our chapels in every town and village visited by the Welsh National Opera Company said: There for you. Let that be a warning to you. Young people who have left their chapels to dress and undress and paint their faces in theatres. The regular theatre-going public did not support the venture being made by these courageous amateurs and a few semi-professionals and the chapel practically boycotted it, so it was bound to be a failure. Mendy, Joseph's son, was general manager and conductor when there was anything to conduct, but the singers relied most on the one they called 'Richards the band'. Mr Richards was a church organist who had decided to support the venture and it was he that played the piano and conducted at the smaller places. The company played in all sorts of places, in up-to-date theatres like the Theatre Royal, Merthyr, and in small halls in villages, some without any sort of stage.

At the Theatre Royal, Merthyr, it was three nights 'Blodwen' and three nights 'Arianwen' and I went to see and hear both performed. I was sorry in my heart when I heard that the tour had ended disastrously – no, not disastrously. It just failed to achieve success, that is all. I was sorry for what it might and could have been had the two operas been well-rehearsed and produced and then supported as they should have been. Then Joseph's words about the beginning of a new era in the musical life of Wales might have come true. Was Joseph doomed to failure? That was the question I was asking myself when I left the Theatre Royal, Merthyr, on the Friday night, after the performance of 'Arianwen'. I went with Edwin and my grand-daughter on the Friday night because I knew that Friday night was the worst night of the week for an audience. It had to be a good company to draw people into the theatre on a Friday night. We were not many there that Friday night. Still, there it is.

Good job Joseph was in America, where, in Portland, Maine, he found his mother, Betty Parry, looking very old. Well, she was old, wasn't she? Joseph had to go half over America to meet all his relations and all of them looking ever so much older. Fourteen years older than when he had last seen them and fourteen years can do a lot to a family. Joseph had to try and earn a bit of money whilst in America too. Lecture-recitals, concerts and Eisteddfods all over again. He thought twice before accepting an invitation to go and give a lecture-recital at Chicago but he went in the end. The year previous Chicago had had its World's Fair and for a week in the Festival Hall of the World's Fair at Chicago the Welsh of America had held one of the greatest of all Eisteddfods. But it was John Thomas, 'Pencerdd Gwalia', not Dr Joseph Parry, 'Pencerdd America', was the shining star of that great Welsh-American Festival at the World's Fair, Chicago. Only one of Joseph's pieces was sung there, his famous piece for male-voice choirs, 'The Pilgrims'. Yes, that was all that the Welsh of America got of Joseph at Chicago in 1893. Now, in 1894, he had a good mind to stay away from Chicago altogether, but his mother advised him to go there as though nothing had happened there the year previous to annoy him.

Joseph should, of course, remember that fourteen years is a long time, and that people and things change very much in that time, particularly in America, which was growing so fast. Now, in 1894, people were asking: Who is this Dr Joseph Parry? In Wales he was 'the Doctor' and practically everyone knew him in Wales. But America ... His one-man shows did not create much of an impression there this time. He went down better when backed with a choir, which Dan Protheroe provided at Chicago, than he did when on his own. He was not a very good lecturer and he did not need to be told that. He knew by now that he was not a good lecturer. But he put on the 'hwyl' and displayed feeling when at a loss to illuminate the subject or work he was dealing with. He was following the example of many of us Welshmen. Welsh 'hwyl' covers many deficiencies in us. It is a sort of smoke-screen of feeling which we put out when we are stuck in front of an audience and Joseph was often stuck. But he got by for he could talk, sing and play and he was a distinguished-looking man, remember.

He worked hard to get a bit of money to go back home with, and he was as good value for the money he got, which was not a lot, less than two thousand dollars after expenses, and he was as good if not better value for that than lecturers from Britain who had made ten times that amount in the same time. Oh, the places he went to and the people he met this time again! More and more convinced of his mistake he was now. America would have stuck to him had he stuck to America. Wrong he now felt he was when he gave himself back to Wales. Yet he was not so sure that he was wrong. It had been easier to make a reputation and to create 'the Doctor' than it would have been in America, where it was so easy for a reputation to get lost and a name such as the 'Doctor' to be forgotten. Compared to America Wales was only a cockle-shell to a ship like the *Etruria* but he was somebody on that cockle-shell. There was an indifference about immense space which made him feel so lost and insignificant. He never felt that way in Wales. He had stamped his personality indelibly on the mind of Wales and his music, good, bad or indifferent, was continually under discussion and he and his music gave rise to many a controversy, the greatest being the sacred or profane, the chapel or theatre controversy arising from the presentation of his operas in the 'chwareudai', the playhouses. Now in America all that would have been a storm in a tea-cup and his movements through the years from one state to another would not have excited more than his own part of one state. But in Wales his moves from Aberystwyth to Swansea and from Swansea to Cardiff had been discussed as matters of national importance to little Wales.

It was funny. The more he went about America the more he longed for Wales, and after seven years in Wales he longed to go to America to open his lungs and get his mind swept clear of all the sand his people had thrown into the machinery of his prolific mind. He wanted to get away from the pressure of his own people, from their jealous pride in him, from all the petty restrictions which Welsh Nonconformity imposed upon him. Yet before he had been a month in America he was longing for Wales, so what could you do with a man like that? Now his mother – there was a change.

Speaking more English than Welsh in America in her old age. She had finished trying to push the Welsh language into the mouths of all around her. Forty years of life in America had made her realize, as Daniel, her late husband, realized long before, that America is greater than all the languages spoken there. So she now spoke English to Jane, Joseph's wife, and to Dilys, his daughter, without any bad taste in her mouth. Betty Parry was a grand woman and a credit to both Wales and America. Great-grandchildren she had now in America and she was not worrying about them not speaking Welsh.

This tour in America was a tonic to Joseph, a tonic he was badly in need of. For between the deaths of his youngest and eldest sons, William Sterndale Parry and Haydn Parry, between their deaths Joseph had worked hard on the editing of the six volumes of the *Cambrian Minstrelsie*, which reminded me of *The Cambrian Minstrel* which Ieuan Ddu had collected and printed at his own expense fifty years ago. David Jones in High Street printed that for Ieuan Ddu, in High Street in the town of Tydfil the Martyr in Wales. A good collection of the melodies of Cambria it was, with original words in English and Welsh. A labour of love for it was little profit in money Ieuan Ddu got out of that first collection of the melodies of Cambria. You must forgive me for remembering Ieuan Ddu for I cannot help it. I am one of those who crucified not his body but his great soul because he was a Unitarian. As a people we knew not what we were doing at the time so perhaps we shall be forgiven after all.

But as I was saying, between the deaths of his talented son and his most promising son, heavy-laden with sorrow Joseph worked on the *Cambrian Minstrelsie* for Messrs Jack of Edinburgh. He had the valuable help of Dewi Mon but even so he had to resign his position as conductor of the Cardiff Orchestral Society to complete the work in six volumes. I ought to say something about Dewi Mon, for there was another great Welshman if you like. Great man, Dewi Mon,

366

but someone else must tell about him for I have all I can do to tell you about Joseph. The work in six volumes was finished and it was part of what he was paid by Messrs Jack of Edinburgh for that work that enabled Joseph to make the trip to America with Jane, his wife, and his daughter, Dilys. Mendy stayed at home and so did the other daughter – but wasn't she married to that Mr Waite? I can never be sure which is which of those two girls of Joseph. It is a funny thing how it was about girls all my days. Compared to boys they were unimportant and a negligible factor. The works, first the ironworks and now the steelworks, the works and the coal-mines wanted boys, and we got to know and remember the names of the boys but not the girls.

The *Cambrian Minstrelsie* was a good piece of work if not a great piece of work in six volumes and it did much to confirm Joseph's position as the greatest living Welsh musician and composer. Then he went and – oh, enough to drive you mad the man was. What good me talk to him like I did that night on the sea-front at Rhyl in North Wales? No good at all. And after what the *Musical Herald* said about his 'Saul of Tarsus', which I knew was a great work as soon as I had heard it at Rhyl. A little pruning here and there and it would hold its ground with some of the works of the great masters. Listen till I tell you what an English newspaper said after it was performed in England and not in Wales, remember. At Newcastle-on-Tyne, which was one of the places at that time which knew good work from bad. And what did the daily newspaper they had at Newcastle-on-Tyne say about Joseph and his 'Saul of Tarsus'? This is what they said and you can take it or leave it. 'A masterly and scholarly production, which entitles the author to rank high amongst eminent modern composers.' There it is for you. That and the editing of the *Cambrian Minstrelsie* in six volumes made us in Wales feel very proud of Joseph. But wait a minute.

Mendy wrote a libretto of a fairy opera, if you please. In

Welsh we call fairies and elves and those sort of beings 'y Tylwyth Teg', and Mendy wrote a libretto about them. More than once I heard Joseph say that Mendy's brains had gone to his legs and into that old bicycle, and now he had evidently ridden his bicycle into fairyland, from where he returned with this libretto I am telling you about. Oh, dear me. Still, perhaps we must make allowances for Joseph now. Mendy was now his only son and Joseph gave him the fond love of the two sons who had gone as well. So when Mendy came to Joseph with the libretto Joseph read it and said: Yes, indeed. Very good, my son. I will write the music for it. We will call it 'Sylvia', said Mendy. Yes, 'Sylvia' will be nice, my boy, said Joseph, and he hurried as fast as he could to write the music. Before long I had a letter from Joseph in which he asked me to come to Cardiff for sure to see and hear his new opera, the best thing I have ever done, he said. No, I will not go to any more old opera of yours, I shouted. What is the matter? said my grand-daughter, The man has written another opera, I said. What man? she said. The Doctor, gel, the Doctor, I said. Well, that is his work, isn't it? she said. No, it is not his work – talk about something you know, good gel, I said.

Go down to Cardiff I did like the old fool that I am. Edwin with me. Back home to Merthyr on the rodneys' train feeling sore all over. Now the old row would start all over again, for it was put on at the Theatre Royal, Cardiff, and all the Welsh chapels of Cardiff represented on the stage. Misrepresented if you like then. Young people, members of Welsh chapels like their mothers and fathers and grand-parents, now stage-fairies with wings and some in tights. I did not wait for Joseph's speech at the end. Come, Edwin, I said. He has done it now. Fairy opera, indeed. If I am any judge those fairies will have the theatre to themselves before the week is out. Don't ever talk to me about it, Edwin. I thought parts of it quite good, said Edwin. Parts! I said. Is it good in parts Joseph should be now? Fifty-five next birthday and only good in parts! Don't talk any more about it.

The rodneys' train back to Merthyr was crowded as far as Pontypridd and the compartment was full of smoke and the smell of beery breath. Two drunken men singing unfairy songs and others joining in the choruses. Me coughing and trying to catch my breath. Never again on the rodneys' train, I said when half those in the compartment got out at Pontypridd. A week in bed I had after that jaunt. On Friday when Edwin came home to his dinner he came upstairs to me first with my *Merthyr Express* and said: Lady Charlotte Guest is dead. No, I said. It is in the *Merthyr Express*, he said. So it was. Well, well ... We still spoke of her when we remembered her as Lady Charlotte Guest, though of course she had to change her name when she went from our district to marry that Charlie Schreiber, who was in Parliament at the time. So I suppose she was Lady Charlotte Schreiber when she died, for I do not remember hearing that she got married the third time.

Well, she is dead, poor woman, and it is not for me in my old age to say nasty things about her. All I wish is that she had paid to have our district cleaned up a bit and put tidy after her. She had taken the money out of the place to wherever she went to live with Charlie Schreiber and had left mountains of muck and ash and slag and clinker for us to do just what we liked with. We have still got it and much more to it as well since she left. I lie in bed and sometimes I wonder where all that money is now, the money the Guests and the Crawshays and all those others took out and away from our town and district. No doubt millions of that money have done its work from London, from where it has gone to develop other places even as we were developed in the first place. Money is a funny thing when you come to think of it. It can be put in a small place and taken away and nobody is much the wiser. Muck and sludge and ash and slag and clinker stays and it grows and grows and we living in the midst of it all get used to it in time. There is a fine view from the tops of some of our slag and clinker-tips.

Now, of course, there is hardly a famous family left in our South Wales coal and steel region, not living amongst us, I mean. They still have what are called 'interests' here but their harvests as families have been gathered in. Now it is the hundred and one companies that are doing the gleaning. Many Welshmen have by now come to the fore, including one of our two M.P.s, Mr D. A. Thomas, and Sir William Thomas Lewis. So the money now being made by the companies of South Wales is harder to get and it has to be shared between ever so many more people than was the case during the hundred years' reign of the coal and iron kings. But we, the people of the place, still get the muck and sludge and slag and clinker and ash.

Still, there are a few more tidy houses going up, on the rise behind our Hospital for one place. The waterworks are giving us a little more water but the companies are not giving our miners very good wages. For the companies have to get more out of the gleaning than our coal and iron kings got out of the harvest, and you would think that impossible. But don't you fret. The companies know how to get it and who to get it out of.

CHAPTER 15

Tone-poem

BEFORE I tell you any more about Joseph I must tell you something about some other men I knew in Merthyr and district and throughout South Wales. You may not know them but no doubt you know what they laid the foundation of, the South Wales Miners' Federation. Now, in 1896, these men had something to show for their work and sacrifice. It will only take me a couple or three minutes to tell you about them. But first I must tell you of the way our miners' wages were fixed. For twenty-one years since 1875, when we were locked-out for twenty-two weeks by the coalowners, it was the 'Sliding-Scale' that determined our wages. A 'Sliding-Scale' based on the selling price of coal at so much free on board and so on. Coal, of course, was sold and sold again and again before it got to the consumer. It was the price he paid in the long run that no doubt kept coal-brokers looking so happy in their offices in the vicinity of the docks. We in the valleys, at the point of production, would not know about that for sure. We would not know what the colliery companies' selling agents made either. Those big pickings had nothing to do with us anyway.

The 'Sliding-Scale' operated in a way too mysterious for most of us to understand, but what we did know was that it was not very good for us as miners. So for years we had been wanting a new and better agreement between ourselves and the coalowners. I know this is getting to be a long story but I will cut it as short as I can. For years we had been trying to organize ourselves so as to be able to pay men able to talk for us. It was hard to get men to undertake the responsibility of office and the risks attached to it. What we wanted were local lodges and district committees and a headquarters for South Wales. All this had to start in the localities and men had to take risks in order to start the local lodges in the back rooms or upstairs rooms of public-houses. Each lodge had to have a chairman, secretary and treasurer, offices for which there was no competition at the beginning. The men who dared to take those offices were marked men, more liable to victimization than the rest of us. They took office, and these are the men I want to tell you about.

Why did they start the lodges in our public-houses? Where else could they start them? Before you say anything let me tell you that many of our chapels started in public-houses. That is another story. The first fearless federationists started our miners' lodges in our public-houses and instead of paying room-rent for the one night each week they had the use of a room they bought so much beer. The three of them sat there waiting for members to come in and pay their dues and for new members to come and join. A dozen loyal members who always came first sat around talking after they had paid their dues. Like a Sanhedrim they sat there to hearten timid members and to encourage new members, for it took some courage to join the Federation with the bosses all against it and against all who joined it. The drop of beer, the purchase price of which was the room-rent, was not guzzled by the men who had dared to take office. In most cases it was used as sparingly as sacramental wine in the confirmation of new members. Drink, said the secretary after he had put the new name down on the book and the treasurer had taken the nominal entrance-fee. The new member took a sup of beer and then went to sit a bit with the others before going out to look fearfully up and down the street.

The 'officers', chairman, secretary and treasurer, left together with books and bag after having sat for a few hours taking dues and enrolling new members. They came out of the public-house talking and they did not look fearfully any way. They were unafraid, had counted the cost and were prepared to meet it in order to create an organization. They are the men I want to tell you about, the foundation members and the men who dared to take office. I knew hundreds of them. Quiet and sober and determined men. Hard-working and honest men whose honorarium for each year's office and risk was next to nothing. They worked in the mines and they did not have to say anything for their presence alone spoke louder than words could on the need for organization. So they were put to work in the poorest and wettest and most dangerous working-places and still they made a living and gave the bosses no chance to get rid of them without causing trouble. So by now, 1896, there was more than the beginnings of an organization.

One more word about the public-houses in which the miners' lodges were held weekly. Most of them were 'free houses', not tied to any brewery, and the landlords and landladies of those 'free houses' did, whatever their faults, believe in freedom. They would, most of them, let a man spend his wages on drink if he had a mind to, some of them would encourage men to do so, but none of them would tell a bosses' scout who it was had passed through to the Federation room at the back or upstairs. That was how it was in 1896, the year they made the National Testimonial for Joseph. Anthony Howells started it with a great concert at the Rosebery Hall, London, a concert which was attended by over nine thousand people. Out of respect to Joseph nine of the best male-voice choirs of South Wales went to London at their own expense to sing at that concert. I did not go to London but I went to the National Eisteddfod at Llandudno to hear the work Joseph had been commissioned to write.

Edwin had his holidays that week and he had privilege tickets for himself and my grand-daughter but I had to pay full fare. Still, it was worth it, for Joseph was back on the right lines again – but for how long? I asked him. How long before you are again wasting your time and talent on some old opera? Only laugh he did and Edwin, my grand-daughter's husband, made me lose my temper by telling Joseph that he thought that parts of the fairy opera, 'Sylvia', were very good indeed. I think so too, said Joseph. Two against one but I do not care, I said. Too bad to remember the thing was. I am not going to try and talk sense to you any more, Joseph. Back on your right horse you are now and if you get off your horse to ride the donkey of opera again then don't ever ask me to come near. Only laugh he did again. So what can you do with him?

Now this work of his that was performed at Llandudno the week I was there with Edwin and my grand-daughter was good, though not as good as his 'Saul of Tarsus'. Still, good enough. 'Cambria' was the name of it, one of these historical cantatas. It had a splendid reception from as large an audience as I have been in at any National Eisteddfod – but wait a minute now. It was not as big an audience as the one at the Rhyl National Eisteddfod four years ago, was it? I do forget. But talking about Rhyl and Llandudno and remembering them after makes me wish all in the dirt of South Wales could have a month by the sea in North Wales every year. We had a lovely week at Llandudno. Good lodging we had and good food the woman of the house put for us every meal. Competitions and concerts at the National Eisteddfod and the sea so lovely and clean. Not a drop of rain or a cloud in the sky all the week. Do you remember such weeks?

Back to Merthyr and its dirt we had to go after all. Joseph was happier than he had been for years when I saw him at Llandudno and the National Eisteddfod there was the best for years. Everything, weather and sea included, combined to make it a great success and a memorable occasion. Yes, I shall remember the National Eisteddfod of 1896. It was the year of recognition for Joseph, for the national testimonial brought him £630, including £100 from admirers in America. So he bought a bigger house in Penarth and called it 'Cartref', which means 'Home'. Big study which was also a music-room for himself now and when I went to see him there he was working as happy as could be. He had got over his disappointment – Oh, I did not tell you, did I? Sir Joseph Barnby had died or retired or something and so a new Principal was wanted at the Guildhall School of Music in London. Now then, said Jane, and Joseph went around seeing people. The Mayor, Aldermen and Councillors of the County Borough of Cardiff most strongly recommended him for the appointment. Hundreds of others also recommended him, including Manuel Garcia and Signor Randegger. Sir John Stainer, Sir George Grove and Sir G. A. Macfarren were only three of many well-known musicians to recommend him and with it all Joseph was not in the short-list of five for the job. Jane had hoped he would get it so that they could move to London but now that they were in the new and bigger house, with a maid and a woman coming on Mondays to do the washing, she had partly got over the disappointment.

This applying and canvassing for jobs was getting to be a great thing in 1896, when ever so many old jobs were becoming vacant and ever so many new jobs created by the progress we were making. More teachers wanted for a start. They have started to build that secondary school in Merthyr that there was talk about. Up by the Hospital they have started to build it and canvassing for the job of headmaster started long before the roof was on the school. As I was telling Edwin, who told me that canvassing for this job had already started, I don't hold with it, I said. How can you get the best man for the job without canvassing? said Edwin, who is not as ready to give in to me now as when he first came to live here with me and my grand-daughter. With canvassing, I said, every one who tries for a job is the best man in the opinion of some. A regiment of people of all sorts said that Joseph Parry was the best man for the job of Principal of the Guildhall School of Music, didn't they? But it was some man named Cummings that got the job. So what good Joseph bother in the first place? I hope I shall be able to get off to go to London to sing under him at the Crystal Palace, said Edwin. I am not going all the way to London, I said. No, too far for you, said Edwin.

He and my grand-daughter belonged to one of the Tonic Solfa choirs which Joseph was gathering from North and South Wales for the performance of his works he wanted to give at the Crystal Palace, London. I hope I am not saying wrong but say it I must. I firmly believe that Joseph wanted to show London and the Guildhall School of Music what they had missed by not appointing him Principal of the Guildhall School of Music. Who can say that they did not lose a great Principal by not appointing him? True, he had

not been a great success at Aberystwyth or Swansea as the
head of a Music Department and as the Head of a College
of Music. Neither was he any great shakes as a lecturer at
Cardiff College now. Yet he might have made a great
Principal outside Wales. Now when I think and remember
everything about him I am sure that he would have made
a great Principal of such a school as the Guildhall School of
Music. For say this I must too, and it is as a Welshman I am
saying it, remember. National testimonial notwithstanding
Wales for Joseph was not good any more. In Wales at the
age of fifty-five – fifty-six next birthday – he was as good as
finished. Only outside Wales could he now crown his life's
work. Whose fault is that? There you are again. Fault on
both sides no doubt. Only saying I am, knowing him as I
did and knowing Wales as I do. Small we are as a country
and a people and the world has taken so much from us. Now
we are not willing to give to the world such men as Joseph.
I don't know. Only thinking I am, that is all.

Mrs Hughes next-door up looked after me the three days
my grand-daughter and Edwin were up in London. A day
to go and a day to come back and a day to sing at the Crystal
Palace under Joseph, though not under him altogether. For
it was a selection of his works, Edwin told me, and my
grand-daughter, who speaks her mind 'front or please more
than Edwin, said that some of the choirs had not half learnt
the pieces. It was awful the way Joseph's 'Cambria' was
mangled, she said, but she agreed with Edwin about the
Tone-poem for choir, organ, four brass bands and I think
she said an orchestra as well. That was grand, they said.
Joseph has been fond of brass bands from a boy, I said.
How have you managed? said my grand-daughter. Splendid, I said. Mrs Hughes looked after me better than you do.
Listen to him now, said my grand-daughter, who is the best
grand-daughter in this world.

You remember the Diamond Jubilee of 1897. Sixty years
a Queen, remember. I do not remember seeing her in

376

Merthyr but never mind. There was Sports in the Big Field and two bands playing there, the Cyfarthfa Band and the Merthyr Volunteer Band – no, it was up and down the High Street the Merthyr Volunteer Band played in front of the Volunteers, wasn't it? I am trying to remember but it was what Joseph did about this time that is full of my mind. An operetta, if you please. Tone-poems one minute and operettas the next. Go to see it? No fear. 'Cap and Gown', he called it. Tut-tut. Leave him alone to do what he likes, was what I said to myself. 'Descriptive of college life', it said on the programme which Edwin brought back. Yes, no doubt. Edwin could get privilege tickets for him and his wife, my grand-daughter, but I would not have gone to see it if they gave me a first-class privilege ticket and dinner at the Park Hotel into the bargain.

Did you tell him what I told you to tell him from me? I said to Edwin. No, for we had to hurry to catch the train, said Edwin. Wait till I see him, I said. Fair play, it was not so bad, said my grand-daughter. I enjoyed it, said Edwin. Please do not say any more, I said. Go now for me to sleep. But I could not sleep. These young people with their 'not so bad' and 'I enjoyed it'. Was Joseph right after all as far as the young people were concerned? Was he trying to give them what they wanted? If he was then only God could help him now. For the young people in 1897, the year of the Diamond Jubilee, did not know what they wanted. Look what they were flocking to see at our three-year-old Theatre Royal. Was a man of Joseph's worth to compete with that stuff with operettas descriptive of college life? God forbid.

He came up to Merthyr for the opening of our new Town Hall. Oh, glad I am to see you for I am going over to America again soon, he said. Stay there, I said. What have I done now? he said. Go now, 'Cap and Gown', I said. Oh, he said. A bit of fun, that is all. I have heard all about it, I said. I am gone I cannot quarrel with you any more. If you promise not to say any more about it then you shall come for food to our house after you are tired of the speeches they are going to make one after the other. I have promised to go back down to Pontypridd to Tom Stephens, he said. Did I tell you that my mother is very ill over in America? Is she? I said. Yes, he said. Well, I am none too good and she is older than me, I said. Already I am tired of standing. I will leave them to talk and go down to the railway station to get a cab to take me home from there. Stay where you are and I will get you a cab and pay for it too, he said. But I would not let him pay for it. Give him his money back, I said to the cabman. Take it, take it, Joseph. And listen now, good boy. I may not be here when you come back from America. If I am not then I will turn in my grave when you write operas or operettas. So try to keep solid from now on.

Laugh he did again and I told the cabman to take me home. I had another look at our new Town Hall as the horse started and that look was enough. I had seen what had cost £15,000 to build and the speeches at the opening I could read in the *Merthyr Express* and me comfortable in bed with my glasses on. It was a red, well-built building right in the centre of the town and no doubt it will be found most useful now that we are getting on towards the end of the century. Another two years and we will be in the twentieth century and we are hoping that before then we will be a Corporation. Five unsuccessful applications we have already made for incorporation. Evidently we are not yet important enough. We have been sending our coal and iron and now steel somewhere for a hundred and thirty years but evidently that is not enough. Then say only a hundred million pounds sterling have gone somewhere out of the place. That is not enough. In the town and district there are eighty thousand people. Not enough for incorporation. I am not worrying. I shall not lie any the more comfortable in my bed if and when we are incorporated, neither shall I live any the longer. I thought Joseph was getting to look old. Didn't you? Fifty-seven, that is all he is. This jaunt to

America will no doubt do him good. But his mother, Betty Parry, God help her, was dead before he could get to her. He cried and cried but what good him cry.

A grand woman. Only God knows all the grand women we have had in this world. Was it the Rev. Silyn Evans said that day at Groeswen ... what did he say about mothers that day in the mother chapel of our denomination, the Welsh Independents? Was it there he said it or at that funeral? Let me see now. God, he said, only gave us all one mother. The material was too precious to give us more than one. No, Silyn Evans put it better than that. There is a preacher for you, especially at a funeral. I hope Betty Parry had a grand funeral in America, for if ever a woman deserved a grand funeral then it was her. I do not know if they are as much for funerals in America as we are in Wales. I have heard many preachers preach at many funerals and when I remember them and their sermons it is glad in my heart I am. Our Welsh preachers were good lime on the poor soil that we are. No poorer, mind you, than any other people of the world but poor after all. Oh, the rich words of our Welsh preachers better than gold when you are getting old like me!

And this old trouble again, trouble not altogether of our making. All our miners out on strike, here in Merthyr and district and throughout South Wales. No, not all. Let me be right. One of our M.P.s, Mr D. A. Thomas, kept his pits in the Rhondda Valley working and paid the men their wages. But all the other pits idle and no wages for scores of thousands of men and boys for six long months. Enough to break your heart to see our miners standing about and their leaders trying to get them their rights. Yes, their rights, that is all. Some of you know what it was like down in the mines of South Wales in '98, and you know what it has been like in the South Wales mining valleys through the years. Were we wrong, do you think, in our demands for something better than what we had had through the years, and in

379

striking for it? The companies with the exception of the one I have mentioned stood firm and so did we. After nearly six months on strike we had to give in again. We were not strong enough yet. I had gone past work but my spirit was on strike with the miners of South Wales for nearly six months in '98, and when they were beaten back to work I said then the day would come. I will not see it but come it will for sure. It is funny that during that six months I was feeling better than I had for years, no doubt because I wanted to help as best I could. I will not tell you of the many incidents and the suffering caused, for you should know what it means for families to be nearly six months without wages and in receipt of very little strike-pay. What I am asking you is what I asked myself many times during that six months. Why must this be? Why can't we live and let live? A man who is ready and willing to go down a pit to work ten hours for five days a week up to Friday night and seven hours on Saturday is entitled to as much if not more than any workmen above ground the world over. You would say so I am sure if you had to go down one of our South Wales coal-mines and work at least fifty-seven hours a week in '98.

But we will leave those miners and their wives and families and go to see how Joseph is getting on over in America. I told you that his mother was dead before he could get to her. He was sad in the train going to Salt Lake City to preside at the great Eisteddfod at the Mormon Tabernacle. Perhaps you did not know that many Welsh-Americans were Mormons. Oh, yes, and good Mormons they were too. I met one of them when he came to Wales to our National Eisteddfod. John James his name was. He took two young chaps he had converted whilst over here back to the State of Utah with him, where they turned out to be very good Mormons.

I heard the record of the singing at the Gymanfa Ganu at Danville, Pennsylvania – but I have gone before my story again. I should have told you that Joseph went to America by himself this time, for after buying the house, 'Cartref', out of the money of the National Testimonial, there was very little left. Neither Joseph nor Jane, his wife, are very good at handling the bit of money. He was engaged for the big Eisteddfod at the Mormon Tabernacle in Salt Lake City, so his expenses were being paid on top of the fee. Anyway, there was no money to pay for Jane to go this time. Joseph and Jane were sorry but there it was. So Joseph went by himself and when he got to Danville they had organized a Gymanfa Ganu ready by the time he arrived. More than that they had men there to record the singing of some of the hymns and make Edison Bell Records of singing in America for Joseph to send home to his wife, and another set of the records he sent to Tom Stephens of Pontypridd. Hearing that I was fast in bed again Tom brought them up from Pontypridd, with the machine, to play them for me. Well, well, I said. What next? Me in bed in our house in Twynyrodyn in Merthyr in Wales and listening to the machine that was making me hear singing over in America. Twice Tom played the records for me.

What a welcome Joseph had at Salt Lake City, where he met another Stephens and another conductor into the bargain. Professor Evan Stephens was the Welshman who was conducting the singing at the Mormon Tabernacle in Salt Lake City. He was a splendid musician and he was waiting for the train to welcome Joseph to the city. So were many other Welsh-American Mormons. They all escorted him to the hotel where he had a suite of three rooms. Never before had Joseph had such a welcome or such hospitality. For a week he was in the Mormon city, where he was honoured as though he were the Prince of Wales. After the Eisteddfod every day they took him in carriages to see places and there were fourteen thousand people in the Mormon Tabernacle to hear him give his lecture on 'The Great Masters of Music'. More Welsh talked on the streets of Salt

Lake City that week than ever before. And what a send-off Joseph had! More singing, of course. Sleeping on trains and going everywhere Joseph was. Opened his eyes he did when he saw how some of the cities had grown since he last saw them. Parks and fine streets and big buildings the cities now had and ten times more people than before some of them had. Chicago when Joseph got there had grown more than any city and Professor Dan Protheroe was at the railway station which they call 'depot' to meet him and greet him in Welsh. A splendid reception in Chicago again and a grand concert there as well. At Scranton Professor Haydn Evans with the Scranton Choral Union to meet and greet Joseph with song in Welsh. Concert at Scranton better than at Chicago. To Tennessee, Colorado, Kansas, Kentucky and other States and from four to five thousand miles on the train before going back to New York to get the boat to go home. He had promised ever so many to come back to America the following year with four of the best singers in Wales to sing the best of his songs. We are holding you to that, Doctor, they said. We shall go right ahead with the arrangements. God willing I will be with you again next year, said Joseph. And he was as good as his word, come you.

Same it was this time again, the best of welcomes everywhere for him and his quartet of grand Welsh voices. This tour was his greatest success in America and if only he had stayed in America after having been on tour there two years running he would have been accepted as the greatest Welsh-American musician and America as a whole would have forgotten and forgiven all the years he had been away from there. Professor Dan Protheroe of Chicago, when he came to Merthyr for the National Eisteddfod we had again at the turn of the century, Professor Dan Protheroe of Chicago himself told me that Joseph had made a great name for himself in America during the two tours in 1898 and 1899. Even at New York he had a grand reception – but I am bound to tell you about New York. Not about the way it had grown or anything like that. You would not believe if I told you how New York had changed since Joseph first went to America on that sailing-ship, the *Jane Anderson*, in 1854. Joseph himself could hardly believe his own eyes now in 1899. Well, forty-five years of change, remember. You remember old Eleazar Jones, whose hotel, 'The Celtic', Joseph used to stay at when passing through New York in the old days. 'The Celtic' was a nice little hotel though not what you could call central. But it was always a little bit of Wales on 33rd Street, New York. It is not there now, neither is Eleazar Jones. He died years ago but now his youngest son, G. Morgan Jones – that G. used to be Goronwy when his father was alive – G. Morgan Jones was managing a very nice hotel on 57th Street, between 5th and 6th Avenues. Joseph knowing G. Morgan Jones from a boy was staying at this hotel for two days and two nights before going on the ship to go back home to Wales again.

Joseph was feeling a bit tired after going about America so much two years running. Remember that he is not far off the sixty mark now and when a man is nearly sixty, especially when he has worked as hard as Joseph had all his days, he gets tired sooner than he used to. Do not think that making music all the time is easy work. Oh, no. Joseph often told me that songs in his head had kept him awake many a night when he was dying for sleep. Even when a boy working in the coal-mine and after that in the ironworks until after he was married and the father of two children songs in his head used to keep him awake. But he was young then. Now he is getting close to the sixty mark and this is what I am going to tell you about him and her in New York now in 1899.

It was getting on for eleven o'clock in the morning and he was walking slowly along 5th Avenue when he saw her and knew at once that it was her sitting in the carriage that was stopped outside one of the fine shops of 5th Avenue. Sitting with her eyes closed like if she was tired too she was and her face was set white like the black mask her father used to wear over his face. She had glasses over her closed eyes fastened to her nose not with things to put over the ears and there was a thin gold chain from the glasses clipped to her nose down to where it was fastened to her bodice near her waist. Two horses in the shafts of the carriage and a coloured man in some sort of uniform up on the seat holding the reins and the whip upright and handy to his right hand. Another coloured man, only younger than the other, standing on the pavement for someone to come out of the shop no doubt. His uniform was the same as the man holding the reins and sitting on the seat.

Myfanwy, said Joseph. Go home, boy, she said like a woman in a trance without opening her eyes behind the glasses. I am going home day after to-morrow, said Joseph, then she opened her eyes and looked at him as though it were a ghost she was looking at. She took off her glasses and blinked her eyes. Me it is, said Joseph, smiling. I knew you glasses and all. The coloured men both stared at Joseph, who was too distinguished-looking for them to tell him not to annoy the lady, and Myfanwy looked and looked. It cannot be you, she said. I was day-dreaming about you and ... and then – but it is you. Of course it is you, she said, reaching for his hand. Come and sit beside me. The youngest of the two coloured men with wide-open eyes lowered a step for Joseph to step into the carriage. This is the most extraordinary coincidence, said Myfanwy. How long have you been in New York? Day before yesterday I came here all the way from St Louis and day after to-morrow I am leaving for home, said Joseph. How long have you been here from Italy? About a week, she said, looking hard at him all the time. I simply cannot – say something in Welsh. I thought you had finished with the Welsh, he said with a smile. Please say something in Welsh, the line of a Welsh hymn – anything, she said. He smiled and began to recite: 'Beth sydd i mi yn y byd – ' She squeezed the hand she was holding and put the fingers of her other hand to his lips. It is you, she said. One of my maids has gone into that shop for something which required some slight alterations before I could wear it at the opera to-night – please go and see where she is, she said to the coloured man on the pavement. Oh, this is so extraordinary and such a delightful surprise. Incredible though it may sound I really was thinking of you, and of that cold douche you and I gave that audience at Merthyr. She laughed and Joseph laughed too. Then, she said, in a sort of old woman's day-dream, I heard you speak my name. And you said what you have always said to me from a boy, said Joseph. Did I really say it? she said. Yes, he said, go home, boy, that was what you said without as much as opening your eyes. How extraordinary, she murmured and then a young woman came out of the shop with something in a cardboard box. Myfanwy told her in Italian to get a cab for herself, and then told the coloured man in English to drive back to the hotel, which he did after the other coloured man had got up on the seat beside him. What are you doing in America? Joseph asked as they were being driven along. She squeezed his hand again and said: When we get to the hotel I may be able to tell you. I am still trying to convince myself that you are real, that you are – well, you. Oh, yes, I am me, said Joseph, laughing. How long have you been in America? she asked. A month – no, nearly six weeks, said Joseph. You do not look much older, Myfanwy. Thank you, she said. No indeed you don't, he said. Strange, but I was not surprised to see you sitting with your eyes closed and me on the pavement. Always and everywhere I am expecting to see you. Always and everywhere I think of you but without expecting to see you, she said. I was wrong. Joseph. It is not Wales or the world but life, short, sad, sweet life. It is not the place but the time that does things to us. Places too, said Joseph. He looked down at her hand holding his. No, never mind, no harm, he said. What? she said. Only thinking aloud I was, he said. No, you are not old. Please do not say that again, she said. I wish you and my wife had met that time in Cardiff, he said.

She released his hand and sat straight and looked the other way. I do not wish to meet your wife, she said. The carriage stopped outside the entrance to the Astor Hotel and the youngest of the two coloured men jumped down on to the pavement to open the door of the carriage for Myfanwy and Joseph to step down and out. I shall not want you again until this evening, then be here in good time to drive us to the Opera House, said Myfanwy to the coloured man. Joseph followed Myfanwy into the Astor Hotel, which was one of the first hotels to have that kind of elevator on which Myfanwy and Joseph went upstairs to her suite of rooms. I had a suite of rooms at the hotel in Salt Lake City, but not such a suite as this, said Joseph. I would like you to meet a protégée of mine before lunch, said Myfanwy, tinkling a handbell. A maid appeared and Myfanwy spoke to her in Italian. The maid went and Myfanwy asked Joseph to sit down. She went to where there was wine in bottles with wicker covering and she poured some into two glasses and gave one to Joseph. To our meeting, she said, and Joseph said: Pob hwyl, then laughed until he spilt some of the wine on his trousers. She dabbed it with a tiny handkerchief and he said: I am sure you still know what Pob hwyl means. It means that you wish me every happiness, she said. Well ... er, yes, that will do, said Joseph. You asked me what I was doing here in America, said Myfanwy. A girl I am interested in is making her debut in 'Traviata' at the Opera House this evening. I arranged it. She has taken my name and will sing under it always. You mean that other name, said Joseph. My professional name, said Myfanwy. The girl is lovely – but you will see. She has the voice and the right temperament for opera. I have supervised her training.

Then the girl came in and Joseph stood up and bowed with some wine still left in the glass in his hand. Myfanwy spoke in Italian to the girl who looked from her to Joseph and smiled. I am telling her that we are old friends, said Myfanwy to Joseph. You will be meeting her again at supper after the opera. She spoke in Italian to the lovely girl, who smiled and nodded her head and looked at Joseph and then went out. 'Traviata,' said Joseph. No, no, it was 'Rigoletto' I heard you in in London that time. That time, said Myfanwy. That time – some more wine, she said. No, not at this time of day, said Joseph. You know I never take drink. Myfanwy took his glass and put it away with her own near the wine-bottles. You shall have another glass with your lunch and after lunch we will talk, she said. Oh, I have promised to go back to my hotel for lunch, said Joseph. I have a quartet from Wales with me and it is little they know about New York. We will send a message, said Myfanwy. We have so much to talk about, you and I.

So she kept Joseph with her until it was time to send him in a cab back to his own hotel to dress for dinner and the opera. It was her he was with nearly all the time till his ship sailed, but please don't think bad thoughts. He slept at the hotel managed by G. Morgan Jones. Both he and Myfanwy were too old for any old nonsense of that sort, remember. And, speaking for Joseph if not for Myfanwy, he was too respectable too. Never mind what goes on at hotels, some hotels anyway. Two old people talking they were, that is all. What would Myfanwy be now in 1899? Sixty-three if not sixty-four. And Joseph gone fifty-eight and tired after a tour of from four to five thousand miles in America. There you are then. But there was not a handsomer couple for their age in the Opera House that night. She had more colour than when Joseph saw her sitting with her eyes shut behind her glasses in the carriage and she was wearing the new dress one of her two maids came out of that shop with in the cardboard box. And it was a box they had to themselves the two of them and opera glasses to look through they had too. To see them looking so distinguished who would think that it was only a boy and a girl from Merthyr in Wales they were in the first place, and a poor boy and girl at that.

That is how it is. You go into a theatre or an opera house away from where you were born and nobody is any the wiser. Look at all the people who were in this Opera House in New York this night. Where did they all come from in the first place? There is a story for you if you like, without the men of the orchestra and all the singers on the stage too. Must have been thousands there that night, for they were one on top of the other in galleries shaped like horseshoes. It was not as big as the Mormon Tabernacle in Salt Lake City but it was much grander in a different way. Myfanwy had been there before, of course, for she had sung there when she was singing all over the world. Now she was nervous as well as anxious about the girl who was that night to sing under her name, Lina Van Elyn. She need not have worried, for the girl sang in a way that thrilled Joseph through and through. She had many in that distinguished audience on their feet shouting as well as clapping their hands. Oh, Joseph enjoyed himself that night. Between the acts many people came from their boxes to congratulate Myfanwy in hers. Like a queen she was receiving their congratulations and she introduced Joseph to the people who came to the box as an old friend and one of Britain's greatest musicians. In the mixture of talk there were some invitations to Joseph, and Myfanwy had to explain that he was leaving for England almost immediately – leaving for Wales, said Joseph, but Myfanwy ignored that. Then after it was all over a man belonging to the Opera House came dressed in evening dress to take them around to the stage while the audience was clapping and shouting.

Well, well ... Talk about excitement. Bouquets and baskets of flowers all over the place and men and women embracing and kissing Myfanwy and the girl who had sang so wonderfully under her name that night. There was no time for any introductions back-stage so Joseph had a look around whilst all this was going on. What a stage! Three if not four or five times bigger than the stage of the Theatre Royal, Cardiff. A big opera I would like to write for this stage, said Joseph talking to himself. An opera about our Prince Llewelyn or Owen Glyndwr or Tydfil the Martyr. Yes, an opera about Tydfil the Martyr would be grand on this stage. Merthyr so lovely a place before they came to make iron or look for coal and Tydfil, daughter of the Prince of Brycheiniog all in white and her black hair hanging down her back to below her waist. Alone in the middle of this stage singing ... what shall she sing first? She will be happy at first. Her lover from ancient Powysland will be on his way to her – some tenor arias for him. Then the two chiefs of the Picts and Saxons – baritone and bass arias for them. Choruses and –

Ah, there you are, doctor, said Myfanwy, calling him doctor in front of people as she had through the evening. Here are some friends of mine who are joining us at supper. She turned right and left to the dozen people she had gathered. He has been introduced to death this evening already, I'm afraid. This is my old friend, Doctor Joseph Parry, one of Great Britain's most eminent musicians. He took his degrees at Cambridge University ... The people were suitably impressed and having bowed to Joseph they stood and talked until the second Lina Van Elyn joined them. Then Myfanwy took one of Joseph's arms and the second Lina Van Elyn took the other and they walked across the stage followed by the other dozen or so who were speaking a variety of languages. The carriages were waiting and off they all went to the Astor Hotel, which was not so far away. One of the supper-party was a young man named Astor and he was following the second Lina Van Elyn all over the place. Myfanwy must be worth a lot of money, said Joseph, talking to himself. Two more came and that made eighteen sitting down to supper which was served by six waiters under the supervision of a head-waiter and there was one man handling only bottles. Joseph watched him and stopped him each time he came smiling with a bottle ready to pour. One glass of wine only Joseph took and having a bit of a headache he asked for strong tea instead of coffee after supper. Tea? said the waiter. Yes, said Joseph. Tea? said the head-waiter, then Myfanwy said: Of course, tea. Tea, tea, tea – you know what tea is, don't you? Joseph had a pot of tea for himself and he drank it all and it made his head feel better.

No wonder he had a headache. It had been a most exciting day for him and the opera and all this talk on top of it was enough to give somebody not used to it a headache. But he would not have missed it for anything. One more day of Myfanwy's company he had before sailing for home. It was with her in her carriage he went across the narrow city and down to where the ship was waiting. Goodbye, Joseph, she said. Goodbye for now, Myfanwy, he said, try to come to Wales whenever you can. She shook her head and then smiled and said: Go home, boy. Then she kissed him the way she had only once – or was it twice before? She turned away from him and went to where the carriage and the two horses and the two coloured men were waiting. He stood looking after her but she did not look back. He stood and looked until the horses had taken her in the carriage out of his sight. There were tears in his eyes and he took off his glasses and felt for his handkerchief. That is the way it is, isn't it?

When Joseph got home there was a letter asking him to write something big for the National Eisteddfod, which was to be held at Liverpool again the following year. The war out in South Africa had started but Joseph forgot all about it as he worked on his cantata, 'Ceridwen', to get it ready for the National Eisteddfod. We in Merthyr were making history, political history this time, as well as music all the time. You know about Keir Hardie, no doubt. Bombshell he was in 1900 in Merthyr in Wales. I had seen him once during the '98 strike but I did not hear him speak then. I did now. Not like a burning fire but like a smouldering fire he was. Not much to look at until you had looked twice. Then you could see the man he was. Never before had I thought of voting Labour but I did now and I did not care who knew it either. All those quiet and tidy men I was telling you about worked and voted for him, come you.

Coal-miners and steelworkers voted for him and Keir Hardie was in and Pritchard Morgan, who was supposed to have a gold mine somewhere in North Wales, was out. This, this is the end, said Washington Morgan to me on Pontmorlais Square. The end of what? I said. The end of all things, he said. The beginning you mean, I said. No doubt you voted for him, he said. What if I did? I said. Now, now, he said, with a war on our hands and all. In Merthyr we have had a war for bread on our hands ever since I can remember, I said. Oh, it was a sensation. The first Labour M.P. for Wales to send to Parliament, for our miners' leader, William Abraham, better known as 'Mabon', was not a Labour M.P. but what we called a 'Lib-Lab'. Keir Hardie was the first independent Labour M.P. for Wales to send to Parliament and we in Merthyr and district were proud to think that we had sent him there. Not all the voters of Merthyr and district, of course, but enough of us to start something which we felt certain would never again be stopped dead.

My century, the nineteenth century, was over and done with and so was I nearly as good as done for. The excitement of the election and Keir Hardie being returned as one of our two members put me back in bed, and although I was up and about in time to go to the National Eisteddfod at Liverpool I was not strong enough for such a long journey. My grand-daughter and Edwin went and Mrs Hughes next-door up looked after me same as before. Edwin

managed to arrange to have his holidays National Eisteddfod week and having privilege tickets for himself and my
grand-daughter helped to make it a cheap week's holiday
for them. They told me that Liverpool was a bigger town
than Cardiff and that bigger ships came there and sailed
from there. They said that Joseph's cantata, 'Ceridwen',
was very good indeed. And we were lucky to get in to hear
it, said my grand-daughter. Three thousand people were
turned away after the place was chock-full. They like
Joseph's work in Liverpool, I said. I wish now I had gone
there to hear 'Ceridwen'. I am glad you did not, said my
grand-daughter. In that crowd trying to get in like we were
you would have died for sure.

Yes, Dr Ward told me that I must keep out of crowds
from now on. Well, I have had my share of crowds, and
most other things in life. I could not complain if I had to go
this minute. No good me complain anyway. But I went to
Pontypridd in a trap all the way from Merthyr to hear
'Ceridwen' performed there. Tom Stephens had written
to say that he was keeping three seats for us and that there
would be no need for me to push to get in to that big building over Pontypridd Market. Wasn't it the New Town Hall
they said it was? Whether or no it was a good work and it
was performed very well indeed. It was done in character
as we used to say, which means that it was half-opera and
half-cantata. Joseph himself conducted and he did conduct
too. Oh, yes, he could conduct when he liked. Foolish I was
to go in a trap on Boxing Day to Pontypridd but I would go.
Wrapped-up well I was with a rug over my legs and all. If I
had gone home as soon as it finished I would not have caught
cold, not so much cold anyway. But I stopped to talk to
Joseph and Tom Stephens and Tom said that we should not
start back in the trap before we had had a cup of tea and a
bit of food to keep the cold out. My grand-daughter said no
and I said no but what good us say no? Come on, said Tom,
our house is just over the bridge and my wife has gone to

392

prepare for you. With the rug over my shoulders now and arm-in-arm with Edwin I went to Tom's house with Joseph and a few others. Lot of old talk from which I gathered that Joseph was up to the same old tricks, writing operas, I mean. Now I heard first that he had written the music for that damned silly comic opera, 'His Worship the Mayor'.

I heard the name of Joseph Bennett, some music critic who was going to write a libretto for Joseph to put the music to 'The Maid of Cefn Ydfa'. Come, it is time for us to go, I said under the talk going on to Edwin. But he was interested and said: In a minute. Such talk. All about opera. The trouble is you have not had good librettos, Joseph, said Tom Stephens. Mr Bennett has written very good librettos for operas but none on such a good subject as our 'Maid of Cefn Ydfa'. Humph, I said. If you will excuse me now, Tom – where did you put my rug, Edwin? No good me talk to you, Joseph. It is a punch and judy show you will finish up with. Only laugh he did and insisted on coming to tuck me up in the front seat of the trap, which was in the yard back of the public-house over the bridge, and the driver now more than half-drunk to make matters worse. He very nearly drove us into the river just this side of Fiddler's Elbow. Come on here and take the reins, Edwin, I said. Not if I know it, said the driver, old Tom Norberry, who was working for Sam Dix. Then try to keep the pony on the road, I said. Don't you try to tell me how to drive the pony, he said. Any more of your old cheek and I will be sure to tell Sam Dix, I said. Tell who the hell you like, he said. Mind I don't make you get out and walk up the Perrott Pitch. For two pins I will get out and walk all the way home, I said. He stopped the pony and said: Go on, get down. Listen, you drunken old thing you, said my grand-daughter from the back seat. Don't you dare try to bully my grandfather. If my husband is afraid of you I am not. I am not afraid of him, said Edwin. Now drive on before I knock you down from where you are. Who is bullying now?

said Tom Norberry. Will you take me home before I die of exposure? I said.

All this old talk just this side of Fiddler's Elbow getting on for midnight on the 26th of December, if you please. No wonder the bed had me for months after that. Clever I was going by trap instead of by train, thinking the trains would be overcrowded on Boxing Day and especially on the rodneys' train on which I would have had to come back late at night. Now I have been in bed for I do not remember how long, reading my Bible and the *Merthyr Express* in turn. I am gone I cannot read for long now. I did not tell Sam Dix about old Tom Norberry getting drunk down Pontypridd whilst in charge of the pony and trap. I would be none the better for getting him into trouble but if I die this time then it will be old Tom Norberry's fault. Or my own for going to Pontypridd in the first place. Pontypridd growing all the time. More coal passing through Pontypridd now than is passing through any other three places put together the world over. Every week now the *Merthyr Express* is half-full of the war going on and on out in South Africa. No pleasure reading the *Merthyr Express* these days. I only read what it says at the top in big letters about the war and then I turn to the Merthyr and district news. After that I read what is going on in the other half-dozen valleys which is served by the *Merthyr Express*.

Before I read about it Edwin told me that the Dowlais Works had been sold. Sold? I said. Yes, to Guest, Keen, and Company, he said. Guest I know but who is Keen? I said. I think it is a Birmingham firm, said Edwin. Then we *are* sold, I said. Where are my glasses? Edwin was quite right. The works was sold. It was done just like that without asking the people whose living it was. The name of Guest, the name which had been a household word with us in Merthyr and district for a hundred years, was still kept by this new company, no doubt not for us to feel too bad about it. But the name of Guest meant little or nothing any more now that the great Dowlais Works was sold to those Brummagem Boys. After a hundred years a great works goes through many vicissitudes and this was one of them. I did not know what to think now. There would, no doubt, be more reconstruction and some changes in management resulting in production drives. Well, they will not drive me any more.

The first year of the twentieth century, 1901, and, according to the *Merthyr Express* and all the talk, we were going to do great things, not only in Merthyr and district but all over South Wales as well. New blood and new methods in Dowlais Works for a start. The Victorian era as some called it was over and now ... Yes, now ... Me in bed and I could hear the voices of the children playing on the road outside. Children's voices ... God save the King now. God save us all I was thinking. All over South Wales the new companies taking over. Dear me. My grand-daughter came upstairs and said: Do you want anything now before Edwin and me go to the Temperance Hall? No, I said. Go you. What is in the Temperance Hall this week? Variety, she said. Sure you don't want anything? No, I said. Then we'll go early to be sure of getting in, she said.

Theatre and Temperance Hall she and Edwin, her husband, went to every week like the clock. Temperance Hall now 'Variety' and Israel Price, who had lost a leg working in the pit now lessee and manager and bringing 'turns', as Edwin and my grand-daughter called them, all the way from London to sing and dance and do tricks of all sorts on the stage of the Temperance Hall. Rosser Beynon and all our other Temperance conductors sure to be turning in their graves. For the Temperance Hall was built to support the cause of Temperance and now they were calling it a 'Variety house', Edwin and my grand-daughter telling me about 'turns' acting drunk there and the people laughing like anything.

Plenty of entertainment for the young people now in 1901, in Merthyr and district anyway. Every week two places to go to and some weeks, when the Drill Hall had a company acting or singing there as well, there were three places to go to. Then on top of all that circuses used to come to the place. The front of the *Merthyr Express* most weeks told of three places the young people could find entertainment at. This week I am telling you about 'A Life's Revenge' with the great duel between two lovely women was at the Theatre Royal and there was 'Variety' at the Temperance Hall and the Myriorama as well as a man in a trance and all the week without food or drink at the Drill Hall. So the young people could not complain of lack of entertainment. What about when we were young in Merthyr and district and only that little portable theatre at the top end of the tramroad to go to if our parents were willing? Yes, indeed.

Let young people have their share of pleasure, I say, for they will have it whether or no. But there is pleasure and pleasure, isn't there? Last time I went to our Theatre Royal it was to see 'The Sign of the Cross' and it was a pleasure for me to be there. But Edwin and my grand-daughter did not like the play. The acting, they said, was good but why all that talk about Christianity in a theatre? We have plenty of that in the chapels on Sunday, they said. So there you are. Perhaps if I was young I would be saying the same now in 1901. When I took Edwin and my grand-daughter to the chapel on a Monday night to hear the Rev. Herbert Evans deliver his famous lecture on Livingstone what do you think they said to me on the way home? That man, they said, would make a fine actor. What if I had said that about the Rev. Methusalem Jones to my father and mother sixty years ago?

Never mind. All I was hoping now was that things would be better for the young people than they were for us when young. The old war in South Africa must have an end and then perhaps another new era would start. New eras ... I had read and heard talk of many in my time but they all got old like me. New eras and new generations ... I will sleep a bit again, I said, putting the *Merthyr Express* down on top of the Bible on the little table near my bed. I took my glasses off and then put them back on. I would read a bit of the Bible before trying to sleep. One little psalm perhaps ...

CHAPTER 16

The World is Yours Now

IT was some committee that was now raising Joseph's sleeve, as we Welsh say when a man is being encouraged to do something we do not agree with. Opera-mad he was now again and this committee they were telling me about was doing its best to send him to the lunatic asylum or his grave. That is talking nonsense, said Edwin, my grand-daughter's husband, who cheeks me to my face now. He is all for opera and he thinks that Joseph is better for opera than with oratorio. That is Edwin for you. Lot like him too. Whoever is on that committee behind Joseph must be like him for a start. Listen, Edwin, my boy, I said. Tied to my bed I am, I know. But from my bed I am a better judge of what is best for Joseph Parry than you are. Sit by there a minute and listen to me, good boy.

It was a Sunday and I had finished my dinner and he had come upstairs to take my tray and the dishes on it downstairs. I will be back up in a minute, he said, and I had time to think a minute before he came back up and sat on the chair beside my bed. Now I am ready for you, he said. Yes, and I am ready for you too, I said. Right. We will say Opera. Now then. If only he would stick to one kind of opera I would not be so nasty to him. It is I that knows Joseph, remember. Comic, romantic, fairy and grand opera, all of them he has tried his hand on and worse he is getting. That is what you think, said Edwin. Right I am in

my thinking, I said. 'Sylvia' and the stage full of fairies.
You were there with me at the theatre that night. The other
nonsense, that comic opera about 'His Worship the Mayor',
I did not go to see. Nor the romantic opera about Bronwen,
'The Maid of Scer', did I bother to go to see either. Nor
will I go to see this one either. I will, said Edwin. This will
be his best – Now you are talking like Joseph, I said. He has
got a good libretto this time and a real opera company, not
amateurs, to perform this work, said Edwin. I cannot stay
long now for we are going for a bit of a walk – Go, go, I said.
Are you and her going to chapel to-night? We may, said
Edwin. There you are again, I said. You may go to chapel
but you are sure that you are going to hear this old opera.
That is Joseph's trouble too. Thinking more of old operas
than of his chapel. Since he gave up playing the organ on
Sundays at Ebenezer Chapel, Cardiff, he never goes to
chapel more than once of a Sunday. Once is enough, said
Edwin. Once may be enough for you but not for Joseph
Parry, I said. He went to Bethesda Chapel here in Merthyr
three times every Sunday when a boy. It is no good you try
to tie an artist to the pulpit of a chapel, said Edwin. Will
you be wanting anything before we go for a bit of a walk?
No, I said. Now you are turning nasty again, he said. It is I
that knows Joseph, I said. Go if you are going – but listen.
I am not nasty to you. You know I could not be. It is thinking of Joseph I am. I have known him from a boy and have
always wanted for him to get on. He do work so hard but
not on what he can do best, God help him. I will try to
sleep a bit.

But I could not find sleep that afternoon after my dinner.
Never mind. Perhaps I will sleep better to-night. Of Joseph
and his work I was thinking all afternoon. This new thing
which was not new at all. Many versions of the story of
'The Maid of Cefn Ydfa' had been played in my time in
little portable theatres all over South Wales. A sad little
story of a girl who was made to marry the rich man instead

of the poor man she loved and dying broken-hearted. It all happened long ago in the Llynfi Valley when that valley was green and lovely and the most that can be said for it was that it was a Welsh story of a love which did not run smooth. Now this Joseph Bennett, some Englishman who was music critic for a London newspaper, was going to write the libretto and Joseph the music, and when that was done the Moody-Manners Opera Company was going to perform it for the first time on any stage at the Grand Theatre, Cardiff.

A representative committee, the one I have been telling you about, was going to guarantee the Moody-Manners Opera Company against loss, but who was going to guarantee Joseph against loss of another bit of his reputation? I was feeling better by the time it was performed, and I had been up and about for three weeks and Edwin and my grand-daughter were going, and there was such a lot of talk in the newspapers until I had a good mind to go myself. Better ask Doctor Ward, said my grand-daughter. What good me ask him when I already know what he will say? I said. What do you think, Edwin? said my grand-daughter. Edwin looked at me like if I was something out of the Ark – you know the way you young people look at us old people without me telling you.

Well, said Edwin. We could travel first-class and take him in cabs to and from the railway stations. Yes, we could do that, said my grand-daughter. Never mind, I said. I won't go. Too much trouble I am. You are saying that not us, said my grand-daughter. Of course I went and glad I am now that I did, glad because Joseph was so glad to see me at the Grand Theatre, Cardiff. I was hoping you would be able to come, he said. I think you will be satisfied with me this time. This is the greatest of all my work and this company is performing it lovely. Mendy was with him and both of them in evening dress and Jane and Dilys and the other girl made a family party worth seeing, come you. Only faded a bit Jane was but as ladylike as ever. Mendy was talking big for his father. The Moody-Manners Opera Company will from now on be including this opera of dad's in their regular repertoire, said Mendy. So it will be performed all over Britain. I am also certain that I shall be able to arrange for its production in America. Oh, Edwin, I said. Isn't this the company Will Full-Moon and his wife were with that time at Merthyr? Yes, of course it is, said Edwin. Then go and see if you can find him for me – see you after if there is time, Joseph, I said, going after Edwin.

No, Edwin could not find Will Full-Moon or his wife for me. Will, the man of the company told us, died suddenly in lodgings at Wigan. And is that where he is buried? I asked the man. Yes, said the man. And his wife? said Edwin. I don't quite know what became of her, said the man. But wait a minute. Madame Fanny Moody would surely know. Thank you, but never mind, I said. His wife is all right wherever she is. Come for us to get back into our seats before the lights go out, Edwin. H'm. Wigan. Well, Will Full-Moon could have picked a worse place than that to be buried at. For Wigan must have reminded him of Merthyr and he decided to die there.

The Moody-Manners Opera Company gave a good performance of Joseph's opera, 'The Maid of Cefn Ydfa', but it was far from being Joseph's greatest work. Edwin thought it was, of course, but I knew better. Passable I would say it was if it was the work of some young Welsh composer, but as Joseph's it was not passable. Forty years ago, in 1862, Joseph was writing the compositions with which he had 'swept the board' at the Swansea National Eisteddfod of 1863. That I was bound to remember this night in 1902 when sitting in the Grand Theatre, Cardiff. Is this, I began to ask myself, is this to be the crowning work of forty years of composition? Joseph himself thought so but never mind him. Was it? No. What could I say to him if he was waiting for me and my opinion after the performance? I did not want to be nasty to him any more for a boy he would always be no matter what I said. I would not be able to force myself to say: Well done, Joseph, and I hate telling lies. Enough lies about his music he had been told already. Mr Manners had told him that this opera of his, 'The Maid of Cefn Ydfa', was as good as the 'Lily of Killarney', and all the principal singers including Fanny and Lily Moody and Charles O'Mara had said the nicest things.

Edwin had a cab waiting outside the theatre and I went out to it without looking right or left for fear of seeing Joseph. There was no fear of seeing him if I only knew, for he was waiting on the stage until called for to say a word in Welsh and English. So I did not have to tell him, thank goodness. My grand-daughter and Edwin enjoyed it very much and it was made much more bearable for me than some of his other operas by the better acting and singing. Now perhaps he would go to work on something bigger and more solid again. He told me when talking to me before the performance began that he had finished his 'Hunan-gofiant' and that he would send me one as soon as he had some copies typed or printed.

The war in Africa was finished and the rejoicing was over and my health was middling and I was able to get about the place a bit before something came one day in a big envelope. It was years since the postman had brought me any sort of letter and now this. It was a typed copy of Joseph's 'Hunan-gofiant', which in English means 'What I Remember' or 'Memoirs' or whatever else you like to call it. At the end a list of his works. He had made the story of his sixty-one years of life nice and short for people to read, he had put it all into twenty-four pages. In one place he put three years into a line and a half. Yes, in thirteen words he covered three years of his life. He had let himself go a bit at the beginning and end but the middle part was a model of compression. So it was easy for me to read.

When he came to Merthyr to conduct a Gymanfa Ganu

401

on towards the end of the year he was looking far from well, I thought, but I did not say anything about that. Plenty ready to tell people when they are not looking well. Took him up in a cab to our house to have a cup of tea and a bit to eat, I did. I have read your 'Hunan-gofiant' twice, I said. The list of your works at the end is nearly as long as your life-story. Isn't that as it should be? said Joseph. Perhaps you are right, I said. Too much old writing there is anyway. But until I read the list of your works at the end of your 'Hunan-gofiant' I did not know that you had turned out so much. Hundreds and hundreds of pieces. Joseph laughed and said: Only Dykes in the musical world has written more than I have. Who is Dykes? I said. The most prolific of all composers living or dead, said Joseph. Funny I never heard of him, I said. What are you working on now? 'Jesus of Nazareth', said Joseph. Well done, I said. The biggest thing I have ever attempted, said Joseph. This oratorio will be made up of the greatest scenes in the life of Jesus. All the tenor solos will be sung by Jesus himself. Wait a minute, good boy, I said. By the tenor soloist, you mean. Catch it you will again from some of our deacons if you put tenor songs into the mouth of a soloist and call him Jesus. How did the opera go during the rest of the week at the Grand Theatre, Doctor? said Edwin. Splendid, said Joseph. But it was very expensive to perform five nights running. The committee behind it lost two hundred pounds. But they are not sorry. I did not want to tell you, Joseph, I said. I was hoping Edwin would have kept his tongue off that opera. I am very glad that that committee lost two hundred pounds on it. Perhaps it is that has brought you to your senses and turned you back to the Bible for your next work. But you had better try to keep Jesus himself out of it. I do not remember that Handel or Mendelssohn or Haydn or any of the masters bring him into any of their oratorios – Another cup of tea, Doctor, said my grand-daughter. No, thank you, said Joseph. I am not going back down to the chapel with you, Joseph, I said. Edwin have got a cab waiting to take you back there, and he and my grand-daughter will ride back down with you. Dr Ward has warned me again about being in crowds. Then one session of hymn-singing is enough for me now. I am beginning to wonder, Joseph. About what now again? he said. About we Welsh and the way we sing our hymns all through the day except for time off to eat. Six to seven hours solid hymn-singing in one day and we call it a holiday. It does no harm, said Joseph indifferently. Well, look after yourself, he said. You look after yourself, I said.

Off he went in the cab with Edwin and my grand-daughter. I went to bed. The Gymanfa Ganu which was such a feature of our chapel-life was getting to be too much for me now. A thousand to twelve hundred voices singing hymns under Joseph was too much for me at my age. Last night it was that Edwin told me that they had discovered Roman remains in Penydarren Park, which I call 'Y Cae Mawr', the Big Field if you want it in English. That is how I feel too, like Roman remains or something of the sort. Thank God for a bed to lie on is what I am saying after being all afternoon at the Gymanfa Ganu in our chapel. The descants Joseph made the sopranos sing this afternoon go through my old head now. Oh, it is nice in bed when you are old like me. Another ten years and I will be as old as old Ben Watkins of Danygraig Farm said he was the last time I saw him the year he died. Edwin told me they are making a Public Park for us up there on the rise by Danygraig Farm. That is one thing I would like to see before I die. Private parks is all we have known in the town of Tydfil the Martyr up to now. It would be nice to have a Public Park for children to play in and old men like me to sit in on fine days. That was one thing the Crawshays or the Guests might have given us out of all the millions of pounds sterling we made for them. No, only the dirt they left us. I know what I will do. I will stay in bed for a week and get up and go about for a week every other. My grand-daughter is on to me about getting false teeth. No. Could not stomach them in my mouth. I can manage with what I have left.

I am glad Joseph has turned back to the Bible and I am glad the war in South Africa is over. Peace even without plenty is worth having. The cannon from the Russian War outside St David's Church did not learn us much ... Yes, a week in bed and a week out and about. That is what I thought of doing but it is not what you or me think, is it? Month I was in bed with my Bible and the *Merthyr Express*, and the one only for the week and the other for ever. I read Joseph's 'Hunan-gofiant' again and the long, long list of all his works. I did not know until now that he had written so much for orchestra and piano. I tried to count all the things he had written through the years but after two hundred I was too tired to finish counting them. The quantity immense but as for the quality ...? What odds now? Those nine old operas weakened him no doubt. Then the hundreds of his things remembered and listed were less than a third of what he had composed and thrown away when moving from place to place. Always about a cartload of compositions to be disposed of each time he had moved from one home to another. Oh, yes, he had worked hard between everything. Too much he had tried to do and only a trier he was now gone sixty-one years old. Pity. His 'Hunan-gofiant', the story of sixty-one years of his life was just like most of the music. Words just thrown and left to stop on paper, leaving great gaps for people to make what they liked of. No time to think or to try and remember he had or would take if he did have. Only on towards the end did he try to write, the rest except for the first few pages he had copied from newspaper cuttings and Eisteddfod and concert programmes. Pity. For the last few pages of the twenty-four into which he compressed his sixty-one years of life were as good as writing as a little of his music was as music. Never mind. Behind 'the Doctor' there was always 'Bachgen bach o Ferthyr, erioed, erioed', the 'Little chap from Merthyr, always, always'. Only thinking here in bed I am. I cannot help thinking about Joseph for I have known and loved him from a boy. Always I have been wanting for him to grow big like Beethoven in music, but Beethoven did not bother his head with old opera. Edwin told me that he tried one, that is all, and then left the old nonsense alone –

It was Edwin when he came home from his work to his dinner that came straight upstairs to tell me about the electric tram running away. I told you about our electric trams, didn't I? Perhaps not. Well, we had them, and electric light, from the light and traction company. The electric trams had almost driven the horse-buses off the road. But not quite, for many people were afraid to ride in our electric trams, same as people used to be afraid to ride in the trains when they first started to run from Merthyr all the way down to Cardiff. Dear, dear, that was sixty-two years ago and how old was I then? Was I married then? Sure to be. Whether or no I remember the old people afraid of their lives of the trains. Now the old people, though not as old as me most of them, afraid of the electric trams. They wait for the bus drawn by three horses. Our main streets and roads between Merthyr and Dowlais are too narrow in parts for the horse-bus to pass our double-decker electric trams, and there are often delays because neither of them will give way. The language then is not fit to repeat. The man turning the power-handle of our electric tram shouting at the bus-driver who shouts back at him and tells him to take his b— contraption out of the way. But it is not easy. A crowd always gathered when the horse-bus and one of our electric trams met on the street where it was too narrow to pass and nine out of every ten of us were on the side of the horses and their driver and his bus. It is true that he could have backed back a bit and then turned his three hor⸲ into one of the lanes, the one between Oliver's bo⸳ and the Albion public-house say. But would ⸳

If he had we who had gathered around would have hooted him. So he stood his ground. Now the driver of the tram could not take his tram off the rails and turn its nose into the lane between Oliver's boot shop and the Albion public-house, so the man who collected our pennies had to pull the cord to turn the pole which went from the top of the tram to the overhead electric wires which some called cables. Then the driver of the tram had to take his handle off and walk through the tram with it to fix it at the other end and drive back out of the way far enough for the horse-bus to pass, say there where Castle Street starts off our High Street. As the tram retreated, followed by the horse-bus which had refused to give ground, we who had gathered cheered the bus-driver and the three horses – and do not think that the horses did not know. The three of them in each of our three horse-buses, nine horses in all, used to nod their heads in acknowledgement of our appreciation of the way they and their drivers had stood their ground against the electric tram. If you do not believe me then ask anyone who was there on any one of the many occasions when our horse-buses refused to give way to our electric trams.

We still had gas-light on the streets but there was talk of having electric light all along our streets and all over Merthyr and district. Our new Town Hall was lit by electricity and so was the Theatre Royal, but the Theatre Royal had an engine at the back of the stage, but right outside of course, to make its own electric light for long before the light and traction company was in a position to supply the Theatre Royal with electric light. But the Theatre Royal had a lot of trouble with that engine after a bit, the generator or something they said it was. Still, they managed to make their own electricity for years before troubling the light and traction company. I think the Drill Hall stuck to gas-light for long after the Temperance Hall had electric light. The Drill Hall only had entertainments off and on 'ut the Temperance Hall, with its go-ahead lessee and manager, Israel Price, was getting to be real music-hall, small, of course, but a real music-hall which had some of Britain's best variety acts week after week. Israel Price often went up to London to book the best turns for us – not for me but for young people like Edwin and my granddaughter. I told you that Israel Price had lost a leg when working as a miner long before he ever thought of becoming a lessee and manager of a music-hall. He had a big black moustache and how he made the Temperance Hall pay as a music-hall proved that he must have been a very good manager. For if he stuffed three hundred into each and every performance the receipts were not much. For the prices of admission were only sixpence, a shilling and two shillings, and there would be no more than fifty seats at two shillings. An average of about £15 per performance was the most he could hope to take, but then there were two performances nightly and a matinee on Saturdays for the children as well. The Theatre Royal only gave one performance nightly.

But I was going to tell you what Edwin told me about the electric tram running away. The three miles from where the electric trams started back from the Bush Hotel in Dowlais down to by the Market House in Merthyr is nearly all downhill. Some of what we called 'pitches' were fairly steep. If the electric tram was going a bit fast sometimes the pole from the top of the tram to the overhead electric wires would come off the wires before the driver knew it. As soon as he knew it he would try to apply the brake but sometimes the brake could not stop the electric tram. So it would go full-pelt downhill as it did this day Edwin was telling me about, and when it came to a turn it would jump the rails and there you are. This day it had jumped the rails on the turn just in front of our Hospital. How many killed? I asked Edwin. No one killed or injured, said Edwin. H'm, I said. I saw Harry Morris meeting Keir Hardie off the train, said Edwin. Harry asked how you were. H'm, I said.

I had known Harry Morris and all his brothers from little boys and they were the last I thought would turn Labour. They had to work hard as miners, of course, but Liberal the family was and always had been until Keir Hardie came to the place. As a family they all went to Tabernacle Chapel and good chapel-people they were. It was a surprise to everyone when Harry took the responsibility and risk of acting as election agent for Keir Hardie, who the Liberals and Tories said was no chapel man. Whether or no many good young chapel-people worked and voted to send him to Parliament, and Harry Morris worked harder and more fearlessly than any for Keir Hardie.

It was Harry brought Keir Hardie up to the house to see me now that I was tied to the bed. My grand-daughter brought another chair and they both sat down to talk for a minute before going. My grand-daughter wanted to put food for them but Harry said they had promised to go to tea with Llewelyn Francis the barber up in Penydarren. Bring them a cup of tea in their hand, I told my grand-daughter. How are they treating you in the House of Commons, Mr Hardie? Harry laughed and said: How is he treating them in the House of Commons you mean. Man-a-man-a-shanko, I said. What does that mean? said Keir Hardie. A bit of old nonsense we in South Wales say to mean that it is the same one way as the other, I said. How are you getting on up there? I'm managing, said Hardie. I'm only one and I have not yet set the Thames on fire. Too many go to London to try and set the Thames on fire, I said. It is the Taff and all the other rivers of Wales and Britain that we must set on fire from now on. Too much talk about London and the Thames there has been. But don't you worry. No, do not worry about being in the House of Commons by yourself. Soon you will have others to help you. That is what I have been telling him, said Harry Morris. High-tide it will be for us some day. I may not be here then but it will come.

They had a cup of tea in their hands and talked for a bit and then they had to go and leave me to my thoughts. I got better soon after that and I was able to go to the Drill Hall with my grand-daughter and Edwin, cab there and back, for the Eisteddfod on the Boxing Day. I met Llew Ebbw again that day. A grand singer who reminds me of Will Full-Moon. Llew was one of the quartet of Welsh singers Joseph took with him to America that time. This day Llew Ebbw won the baritone and the champion solo competitions. Well done, Llew, I said. Where is the Doctor to-day? he said. No doubt adjudicating or conducting one of his works somewhere else, I said. Joseph is in great demand round about Christmas always. Yes, said Llew, he is a very busy man.

Next I heard was that Joseph had had an operation, though the *Merthyr Express* did not say what he had been operated on for. Better go down to see him, I suppose, I said. What for when it says here that the operation has been successful? said my grand-daughter, pointing to the paragraph in the *Merthyr Express*. Yes, but since I have been on the committee of our Hospital I have known more than one successful operation go the other way, I said. I would not like him to die thinking I did not care. But will Edwin be able to get off to take you? she said. Now I am better I can go by myself, I said. Indeed you are not going by yourself, she said. If Edwin can't get off then I will take you. That is how they talk to you when you are getting old.

Edwin could not get the day off, for he was now the head-clerk in what some had now taken to call 'the booking-office'. So I went with my grand-daughter, left Merthyr with the ten train in the morning and had a cup of tea and a bit to eat before taking another train from Cardiff to Penarth. How do you feel now? my grand-daughter kept on asking me. I am all right, good girl, I said, turning nasty at last. When was I in Cardiff last? Was it that time when I lost the rodneys' train and had to travel on the other line and walk home from Rhymney? Now, now, try to think, she said. Twice if not three times you have been here since then. Twice I know to see Doctor Parry's two new operas with me and Edwin. But I must think too. Only once with the two of us and once it was only Edwin was with you, wasn't it? Was it? I said, not caring for I was thinking of that other night, the night when me and Joseph took wine with Myfanwy at the Park Hotel, Cardiff. Late dinner and two sorts of wine and she looking so lovely under her white hair. Where is she now? I was asking myself. Italy? Perhaps dead. No, no, not dead, don't die before me, Myfanwy. Perhaps Joseph when I see him in a minute will tell me where you are. Remember me and him that night? We will never forget you. No, never. No more bad thoughts come to my head. Clean. Dear me ... You now older than your poor father was when he was found in the lock of the canal. Yes, we are getting on.

Talking to myself and through myself to Myfanwy as on the way to see Joseph after his operation. How is he? I said to Jane, looking a little more faded but as ladylike as ever. The doctor thinks he will be all right, said Jane. Tom Stephens is with him at the moment so perhaps you will – have you had lunch? We had tea and a bit to eat at Cardiff, but this girl would no doubt like another cup, I said. I will go on up to Joseph. You need not trouble to come up to show me the room for I will be sure to hear Tom Stephens talking or laughing – Then I saw Joseph's married daughter, Mrs Waite. May as well ask you first as last. I have been trying to think but as dull as ever I am. Tell me your name. She looked at me. Name, your name, I said. My married name? she said. No, no, I said. That is what I am mad with my old head for. It will tell me your married name but not the name I called you when a baby. Your first name. Edna, she said. Of course it is Edna, I said. Remember that for me ready for when I ask you, I said to my grand-daughter. Her name is Edna.

Upstairs I went by myself and I could hear Tom Stephens in a bedroom so in I walked. Oh, look who is here, said Joseph. Sit down, said Tom, putting a chair for me. By yourself you came all the way from Merthyr? said Joseph. No, I said, my grand-daughter brought me. She is downstairs with Jane and Edna. Months if not years I have been trying to remember that name – how are you feeling? Middling, said Joseph. How have you been lately? Up and down, up and about one week then perhaps a month in bed after, I said. But it is you I have come to see. How are you, Tom? All right except for something that took me on the way home from Llanelly the day after Boxing Day, said Tom. Or it may have been a damp bed Boxing Night. I was conducting there Christmas Night and Boxing Night and I stayed the two nights at that hotel – that Llanelly choir is a splendid choir, Joseph. Well, I must be off back to Pontypridd. I have called a rehearsal for this evening and I have to get some copies of the work we are rehearsing from the music shop at Cardiff. Hurry up and get well now. And you look after yourself too, he said to me. Let me see now ... Yes, I shall be over to see you next Wednesday and I hope to see you up out of bed then. Goodbye for now.

Off he went. Busy Tom is all the time, I said. Yes, said Joseph, but never too busy to come and see me. It is nice to see somebody when you are in bed like this. No doubt, I said. But I am gone I do not care much if people do not come to see me when I am fast in bed. I have got used to the bed. I will never get used to lying doing nothing in bed, said Joseph. Never is a long time, I said. You are getting better? Yes, I think I am, said Joseph. Have you ever had an operation? No, I said. Funny feeling, he said. I was telling Tom just before you came. Like a dream it was. Under the chloroform I mean. All mixed up with the war that finished last year in South Africa. I have always hated war but there I was in this dream under the chloroform. Not me but my works like a regiment of soldiers. Four hundred and forty hymn-tunes, three hundred songs and another three hundred anthems, choruses and things. My operas and oratorios – all there like fighting soldiers. Then I could hear the firing of the guns and they were all shot down, all with the exception of one. Over a thousand shot down and one still lived. H'm, I said. A thousand is a lot of things to compose. I did not know you had composed so many things. More, he said. But only the one stood up in my dream. One hymn-tune, the one I called 'Aberyst-wyth'. A good tune but no better than some of your other tunes, I said. How is that big work of yours getting on? I will finish it in less than a month after I am better, he said. You will be satisfied with my 'Jesus of Nazareth'. I am sure I will be satisfied, I said. You look like if you want to sleep. No, I want to talk or listen to you talk, he said. Tell me how things are in Merthyr.

I told him how things were in Merthyr and district and he listened until he fell asleep. Merthyr he always wanted to hear about, even after that affair which hurt him so much. He wanted to conduct his 'Emmanuel' at Merthyr but the choir said no. They would have their own conductor, Lewis Morgan. Joseph felt that more than all the other slights of his life. A little chap from Merthyr, always, always, and he had composed the music of and for 'Emmanuel' and he wanted so much to conduct it in the town where he was born. But the Merthyr United Choir said no, Lewis Morgan we will sing under and no other. All so long ago now and me back in bed again. That jaunt to Penarth to see Joseph had put me back in my bed.

One day Edwin came upstairs as soon as he came home from his work to his dinner. He did not say anything for nearly a minute. Well? I said. He is dead, said Edwin. Joseph? I said. Yes, he said. H'm, I said. How did I know before you told me? Did you? said Edwin. Yes, I said. As soon as you came up to me I knew and I do not know how

I knew. What odds now? Bachgen bach o Ferthyr, erioed, erioed. That is what he was. Go down to your dinner, Edwin. I was not able to get up out of my bed to go to Joseph's funeral but Edwin went for me and took a wreath. I was in bed thinking of Joseph and his life and his work and his death – but what death am I talking about? The ceiling of my bedroom is low, as ceilings of upstairs rooms are in all the little houses climbing the hill of Twynyrodyn in the town of Tydfil the Martyr. You know the kind of day that we call 'heavy', days when cloud without a break is low and heavy like the grey ceiling of an enormous room. Right. Then there are days when the ceiling of the sky is higher, hundreds, thousands if not millions of miles higher, and on those days the ceiling of the sky is blue. There you are then. Above that high ceiling of blue sky there is somewhere else again and that is where Joseph now is. He left behind him another cartload of compositions partly finished and awaiting the revision so necessary for his work yet so hateful to him. He had no money to leave behind him, he had never had any anyway. Poor Jane.

Thinking of Joseph I am, now without those two Royal Academy medals on his watch-chain. Free and with the great masters of music he tried to emulate. He did his best and they will let him walk the courts of Heaven with them. Now there are young men in Merthyr and district who may do better than Joseph did. He will be glad if they do and so will I. Only once have I been out since the day when I sent Edwin with a wreath from me to Joseph's funeral. I went in a cab with my grand-daughter and Edwin up to the new Public Park the day they unveiled the Memorial to those who had fallen in South Africa. It was a fine day but I did not get out of the cab. Too much of a crowd. The new Park is up on what we used to call the 'Thomas Town Tips'. It is on 'made' ground most of it, made over ash and clinker from the old ironworks. But one part of it, where the flowers grow, the part with the bandstand in the centre,

413

is on good ground, for it is part of the old Danygraig Farm. So the flowers grow there.

The Memorial to those who fell in South Africa is in the other part, the part where no flowers grow, on 'made' ground. The Park is high up and I sat in the open cab looking at the crowd and beyond the crowd. All Merthyr and district I could see and the smoke rising from Cyfarthfa and Dowlais steelworks and collieries down the Vale of Merthyr. The Memorial is just a stone pointed like a huge finger heavenwards. The Memorial of stone will no doubt be there for long after we have forgotten our lesson. One last look and back home in the cab I went with Edwin and my grand-daughter.

In bed I am and in bed I shall be now. I am not getting up any more. Satisfied I am. Now the world is yours. I am not flinging it at you or spitting it in your eye or anything like that. In the best spirit I am leaving it for you to try and make it better than we were able to make it. It is a grand world and to have known a little of it I shall regard as a great privilege for as long as I can breathe and remember. Yes, yours the world is now. I am not sad. Why should I be? Four-score years and odd is enough and perhaps too much. I am lying here full of music and remembering only the good and lovely things. Joseph, Myfanwy, Will Full-Moon, Blind Dick, Daniel and Betty Parry and all the others. Oh, the grand company I shall have. Yes, friends, the world is yours now.

Two New Penguins by J. B. Priestley

THE PRIESTLEY COMPANION (860)

In this volume J. B. Priestley has accepted a Penguin invitation to make an anthology of his own writing – and Ivor Brown has contributed a special appreciation of Priestley for the occasion. The selected passages range far and wide over the work of this pungent and vivacious novelist, and they include also a generous representation of his essays and social commentaries. Here are scenes and portraits by the score from Priestley's cavalcade of English life and here, too, many of those subtle and delicate meditations from such bedside books as *Delight* or *Midnight on the Desert*.

BRIGHT DAY (861)

Bright Day, one of J. B. Priestley's later novels, reveals two of the most accomplished qualities of his writings; the robust and the reflective. No one can more abundantly depict than he the life and action of a city or a generation. But he possesses also that gift of meditation which adds a third dimension to his drawing of a place or a character. In this absorbing story Gregory Dawson, a film-writer, goes off to a remote spot in Cornwall to finish a script, and meets by chance two people he had known years ago in Bruddersford, the Yorkshire wool city. This encounter sets his mind exploring the labyrinths of memory between Hollywood and the West Riding, following the clues that lead him back to the golden days of his youth and to the re-discovery of himself.

Non-Fiction

PEOPLES OF THE WORLD

In the Pelican series are a number of books which describe the history, culture or civilization of a particular race or country. These now include:

THE SCOTS *by Moray McLaren* (A 256)
THE IRISH *by Sean O'Faolain* (A 184)
THE GREEKS *by H. D. F. Kitto* (A 220)
THE ROMANS *by R. H. Barrow* (A 196)
THE WELSH *by Wyn Griffiths* (A 215)

THE HOUSE OF COMMONS AT WORK

Eric Taylor

A257

The author is Clerk to the Committee of Privileges of the House of Commons. He has written an account of the daily working of the House of Commons at the present time – its procedure, rules, committees and methods of dealing with proposed legislation.

ATTITUDE TO AFRICA

W. Arthur Lewis, Michael Scott,
Martin Wight and Colin Legum

S159

This Penguin Special is a study of the present day problems of British Africa. It is divided into four parts. The first is a survey of the general situation in Africa and the second treats of Britain's political responsibilities: while in the other two Michael Scott takes the particular case of the High Commission Territories of South Africa and discusses a policy of social development in the Bechuanaland Protectorate, and W. Arthur Lewis puts forward a programme for peasant agriculture.